# Conservation of Fishery Resources

## The Author

**Dr. K.P. Biswas**, M.Sc, Ph.D, D.F.Sc (Bombay), E.F. (West Germany), F.Z.S, F.A.B.S. (Kolkata), Former Joint Director Fisheries (L-I), Govt. of Odisha, Fishery Technologist, I.C.A.R. and Director of Fisheries, Andaman and Nicobar Islands, and at present Faculty Member, Marine Science Department, University of Calcutta and West Bengal University of Animal & Fishery Sciences is associated with fish, fisheries and marine sciences for more than fifty years.

He has published twenty one books and 167 research and review papers on fish, fisheries, environmental and ocean sciences and fish processing technologies.

He is a Fellow Member of Zoological Society, Indian Association of Biological Sciences, Kolkata.His latest book, "Marine Biology" was published in 2013.

# Conservation of Fishery Resources

K.P. Biswas

2014
## Daya Publishing House®
*A Division of*
## Astral International Pvt. Ltd.
New Delhi – 110 002

*Published by*          : **Daya Publishing House**®
                          A Division of
                          **Astral International Pvt. Ltd.**
                          – ISO 9001:2008 Certified Company –
                          4760-61/23, Ansari Road, Darya Ganj
                          New Delhi-110 002
                          Ph. 011-43549197, 23278134
                          E-mail: info@astralint.com
                          Website: www.astralint.com

*Laser Typesetting*     : **Classic Computer Services**, Delhi - 110 035

*Printed at*            : **Replika Press Pvt. Ltd.**


PRINTED IN INDIA

*— Dedication —*

# Dedicated to Mrs. Manju Biswas for her Encouragement

# Preface

The origin of intensive marine fishing started a thousand years ago (AD 955-C 1020) when the English people changed their diet from mainly fresh water species to mainly marine ones, principally herring (*Clupea harengus*) and representative of cod families, the "gadids" with cod (*Gadus morhua*) dominating. The period should serve as a base line when evaluating the present state of marine ecosystems and its fisheries.

The transition towards marine species was due to a decline in freshwater fishes. This decline was caused by pollution from mills, from agricultural runoff (farming was expanding during the period) and by overfishing of what are afterall, limited resources, relative to the demand from then-growing urban population. During the transition from fresh water to marine fishes (950 and 1050) in the English diet was relatively warm. Such conditions were not favorable to herring or cod in the seas around England, where both the species are near the southern end of their ranges. Hence a massive increase in trade with Norway, where the abundance of cod and herring does tend to increase with temperature, could link the observed dietary transition to shifting abundances resulting from environmental change.

Fishermen at that time used to catch herring and salmon, porpoise and sturgeon, oysters and crabs, mussels, cockles, plaice and flounders and lobsters and many similar things. Flat fishes which include species that migrate between fresh water and marine environment.

This transition from eating fresh water fish to marine fish, before the invention of agriculture, tens of thousands of years ago leds most humans to live and migrate along coast line relying on shellfish and started from Africa gradually reaching inlands as far flung as Tasmania and Tierra del Fuego.

These migrations, which brought our African ancestors to Europe and Asia and thence to Australia and Ocenia and to the Americas, were in most cases followed by migrations inland, driven by hunting of larger animals and later by agriculture and there is documentation also from Britain of a change of diet some 5200 years ago, at the start of Neolithic and of British agriculture from marine animals to inland animals and plants.

The transition from eating fresh water fish to eating marine fish, documented by Barrett *et al.*, is thus part of a secondary transition. Marine fisheries catches are declining world wide and the global demand for fish is increasing. So will another transition back to fresh water fish and inland species occur, or will we be able to row even more and maintain our present level of marine fish consumption.

*K.P. Biswas*

# Contents

*and Black Sea (FAO Area 37)–Southwest Atlantic (FAO Area 41)–Southeast Atlantic (FAO Area 47)–Western Indian Ocean (FAO Area 51)–Eastern Indian Ocean (FAO Area 57)–Northwest Pacific (FAO Area 61)–Northeast Pacific (FAO Area 67)–Western Central Pacific (FAO Area 71)–Eastern Central Pacific (FAO Area 77)–Southwest Pacific (FAO Area 81)–Southeast Pacific (FAO Area 87)– Arctic (FAO Area 18) and Antarctic areas (FAO Areas 48,58,88)–Conclusion– Global Capture Fisheries for the Year 2011.*

## 5. Marine Productivity in India — 60

*Depleting Marine Fisheries Resources–History of Fishing and Export from Indian Seas–Remedial Measures.*

## 6. Resources and Environment — 67

*Resources and Environment–Multi-Species Fisheries–Change in Resources– Fishing and Assessment of Stocks–Exploitation and Future Prospect–Exploitable Fishery Resources–Fishery: A Living Resource–Potentially Usable Resources– Monitoring the State of Stocks–Assessment of Potential Maximum Catch– Assessment of Tropical Fish Stocks–Deck Sampling and Catch Recording Procedure–Statistics: Regression and Correlation–Linear Regression– Correlation–Length-Weight Relationship–Methods for Obtaining Growth Parameters from Length-Frequency Data of Tropical Fish–Methods for the Analysis of Length-Frequency Data–Estimating Total Mortality–Estimating Z by Means of a catch curve–Splitting Z into M and F–Stock Assessment–Estimating Stock Sizes–Methods for Estimating the Stock Sizes of Pelagic Fishes–Methods for Estimating the Stock Size of Reef Fishes–Estimating the Biomass of Demersal Stocks–Estimating Maximum Sustainable Yield (MSY)–Stock Assessment of Small-Scale Fisheries in the Bay of Bengal–Status of Exploited Coastal Fisheries in the Bay of Bengal Region–Craft and Gear–Species Composition–Stock Assessment in the Region–Measures for Proper Development/Management of Coastal Fishery of the Bay of Bengal–Biological Over-Fishing of Tropical Stocks– Characteristics of an Exploited Stock–Effects of Fishing–Estimation of Potential Catches with different Fleet Sizes, and of State of Exploitation of Stocks–Exercises Characteristic of an Exploited Stock.*

## 7. Species in Stress and Extinction — 117

*Fisheries Productivity in the Northeastern Pacific Ocean over the Past 2200 Years–Commercial Fishing-Reduce the Fish Age and Size at Maturity– Threatened Sturgeon–Icy Death of Cod–Endangered Fishes–Distortions of World Fisheries Catch–Unregulated Commercial Whaling in the Name of Scientific Studies–Conflicting Opinion–For Review–Military Maneuvers and Whale Death–Off-shore Army Base will Affect Local Sea Life–Harbor Threat for Coelacanths–Massive Fish Kills.*

## 8. Conservation in World Oceans — 128

*Towards Sustainable Fisheries–Single Species Stock Assessments–Impact on Ecosystem and Bio-diversity–Trophic Levels as Indicators of Fisheries Impact– Reducing Fishing Capacity–Biological Constrains to Fisheries and Aquaculture–*

*Sustainable Coral Reef Fisheries–Perspectives–Conservation of Fish Stocks–Fishing's Secretive Controllers–Population Structure of Bluefin Tuna–Recruitment of Cod–Whale Population at Risk–Tracking Whales–Detection of Endangered Species–Threat to Olive Ridley Turtle–Conservation in Indian Seas–Indian Marine Protected Areas–Biosphere Reserves in Marine Areas.*

# Introduction

History of Marine Animal Populations (HMAP) aims to determine what used to live there. By 2010, researchers have examined more than a dozen of key sites around the globe. Historical studies are already under way in southwest Africa, Australia, Europe and the United States, including the latest, a study of the Florida keys. Further work is planned in southeast Asia and New Zealand.

But the researchers base their understanding of healthy fish populations on what fish stocks are like during their life times, with no frame work for incorporating how much more plentiful fish might have been in generations past.

Along the Florida Reef and among the keys, a great abundance and variety of fish may be taken, such as, hog fish, grunts, yellowtails, black, red and grey snappers, mullets, bone fish, amber fish, margate fish, barracuda, cavallos, pompai, groupers, king fish, siber fish, porgys, turbots, sting rays, black drum, jew fish, with a prodigious variety of others, which in present situation was found excellent.

William Dampier, the pirate was one of the most scientifically significant and reliable. Even Charles Darwin recognized the value of Dampier,s work and describd Dampier as a very accurate person on evolution and natural selection. It was Dampier's thought on "bastard" species of Galapagos sea turtles, a mix of species from different geographical areas.

In 1796, Scottish surveyor, George Gauld described that among the roots of mangroves and around every old log, or piece of rotten work, there were much quantities of the largest cray fish (spiny lobsters), that a boat may be loaded with them in a few hours. To day divers spend hours filling just one bag. Other accounts spoke of plentiful fish and coral reefs, where now only sand and rubble are found.

Historical analysis can provide powerful tools for quantitative assessments. If records suggest that sea turtles in a region were once plentiful, but are now scarce, that provides important ecological information about the past- even without details of exactly how many there were.

During medieval times, fish population in rivers and lakes connected to the Wadden Sea began to drop as people over-fished it and built dams, which blocked the spawning migrations. Later dyke building also cut off estuarine nursery areas.

Sturgeon was once popular even for common folk, but by fourteenth century, they were so rare that they were only served at the King's table.

As the more easily accessible fresh water fisheries collapsed, medieval fishers turned to coastal waters and then moved farther a field as fish populations there dwindled. The Wadden Sea is not the only place where over-fishing hit hard.

More than four-and-a-half centuries before 1990s collapse of the Atlantic cod fisheries, there was an astonishingly rich population. In 1623, a fisherman, Emmanuel Altham wrote in a letter to his brother, that in one hour, they got hundred very large cod and if they have stayed after the fog broke up, they could quickly load their ship, they got 1000 in all. After that they took delight in catching and throwing them again in the sea.

Fisheries managers may apply such historical records to their efforts. The historical perspective is certainly important in developing long-term public policy. In the absence of that, it will be like shooting in the dark. A better understanding of the historical populations could help fishermen appreciate their collective impact.

The hybridization of history and ecology has really put a set of new questions on the table that together the scholarly community has been able to answer. And overall the work has potential to make a real impact. It's a whole new way of viewing the world. If in some small way they can shape ecological research for the future and help to conserve biodiversity, then that will be wonderful.

Humans have a history of driving once abundant species to extinction. Extinctions approaching this magnitude may be under way with some sea-turtle populations. It is estimated, for example, that there were tens of millions of green turtles in the Caribbean, when Columbus arrived at 15th century, but human harvesting has since reduced this number by around 95 percent. Some populations have already driven to extinction, the last green turtles nested in Bermuda in the 1930s.

The survival of sea turtle populations is now dependant on conservation efforts. In Ascension Island, the population of nesting green turtle had grown since the previous census twenty years before a success story reflecting conservation efforts both at Ascension Island to protect breeding turtles and in Brazil where these turtles forage. Monitoring of green turtle populations in Hawaii and Costa Rica for the past 30 years has revealed upward trends at both sites.

But turtle populations continue to suffer high mortality at the hands of the human. For example, leatherback turtles face the gauntlet of literally millions of hooks deployed each day on long lines set for tuna and sword fish. But there is important recent work showing how changing hook and bait types can greatly reduce turtle by-catch without affecting the catch of target species.

Are there plenty of fish in the sea? The question continues to reverberate around most of the world's fishing grounds, but scientific data on the subject can sometimes prove elusive.

Researchers interested in the species conservation, oceanography and fisheries management are keen to get more reliable information on the movement of marine animals. On the Pacific sea board of the United States, marine biologists took a big step towards understanding these migrations.

Tagging of Pacific Pelagics (TOPP), which aims to tract bluefin tuna, several species of shark and albatross, elephant seals, leatherback sea-turtles and other free ranging species, have electronically tagged 80 tuna under the project.

The tagging will create a data set by observing animals that will present a better picture of the ocean. The project is the first of about a dozen of similar schemes around the world involving 60 biologists, oceanographers and computer scientists, that will be carried out as a part of the marine census and exploits the latest technological advances in tagging devices that can be attached to the animals. Its tag store data on species location water temperature and depth. The project uses both archival tags, which are recovered when species are caught or found dead, and transmitting ones-some as small a deck of cards-that send information regularly for analysis via a French satellite instrument called ARGOS.

TOPP's participants have also launched tagging operations to track salmon, sharks off Alaska, blue sharks off Los Angels, humpback whales off Oregon and albatross near Hawaii and the Galapagos Islands.

The data obtained from the tagging will help researchers to understand why animals venture to certain oceanic regions. The information will complement that obtained from several other exploratory systems. For example, elephant seals, which plunge to depths of more than 600 meter several times an hour when at sea, will be monitored by the Argo-float system that is being deployed to chart deep ocean currents and their impact on climate.

It is hoped that the tagging of tuna and other species will reveal migratory routes that will help biologists to understand Pacific fisheries.

In a bid to protect an ecologically valuable deep sea environment from damage caused by commercial fishing, the European Commission (EC) has banned the use of bottom trawled nets on the Darwin Mounds, the largest known British deep sea coral reefs.

The mounds make up an unique marine habitat covering around 100 sq. km. at a depth of about 1 km. Under water video footage showed that the reefs were already critically damaged by French trawlers, which are known to have fished in the region.

The European Commission, which oversees fisheries off most of Europe's coast line, has banned trawling in the area with immediate effect. The emergency measures have been adopted to protect marine ecosystems from damage caused by fishing.

The real state of fisheries depends more on the role of females in the replenishment of fish populations. Contrary to the popular wisdom, that in the black fish, older and larger female fish produce eggs and larvae that are much more likely to survive.

Larger female fish are vastly more productive than the smaller ones. A single 61 cm long red snapper (*Lutjanus campechanus*) has been estimated to produce, as many eggs as 212 snappers of 43 cm long. This is largely because eggs are produced in proportion to a fish's volume, which is proportional to the cube of its length. The profligate fecundity of larger females has long been cited as a good reason to preserve fish populations in " no-take" marine reserves. In some cases, larger fish in these reserves may double a species egg production- even if the reserve encompass only 5 per cent of the marine habitat.

In rock fish of the genus *Sebastes*, it has been found that eggs from older females produce larvae that grew faster and were more resistant to starvation than larvae from young females. The differences were huge, on the same diet, larvae of 12 rear-old rock fish grew four times faster than larvae produced by 5-year old rock fish. At the same time, offspring of older females had more metabolic reserves, larvae took an average of 12 days to starve, whereas offspring of 5 year-olds starved in less than half that time.

The central difference lies in a small post hatching gift each mother gives her offspring, a little oil droplet that serves as a metabolic reserve after the yolk-sac has been absorbed. Older females provide a larger droplet than younger ones, ensuring a better head start for their larvae as they drift through the oceans, feeding and developing into juvenile fish capable of settling to the sea floor. Larger females and females in better physical condition, produce better larvae as well, but these effects are slight compared with the effects of age.

These data are also important for attempts to rebuild, overfished sock populations. Fishers value larger, older fishes and strip away these larger individuals from the reproductive populations. In other fish, such as, grouper species that change sex from smaller females to larger males, this tendency to take larger fish has long been known to reduce the number of mature males. Some grouper spawning aggregations have fewer than one male for a dozen of females and this imbalance exhausts the fertilization abilities of few surviving males. The opposite problem is seen in the shrimp and crab populations, where small males change into larger females. Fishing down the family tree in these cases removes females first, and cuts production dramatically.

The new data show why heavy fishing pressure on older fish is also a serious problem in species that don't change sex. For example, a decline in the average age of female rock fish from 9.5 years to 6.5 years during a period of intensified bottom fishing from 1996 to 1999. Such a culling of the older females reduces the average growth rate of larvae in the population by about 50 per cent and probably reduces the ability of these larvae to grow and survive to the next stage in their life history. Data on cod and haddock also show that larger females produce larger eggs and these larger eggs produce better larvae. The conclusion is that standard fisheries management tools that consider every female to be reproductively equivalent can be far off the mark.

Marine reserves change the landscape of fishing regulations by protecting the entire local populations of fish and invertebrates. The resulting dramatic reduction in mortality has an immediate benefit in producing larger fish in reserves- an effect that has been seen in tropical and temperate settings, along reefs, kelp beds and in estuaries. So protecting larger and older females can be more efficient in producing larger numbers of higher-quality offspring. But reproduction is the fuel that keeps all fisheries alive from one generation to the next, enhancing the success of larvae is a key to a sustainable fishery.

# Chapter 1
# Importance of Marine and Coastal Ecosystems

Marine and coastal ecosystems provide a wide range of important products and services. Fish, crustaceans and mollusks are major food. Marine fish provided about 84 million tons of human food and livestock supplements in 1993 (FAO, 1995). Fish accounts for about 16 per cent of the average individual's intake of animal protein worldwide (FAO, 1993), and the proportion is higher in many developing countries (WRI, 1996). The fisheries producing this catch are a major source of employment for many of the world's coastal states.

Marine and coastal ecosystems also provide many critically important services for humanity such as a) storing and cycling nutrients, b) regulating water balances, c) buffering land and protecting it against erosion from storms and waves, d) filtering pollutants, e) play an essential role in regulating planetary balances in hydrology and climate, and f) through the ocean's photosynthetic pump, removing the primary greenhouse gas, carbon dioxide from the atmosphere and producing 33 per cent to 50 per cent of the global oxygen supply.

Coral reefs, estuaries, lagoons and shallow coastal water are particularly valuable for human populations because of the goods and services they provide. They are among the most biologically productive systems on earth. Reefs and mangroves provide sea defenses and buffer the impacts of tropical storms, mitigating the erosive effects of waves and storm surges. All these systems provide nurseries and feeding grounds for many coastal and pelagic fishes.

Marine species provide many other products as well, including edible seaweed, ingredients for food and cosmetics, industrial chemicals and dyes and a host of other products. Medical researches have already identified a number of marine organisms that produce previously unknown bioactive compounds, including anti-viral and anti-tumor agents, which may soon have medical applications. One compound derived from a sea sponge to treat herpes, for example, is worth 50 to 100 milion dollars annually (Norse, 1993).

Marine and coastal ecosystems provide important ecological services that are rarely perceived until they are lost. Species do not live in isolation, but are part of, and dependent upon, vast ecological communities and systems. Thus overexploitation/ disappearance of any one species may lead to, in due course, to a biodiversity crisis. The conservation of biodiversity is therefore an important part of managing economically valuable living resources.

## Global Fishery Resources

A full review of the state of global fishery resources should give an account of the state of the individual fish stocks in terms of their biomass, their growth and mortality rates and the general ecological conditions affecting the productivity of these stocks. Desirable as such information may be, it is available for only a small proportion of all stocks. In the main the knowledge of the state of the stocks has to be deduced from an examination of the trends in catches over a period of years. It is the statistics of catches that provide the main source of information.

The interactions between different fish stocks between fisheries based on different species, and the effects of environmental and climatic fluctuations on fish stocks are matters now calling for attention in many areas, the number of which is increasing, namely, in the North Sea, off Peru and Nambia and in the northwest Pacific. The existing simple single-species models have been effective as a means of determining the immediate impact of fishing on the stocks directly concerned, namely, in determining that the North Sea herring and Peruvian anchovy were becoming, heavily fished, and where management has been ineffective, as it has in many fisheries, it has been so more often because of taking action too late or too weakly than because of scientific weaknesses in the advice. However, the simple models have not been able to give full or convincing descriptions of all the events in these fisheries, namely, the extent to which the decline in North Sea herring is associated with, or even to some extent the cause of the increase in some other species or the degree to which the Peruvian anchovy has been affected by environmental changes and more especially, the extent to which the anchovy and the fishery on it, might have been less vulnerable to environmental fluctuations if it had not been so heavily fished in the period 1965-1971. These are questions to whose solution intensive, and probably expensive, scientific research at the highest level will have to be devoted.

These questions of the interactions between species, the influence of environmental fluctuations and the uncertainty of the general applicability of the single species models, are making it apparent that the greatest yield from a region that can be taken continuously year after year is not the arithmetic sum of the individual estimates of the maximum sustainable yields (as normally calculated) of the individual species in the region. Generally it will be less, possibly to a considerable extent. For example, in the northwest Atlantic, the tendency of the management policies of the coastal states seem to be towards, maintaining the stocks of fish at a level some what above that giving the theoretical maximum sustainable yield. This strategy exchanges some loss in catch (at least under average conditions) for improved economic performance, and for a greater ability of the stocks, and of the fisheries on them, to withstand unfavorable environmental conditions. This policy has been recommended in respect of other resources, notably marine mammals and would seem to be in accordance with the United Nations Conference on the Law of the Sea (UNCLOS) policy of full utilization, except on the most narrow interpretation.

## Effects of the Law of the Sea

The general extension of national jurisdiction, associated with UNCLOS discussion has of course been one of the major factors affecting fisheries in recent years. Although the United Nations Conference on the Law of Sea is still moving towards a comprehensive agreement, extended jurisdiction out to 200 miles has became an established fact in many parts of the world. Apart from the high seas fisheries on tuna and whales, and a few areas, namely, in some parts of the southeast Atlantic, nearly all fisheries are now carried out in waters which are already or will soon come under a single national jurisdiction.

The magnitude of the overall impact in different regions was reported to FAO's Committee on Fisheries (COFI), which set out the catches taken by medium to long-range vessels off the coasts of foreign countries in each major sea area. While a distinction was made between developing and developed countries in respect of both fishery area and flag state of the fishing vessels, individual countries were not identified. In view of COFI's request to FAO to prepare a program for the development of the extended economic zone, a more detailed tabulation, setting out, albeit in somewhat general terms, the likely impact on each country would be helpful. In particular it would help to identify where the major opportunities and problems lie.

The potential looser are those with catches taken off the coasts of other countries. The potential gainers are those with fisheries by other countries off their coasts. The third category of countries with continuing opportunities in the sense of unexploited or lightly exploited resources off their coasts. As regards, the first two categories, it must be stressed that the gains and losses, in the first instance are only potential, the actual gain and losses if any, will depend on the policy followed by the coastal state. As regards the third category, extension of legal jurisdiction over an area of water in which there are unexploited stocks has little, if any, direct effect on the ability of the coastal state to utilize those resources. However, it does draw the attention of national policy makers to the resources, and to this extent their identification is relevant to a discussion of the effect of extended jurisdiction.

The greatest impact has been on the fleets of long range vessels, notably, those of the USSR and Japan, whose freedom of action has been greatly reduced. However, it is clear, that most of these vessels will be able to operate, though at a reduced intensity and with strict controls, under extended jurisdiction. There has therefore been some drop in catch in areas where they have been operating, and this has been most noticeable in areas, namely, the northwest Atlantic, where distant water fleets have taken a large proportion of the total catch, where they now compete for the same stocks with fleets from coastal states, and where these stocks have been heavily fished, and are in need of rebuilding. In these areas some temporary, though significant drop in total is likely or is already occurring, while the stocks are being rebuilt, and coastal states develop their own capacity.

## High Sea Resources

High sea resources are considered as those resources which exist beyond 200 miles from shore, generally beyond national jurisdiction. The FAO data base lists close to 400 species that can be considered as high seas or oceanic; about 50 species of cephalopods, 40 species of sharks, 60 species of marine mammals and 230 species of fish. The biological information available on these species is generally poor, except for some whales and large tunas, and their management and conservation is a matter of serious concern.

Most oceanic high sea resources are dispersed, difficult to harvest economically, and extremely difficult to study with any degree of accuracy. They are usually exploited by long-range fleets operating in areas where target species concentrate for feeding or reproduction. Average densities available in the high seas are much lower than in upwellings and coastal zones. The increasing scarcity of coastal resources to distant water fishing nations, due to over fishing and transfer of resources to coastal states jurisdiction is an incentive to increase pressure on these areas and often fragile species.

Most baleen whales and the sperm whales are heavily over fished or depleted with some rare exceptions, and some species may even be beyond recovery. Future attention should be directed towards smaller cetaceans (toothed whales and dolphins) which are not properly protected and represent a potentially serious management problem.

Most tuna stocks in temperate and tropical waters are under heavy pressure and are intensively to fully fished locally. Further development is facing constraint with the emergence of the problem of accidental mortality of dolphins in purse seines and of various non-target species including mammals, birds and turtles in large-scale pelagic drift nets.

Management of salmon stocks on high seas needs strengthening in order to fully implement the relevant provisions of the Convention of the Law of the Sea.

Oceanic squids offer obvious potential for development on new species and areas, while the main species already targeted are fully fished or over fished. With the present conflicts about drift netting, possibilities to develop commercial fisheries are limited on oceanic dispersed species, but are not inexistent. The oceanic sharks may offer more potential for concern than for sustainable development and research on these species is badly needed as most fisheries have shown to be unsustainable. The oceanic horse mackerel appears heavily fished off Peru, while its future is obscured by the lack of an international mechanism for its management, and cooperation in research, and coastal countries are presently expressing their concern.

In the Antarctic, depletion of commercial species of fish has followed depletion of marine mammals, and management performance could be improved. Krill is the exception, saved probably by the difficulty to use it profitably. The concept of ecosystem management, particular to this area of the world, still has to be put into practice.

Demersal resources, extending on high seas shelves, are fully fished if not over fished. Progress in net making technology will facilitate the intensification of the exploitation by island countries of non-conventional large pelagic species, such as dolphin fish, flying fish, as well as large tuna-like species, presently assumed under-exploited with unknown potential. However, problems of accidental capture of low-resilience and ecologically sensitive species could emerge as in the large scale drift net fisheries.

One of the main issues in the high seas fisheries, as any other fisheries, is sustainability. This concept implies that resources can be reduced by fishing to some agreed average level, at which its existence (reproductive capacity) is not threatened. A particular problem concerns non-target species, sometimes fragile or already endangered, which could be inadvertently threatened by incidental capture while "optimizing"the use of a target species. It is impossible to extract living resources from the marine ecosystems without affecting it and, there is some trade-off between the intensity of fishing allowed and the degree of resources allocation. The difficulty is that, it is hard to forecast and attach a value to the potential damage to the pristine populations, resulting from planned development. Precautionary principles are beginning to be used, explicitly or implicitly. Although they could be useful especially in cases of high uncertainty, its use might need to be codified to avoid development paralysis.

The relative failure of international management to establish sustainable fisheries in many areas, despite the high quality of the research base some times provided, is clearly demonstrated by the dwindling resources, excessive catching capacity, uncontrolled transfers of fishing effort between resources and oceans, and depletion of many highly valuable resources, including those in the Antarctic, and for some whales. The fact that uncontrolled development of fishing effort leads to disaster has now been widely acknowledged in the scientific literature, and by high level fisheries management and development authorities. This was demonstrated by the discussion and agreements in two world conferences on management and development of fisheries held in Vancouver (1973) and Rome (1984). In practice, however, this verbal recognition does not always seem to translate into facts and the future of high sea resources must therefore be considered carefully.

It is a source of concern that most high sea resources under international management suffer from excessive effort and depletion. Improvement of the state of resources has often not been obtained through traditional international fishery management, but through either establishment of eezs (although many EEZ resources are also over fished) or through intervention of non-fishery users interests (e.g whales, dolphins). UNCLOS seems to provide a board, useful frame work, but it would appear that practices for responsible fishing need to be agreed upon, perhaps through the elaboration of a code of practice for the high seas, shared stocks, straddling stocks, some endangered species in the EEZs, etc.

## Present Status

For centuries, The Canadian Grand Banks off the coast of Newfoundland were the prime fishing grounds. The region's abundance of Atlantic cod (*Gadus morhua*) supported the entire communities. At its height, in 1968, the industry employed 40000 people and landed more than 800000 tonnes of fish.

But the factory trawlers that subsequently moved on to the banks exacted a dreadful toll. Stocks collapsed, and in 1992, Canada's Department of Fisheries and Oceans belatedly closed the fishery. Thousands of fishermen and workers in fish processing industry lost their jobs, others redirected their efforts to crabs and shrimp. A decade later, the Grand Bank's show little sign of recovery.

The Grand Bank's disaster shows just how badly fisheries policies can go wrong. And unfortunately, the same mistakes are being committed across the world oceans. In many cases, scientists are warning that populations are being over exploited. But all too often, their advice of setting lower catch quotas, reducing the size of fishing fleets and using less harmful fishing gear is ignored or watered down. When push comes to above, it seems that short term economic interests steam roller scientific arguments.

In the past, fisheries scientists are cursed by the uncertainties that swathe their work. At best their models of the dynamics of fish populations produce in precise estimates of the maximum catches that can be taken without driving a stock into extinction. Here it is easy for those with vested interests to ignore unpalatable messages and to argue that larger catches might be sustainable. At worst, the models can incorporate misleading data that simply give the wrong answer, causing scientists to help speed fisheries towards collapse. In the case of Grand Banks both scenarios came into play.

Given such failures, some conservation biologists are now arguing that fisheries scientists must abandon their focus on individual stocks and adopt a whole ecosystem perspective. But whatever methods are used to determine the advice given to the policy-makers, scientists need to find ways to involve fishermen in their work, to break down the "us-and-them" interaction that helps to foster the current gulf between science and policy. It is utterly important to get fishermen's legitimate interests involved.

## The Problem

Sticking to business as usual would be a recipe for disaster, warn scientific critics of current fisheries management practices. According to global statistics compiled by the United Nations Food and Agricultural Organization (FAO) in Rome, the number of stocks that are being over-exploited is high and rising. In fact, the FAO may be painting an unduly optimistic picture, having for years incorporated inflated figures that over-estimate the health of China's fisheries. If current trends continue, fisheries could collapse throughout most of the world within a few decades.

The single species stock models that are used to calculate "safe" allowable catches, can be labyrinthine in their complexity incorporating hundreds of parameters. At their heart, however, they all rely on assessing the size and age structure of fish populations on the basis of data from experimental fishing cruises and commercial catches. The routine work of government fisheries laboratories consists largely of compiling these data and feeding them into the models.

But factors, such as, varying climate can exert a dramatic influence on fish population dynamics, obscuring the effects of fishing pressure. And the data fed into the stock assessment models can be seriously deceiving. In the case of Grand Bank fisheries, scientists knew that stocks were declining, but were some what reassured by the relatively healthy catches still being landed. They were, however, neglecting to consider the fact that fishermen were spending more time at sea, with improved equipment, fishing selectively in warmer waters where the remaining fish were congregating. Across most of the banks, there was barely an adult cod to be found.

Even scientists who regularly work with single species stock models accept that these tools have limitations. The links between fishing pressure, environmental changes and breeding success are not fully understood.

One important area of doubt is how the breeding success of different fish populations changes when their population become diminished. Ecological theory suggests that the remaining fish competing less intensely for food, should come to sexual maturity quickly and boost their rate of reproduction. But a phenomenon known as depensation- a reduction in reproductive success at low population densities, caused for example, by the difficulty in finding a male-can also come into play. A key question in fisheries science is why, after a reduction of mortality, some species recover and some do not. The presence or absence of depensation could be an important factor. As regards some grounds for optimism, the researchers examined 128 fish stocks looking at catch data to determine number of spawning fish and recruits- the young fish that have survived to adulthood. For only three of the stocks did these data fit with a model of population dynamics incorporating depensation. It is therefore, concluded that the effects of over fishing are, at this point, still generally reversible. But if over fishing is reversible, the situation can't be turned around over-night. Many of the stocks had experienced massive declines due to over fishing. With the possible exception of fast maturing species, such as, Atlantic herring (*Clupea harangus*) these stocks showed little sign of recovery as much as 15 years after their collapse. The life history of the species matters. Small early maturing mid-water species, like herring might recover faster than late maturing bottom living species, such as, cod. There was no association between a depleted population's recovery and the extent to which it continued to be fished after the collapse. What exactly is holding back the recovery of over exploited stocks remains unclear- depensation might still be a factor despite the earlier indications to the contrary. These findings demand a more precautionary approach in setting catch limits to prevent stocks from collapsing in the first place. If there is not much can be done after the damage is occurred, then it is an even stronger case that fish stock should not be let fall beyond safe levels.

There is also a growing awareness that the dynamics of individual fish populations need to be considered in a wider ecological context. Changes in predator-prey interactions and in food web structures may interlink to cause an irreversible downward spiral. Fishing for one species may also cause collateral damage elsewhere in a marine ecosystem. The barndoor skate (*Raja laevis*) for instance, has been driven to the brink of extinction largely as a result of being caught incidentally by vessels trawling for cod in the northwest Atlantic. And recently marine scientists have began

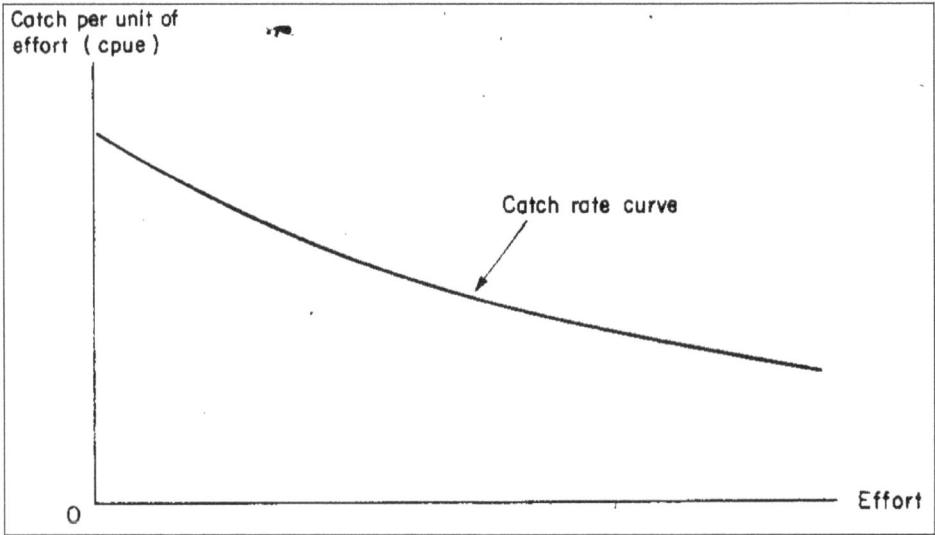

**Figure 1: Relationship between Catch per Unit of Effort and Effort.**

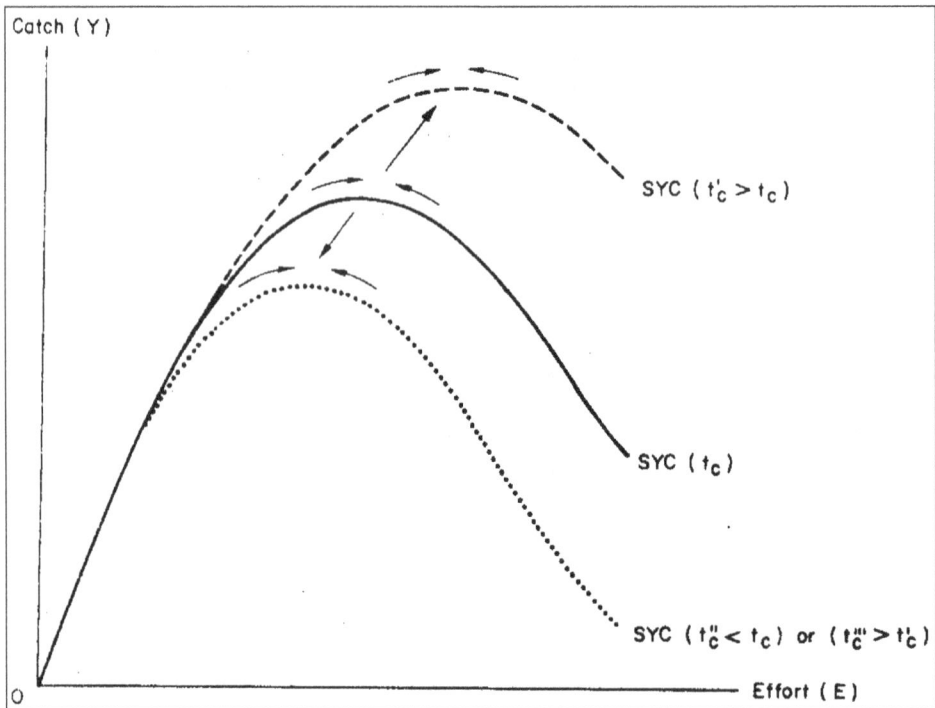

**Figure 2: Sustainable Yield Curve (SYC) under Alternative Ages at First Capture ($t_o$) and the Adjustment of Fishing Effort and Age at First Capture for Maximizing the Sustainable Yield from a given Stock.**

to document the damage brought on important habitats by trawling or dredging gear. Sea grass meadows off Spain, which serve as spawning grounds for many species of fish, have been extensively disturbed. Trawlers have wrecked ancient cold water corals in the northeast Atlantic.

To conservation biologists, these findings strengthen the case for abandoning the single-species approach to fisheries management, and turning instead to the analysis of entire marine ecosystems. Refinements to single species stock models, and to the data that are plugged into them, offer little hope of improving the "dreadful shape" that these ecosystems are in.

When fisheries are considered from an ecosystem perspective, trends emerge that otherwise are not readily evident. In 1998 for instance, Pauly and his colleagues assigned fish to different trophic levels in marine food webs. In their scheme photosynthetic algae represent level I, the animal that graze on these algae are level II, their predators form level III and so on. Looking at FAO catch statistics from 1950 to 1994, the researchers found the world's fishing fleets have been steadily fishing down the food web towards lower trophic levels. This is worring, as the trend will reduce the complexity of marine food webs, which is likely to make ecosystems inherently more vulnerable to damage.

In sea around us project FAO data is investigated for impact of large scale fisheries on North Atlantic ecosystems. One goal to map large marine ecosystems that share common fauna and oceanographic characteristics and to advise policies that can mitigate and reverse stock depletion and habitat destruction.

## Sustainable Fishing

Sustainable fishing will only be possible if protected areas are set aside in which no fishing is allowed, where fish are able to reproduce in undisturbed habitats. Historical evidence provides some support for this view; fish stocks increased substantially during the second world war, when fisheries in the North Sea came to a stand still. And stocks around Cyprus increased in the mid 1980s after the no-fishing period enforced during the summer breeding season was extended.

Encouragingly, the marine reserves established off Florida and in the Caribbean Sea have increased catches in surrounding waters. In particular, a net work of reserves off St. Lucia established in 1995 to preserve important coral reefs has increased adjacent catches by small scale fishermen by up to 90 per cent .

Instituting similar policies on a larger scale will require huge changes in the way in which decisions on fisheries management are made, however, conservation biologists want to see a reversal of the traditional "burden of proof" .Rather than erring on the side of avoiding immediate economic pain, they would like to see precautions being taken to avoid damage to ecosystems. The public, not industry is the owner of the resources. But so far all form of fisheries management have been industry friendly to a misplaced degree.

In the long run industry have everything to lose if the fish stocks continue to decline. And although most fishermen still tend to regard scientists as opponents, who are trying to limit their ability to earn a living rather than partners in ensuring that their industry has a future, hints of a more productive relationship are beginning to emerge. Fishermen have realized in the last decade that there is only a limited number of fish in the ocean.

For productive dialogue more meetings of Responsible Fishing Conferences can be arranged with fishermen, fisheries scientists and government representatives. Fishermen can swap practical knowledge and expertise, for example, on techniques of reducing incidental catches of non-target species, while sharing their perspectives on fisheries management with policy makers.

## Team Effort

The initiative has proved mutually beneficial. Fishermen have brought in data from remote sea areas to assist scientists with stock assessment. And regulators have received valuable feed back on the impact of new management policies on fishing communities. Most importantly, the fishermen who have taken part say that they are now less suspicious of the scientists who advise government regulators. Initiative, such as fishermen's may be particularly relevant in Europe, where competing national agenda make the adoption of sustainable fishing policies even more problematic.

The desperate race for fish has to stop, while launching a far-reaching proposal to reform European Union's common fisheries policy.

Directly or indirectly Europe's fishing industry employs more than 15 million people. But European Union's Commissioner for Agriculture and Fisheries wants to reduce the European Union's total fishing effort by up to 605 from January 2003. He aims to cut the current fleet of almost 100000 vessels by 10 per cent, while forcing the remainder to reduce their activity. Subsidies worth 460 million Euros (450 million dollars) for 2003-06 currently earmarked for renewal and modernization of vessels would be redirected to pensions and retraining for fishermen. In 2004, an inspection scheme was set up to tackle illegal fishing and the misreporting of catches. He also want to introduce management plans lasting several years, in which advise won't be twisted competing national agendas. And to bring policy-making closer to fishermen, he aims to create regional advisory councils, to which stakeholders can submit their own ideas about fisheries management.

It is a bold plan and one that fisheries scientists argue is necessary if Europe's fisheries are to escape destruction. Since 1991, more than 70000 fishermen have been driven out of a job by dwindling stocks and diminishing catches-adult cod are only half as abundant in Europe's fishing grounds as they were in 1970s. But can the man from land locked Austria succeed where his predecessors failed and reconcile competing national interests to achieve a sustainable reform of the European Union's common fisheries policy (CFP).

Time and again, efforts to reduce the EU's over exploitation of its fisheries have floundered, mired by opposition from countries with large fishing industries, such as, Spain, Portugal and France. The commissioner's plan could yet be blocked or watered down considerably.

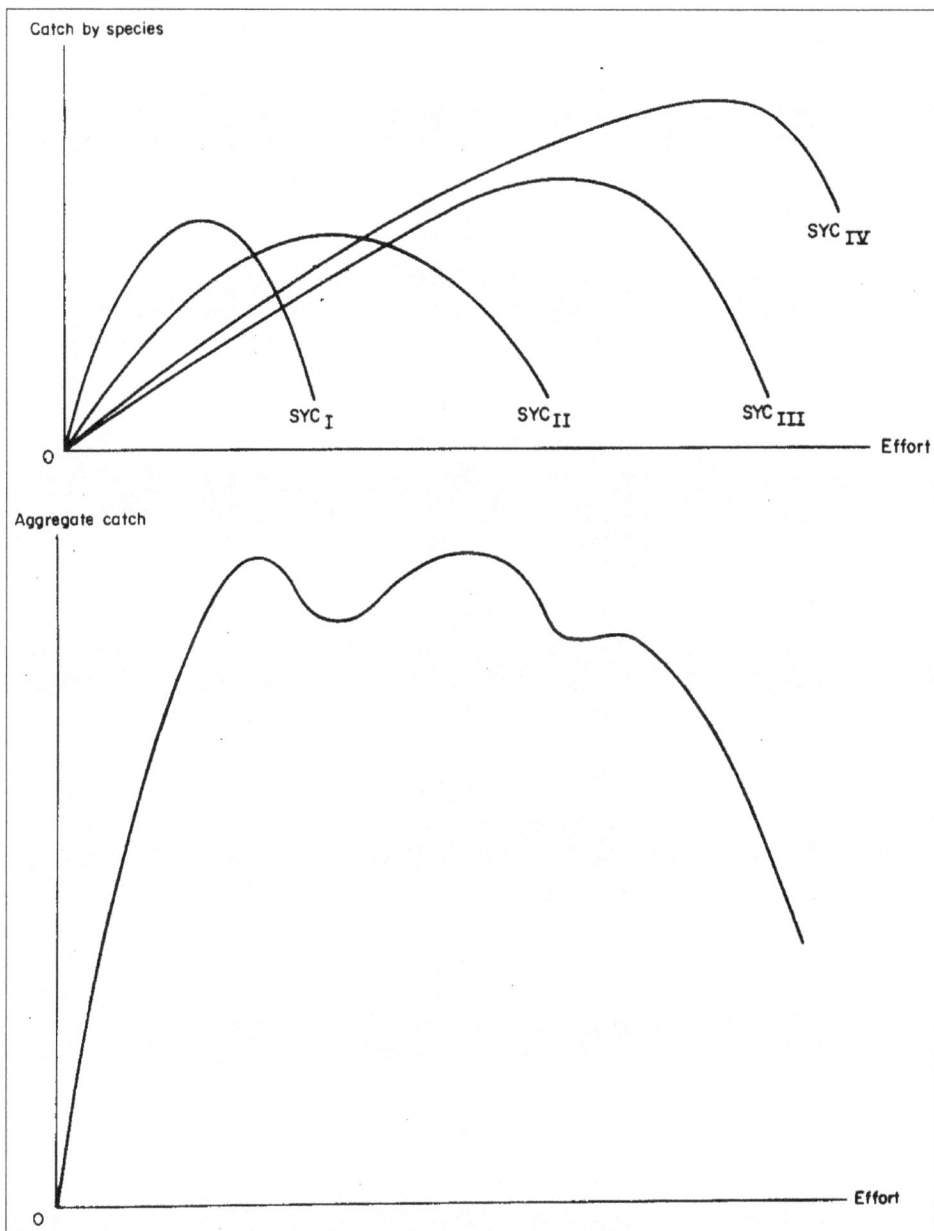

**Figure 3: Derivation of the Aggregate Sustainable Yield Curve for a Multispecies Fishery through Vertical Summation of the Individual Susainable Yield Curves of the Component Species. The waves in the aggregate SYC signify the dwindling of the share of the indicated species in the catch at certain levels of fishing effort.**

If Europe can't get the fisheries in order, the problems seem certain to be exported. With European fishermen increasingly loosing farther a field for their catches, the European Union is already paying compensation to some West African countries for fishing rights in their coastal waters.

Other positive signs include the growing number of nations that are adapting aspects of the FAO's Code of Conduct of Responsible Fisheries, a 1995 document that suggests legal, technical and economic arrangements for national authorities seeking to put their fisheries on a more sustainable footing. Iceland and New Zealand for instance, have reduced their fleet sizes and are strictly enforcing total allowable catches (TACs).

The same two countries have also led the way in dividing their TACs into individual transferable catch quotas (ITQs) for each vessel. New Zealand introduced ITOs in 1986. Iceland after a successful experiment with its herring fishery applied ITQs across the board in 1990. Without ITQ fishermen race against one another to land as much fish as possible, early in the search. Total catches as a result, frequently exceed the TAC and illegal fishing is common. With the security of ITQs however, individual boat no longer compete as fierce, so fishermen can spread their harvest over the season and sell any unused portions of their ITQ. The return come is that total catches tend to below ITQ.

The policies, according to analysis of the Organization for Economic Cooperation and Development, have actually increased the profitability of the two countries fishing sectors. What's more some stocks that are fished by their vessels are now showing signs of recovery.

But will the fishing industry ever embrace the widespread introduction of large marine reserves? Despite recent progress in building bridges between scientists and fishermen, and the evidence that reserves can boost catches, many experts still can't see it happening.

Pauly believes that involving the public in the debate will be crucial. Consumer preference for products labeled as eco-friendly, for instance, could be a powerful factor in changing attitudes within the fishing industry and particularly if the public is informed of the consequences for consumer choice, if fisheries are not put on a sustainable track. If the fishing fleet refuse to withdraw from large areas of the oceans, future generations won't have the option of dining on cod or other familiar favorites. Instead they will have to make do with jelly fish and plankton.

# Chapter 2

# Resource Potential and Population Dynamics

## Fishery Resources in Shallow Waters

Ocean area 361.059 X 1000 square kilometers account for 70 per cent of total earth's surface. Sub-marine topography consists of a gentle slope extending out from most shore lines to 100m-200m.This section is called continental shelf, a common topography to almost all sea areas in the world. The continental shelf is thought to have been a part of the land at the time of Glacial age. Out from the continental shelf, the sea bottom slopes down rather steeply. This section is called continental slope. Reaching a depth of about 3000 m, the sea bottom resumes a gentle slope, until it reaches a depth of about 6000 m, which is called "deep sea floor". Sometimes, there are trenches, which are 6000-10000 m deep at points on the deep sea floors.

## Basic Productivity of the Sea

Biologists and Oceanographers call the waters above continental shelves, "coastal waters". Although the coastal waters constitute in terms of area 9.9 per cent of all the oceans, they are very rich in biota, with productivity of the living resources being estimated at approximately 2 times that of high sea waters. The features of the coastal waters include a constant supply of inflowing land waters with nutrient salts, facilitating propagation of phytoplanktons and zooplanktons on which fishes and other marine animals feed. Coastal waters often have upwellings or vortexes, which cause vertical mixing or agitation of sea water providing biological environments which facilitate the propagation and growth of planktons. It can be said that the original forms of life on the earth were microscopic water plants, called phytoplanktons.

Phytoplanktons drift in enormous quantities in the surface waters penetrated by sun-rays and form carbohydrates and other organic materials through photosynthesis, using the solar energy and nutrient salts in the water.

The most important and most numerous phytoplanktons are diatoms. They are primary producers in the marine ecosystem and therefore, often called "marine pasture".

## Ecosystem and Food Chains

All forms of life have undergone a long evolutionary process to reach their present forms and places in the ecosystem. Each species has its own habitat suitable to its life cycle. Organisms can not lie in isolation. Except for plants which are capable of forming nutritive substance for themselves, all animals live on other organisms, while they are in turn, preyed on by some other animals.

There is also competition between different animals for common preys. These food relations are most important among living organisms. Animals and plants inhabiting given areas have certain food chain relations, which find each animal and plant holding a certain ecological position in the habitat. However, food chain relations are never uniform. In each individual habitat, there is an unique ecosystem consisting of certain food chains. Even in the same habitat, the patterns of food chains also vary with the seasons, as animals feed on different organisms during different stages of their life history, namely, fry, yearlings, adults.

The patterns of food chain reflect the structure of reproduction of the given area. Therefore it is essential to understand the ecosystem in which a given fishery resource exist, if their increase is to be ensured.

Nauplius – Floating after breaking out of eggs – Micro-organisms drifting in water
   I
Zoea     – Floating after breaking out of eggs – Phytoplankon (Diatom)
   I
Mysis  –              -do-            – Zooplankton
   I
Post larvae         -do-          -do-
   I
Juveniles – Inhabiting the sand & mud – Microscopic organic life inhabiting the sea
           Bottom of inner bay        bottom, such as plankton, short necked shell
   I                         fish and worms.

Adult prawn – Inhabiting the sand and                -do-
           mud bottom of the open sea

## Marine Primary Producers

Primary producers synthesize organic matter-ultimately becomes the substance and energy source of all forms of life. Not all of the primary production is available to man, a portion is utilized in metabolic processes by the plants and organisms of successively higher trophic levels. Until man can stimulate photosynthesis *in vitro*, even he must depend on photosynthetic production of organic matter by plants. The function of plants in marine ecosystem is not limited to the production of energy rich organic material, since they also cycle nutrients, including trace metals, reduce the effects of winds and tides, stabilize sediments and provide substrates and habitats for other organisms. Many marine plants are also important to man, since they are used as sources of food stabilizers, preservatives, drugs, fertilizers, fodder and for other insulation and other building materials. In addition, many marine plant communities, Spartina marshes, because of their assimilative capacity are highly effective natural filters for sewage treatment.

Marine environment includes open ocean, coastal waters and estuarine areas. Although the biomass of marine primary producers is small compared to the biomass of terrestrial plants, the relative contribution of these system to the earth's fixed carbon budget is similar. Assuming net production by plants is 50 per cent of their gross production, production by marine plants is about 2.2 X 10000000000000000 g Carbon per year and by terrestrial plants about 2.9 X 10000000000000000 g carbon per year.

Phytoplankton dominates the open ocean in terms of both biomass and production and consists primarily of diatom, dinoflagellates and cocolithophores, although blue-green algae and green flagellates on occasion can be abundant. Regional difference in the occurrence of species and in the production of phytoplankton are a result of many conditions. Three of the more important ones are the supply of nutrients, the quantity of light and the ambient temperature. Within each region there also are seasonal changes and gradients in these factors with depth. Mean net production values have been found to be 500 mg carbon per square meter per day for neritic waters, 170 mg carbon per square meter per day. For inshore waters, 100 mg carbon per square meter per day for sub-polar oceanic region and waters of equatorial divergence, 70 mg carbon per square meter per day for transition waters between sub-tropical and sub-polar zones and 35 mg carbon per square meter per day for oligotrophic waters of central portions of sub-polar regions.

In shallow coastal waters and estuaries, macroscopic vegetation dominates the biomass and often the total production as well. These macroscopic plants include submergent sea grasses and algae and emergent marsh grasses and mangroves. Thus coastal regions provide a rich variety of organic substrates, both microphytic and macrophytic origin. The occurrence of macrophytic species varies geographically and rates of production vary in response to regional and seasonal changes in nutrient supply, quantity of light and temperature. Estimates of the net organic production by marine macrophytes range from 500-5000 mg carbon per square meter per day.

The primary producers of the marine environment possess the capacity through physiological and morphological adaptability, not only to persist during environmental extremes, but also to thrive over a wide range of environmental conditions. The difference in the form and function of these plant groups are the result of adaptive responses to their specific environments. The ecological success of the various primary producer groups within the marine environment results in high level of organic production. Marine plants can not however, always cope with changes brought about by Man's increasing use of the natural environment.

Primary production in the marine environment – Algae and vascular plants, the primary producers of the marine environment, have become adapted to the salinity range of marine waters. Free floating unicellular algae, the phytoplankton are ubiquitous, only a few multi-cellular algae, such as, *Sargassam* have adapted to a planktonic existence. Benthic algae and vascular plants are restricted to relatively shallow water or inter-tidal bottoms. Vascular plants can be subdivided into submergent and emergent species. Phytoplankton are dominant plant life in the ocean, while submergent vascular plants, the sea grasses are limited to approximately 1 per cent of the sea floor. It is only in the narrow band along the coast of islands and continents that sufficient light for the growth of rooted marine plants reaches the bottom. The emergent vascular plants occur in inter tidal water or where the saline water has saturated sediments in the coastal zone .Emergent marine vascular plant occupy the transition zone between marine and fresh water environments and between aquatic and terrestrial environments.

## Productivity

The open ocean area of approximately 326 X 1000000 square kilometer is dominated by phytoplankton production. The area of diverse producers, the estuaries, amounts to only 1.8 X 100000 square kilometer on a world wide basis. Of this, approximately 1.4 X 1000000 square kilometer is open water and 3.8 X 100000 square kilometer is marsh or mangrove communities. Although higher plants growing on land maintain a biomass more than 1000 times greater than plants in the marine environment, the annual amount of organic production on land and in the sea is about the same. The annual gross production for the world is approximately 100000000000000000 gram carbon of which 44 per cent occurs in marine environment. Assuming 50 per cent of this production is utilized in catabolic process of the plants, then net annual primary production in the marine environment is 2.2 X 1000000 gram carbon. The gross production of marine and terrestrial ecosystem ranges from 20 to 2000 gram carbon per square meter per year.

Phytoplankton are not distributed uniformly throughout the oceans, either horizontally or vertically. The species of phytoplankton present in a geographical area at a given time will consist of endemic species and those that have been transported into the area by movement of water. Species transported into an area may be pre-adapted to existing environmental conditions or in the process of becoming adapted. Any species that does not become adapted can persist for a considerable period of time and constitute a significant part of the biomass, while contributing little to primary production.

The species present in a given area and their abundance are in a constant state of flux. Diatoms and dinoflagellates are the most important in relation to the numbers of marine species. Diatoms form an important part of every collections of phytoplankton. The number of diatom species varies from 2 to 400 at the stations sampled.

Dinoflagellates are a diverse group of primary producers. Some are animal like ingesting particulate food, and some are saprophytic. Species of dinoflagellates at certain time divide rapidly, increasing in numbers to form a "bloom", which can be both spectacular and toxic and for some species is referred to as "red tide". Coccolithophores make up a significant fraction of phytoplankton in open ocean areas. These flagellates can occur in large numbers and constitute a significant portion of biomass of tropical and sub-tropical oceans. The cryptophyceae are small red-brown, bluish or colorless flagellates which at times occur in large numbers in inshore waters. The chlorophyceae are mostly flagellates that occur chiefly in temperate coastal regions, especially in late summer and early winter. Blue green algae appear to be important primarily in brackish waters or in warm and nutrient poor oceanic waters.

Micro-algae are found on and within sediments in inter-tidal and shallow sub-tidal zones. In areas of turbulence these species are often resuspended and become part of phytoplankton community. Diatoms dominate the microbenthic algae, although dinoflagellates, green algae and blue green algae can be abundant on occasion. The diatom community of shallow benthic habitats is diverse. For example, on the inter-tidal mud-flats at Beaufort, North Carolina, Hustedt (1955) found 369 species and 19 varieties of diatoms belonging to 63 genera, 74 species of *Navicula*, 48 species of *Nitzschia*, 32 species of *Amphiprora*, 19 species of *Mastogloia*, 13 species of *Diploneis* were recorded.*Nitzschia* was most characteristic of the area and 18 of the Mastoglesia species found in Beaufort appear to be restricted to the Atlantic coasts of sub-tropical and tropical America.

## Macroscopic Plants

Vascular aquatic plants are those angiosperms and pteridophytes which grow in soil saturated with water or covered with water during a major portion of the year. The geographic distribution of submergent sea grasses has been reviewed by Hardog, 1970, who reported that two families, 12 genera and 48 species of submerged aquatic angiosperms have successfully colonized the marine environment. The two families Potamogetonaceae and Hydrocharitaceae are in the class Monocotyledonae of the divisionAnthophyta. It is remarkable that there are few parts of the world's coastal zone where one or more of these species of sea grasses have not adapted.

With few exceptions, sea grasses can be sub-divided into tropical-subtropical and temperate and into new and old world species. Genera of Potamogetonaceae occur from the tropics through the temperate zones, but on one species extends over this range. On the other hand, the Hydrocharitaceae are tropical. Of the temperate species, only *Zostera marina* has an extensive range, while the distribution of *Posidonia* is discontinuous between Mediterranean coast of South Europe and the coast of Australia.*Phyllospadix* has two major centers of occurrence, one on the Pacific coast of North America and the other in eastern Asia. The tropical-sub-tropical species occur either in the Indo-Malaysian region or in the American tropical region. Within these two regions, the species present have discontinuous distributions and in many instances species of the tropical Americans are highly localized.

The distribution of species of sea grasses is also stratified vertically in the tidal zone. For example, the species of *Holodule* and *Halophila* generally extend from the upper intertidal to the lower sub-tidal zone. *Zostera* generally is distributed from the lower intertidal to the lower sub-tidal zone. Both *Thalassia* and *Cymodocea* are distributed throughout the lower intertidal and upper sub-tidal zones, but *Posidonia* and *Syringodium* are restricted to sub-tidal habitats

Macroscopic algae are also important submergent plants and are distributed along both horizontal and vertical gradients of the marine environment. Dawson (1966) reported that the green algae, Chlorophyceae, have their maximum evolutionary development in the tropics, the brown algae, Pheophyceae are dominant in cold temperate waters, and the red algae, Rhodophyceae, occur at all latitudes.

The geographic range of many species of macroalgae depends on suitable water temperature. The Gulf Stream influences water temperature on the east coast of North America and favors the occurrence of many tropical species at least as far north as Beaufort, North Carolina. *Macrocystis*, the giant kelp, occurs along the west coast of North and South America, except between Baja California and Peru. The occurrence along the south American coast is a result of the upwelling of cold water. The geographical and seasonal distribution of many other algal species varies with latitude because of the effect of currents on local temperature patterns. For example, the cold water current originating in the Antarctica and traveling up the west coast of Africa is responsible for water temperatures that are suitable for the growth of *Ecklonia*, *Laminaria* and *Macrocystis* at relatively low latitude.The gulf stream warms high latitude coastal waters of Great Britain, which are thus favorable for growth of tropical brown algae, *Cystoseira*. Stratification of marine algae generally indicates that red algae are dominant in deep waters, brown algae at intermediate depths and green algae in shallow water.

Salt marshes and mangrove swamps are two broad habitat types dominated by species of emergent vascular plants. Salt marshes dominate the intertidal shores of mid- and high-latutude regions, while in the tropics and sub-tropics they largely are replaced by mangrove swamps. Vegetation in salt marshes includes herbaceous plants and low shrubs, but is generally dominated by grasses or reeds. Benthic green, red and brown macroscopic algae, benthic microalgae and phanaerograms, such as, members of the Chenopodiaceae, *e.g. Salicornia*, also are important and may be locally dominant. Most salt marshes are remarkably uniform in appearance due to dominance of one or few species. The list of representative or dominant salt marsh species of 8 geographical regions of the world includes at least 13 genera.

Mangroves swamps are dominated by mangrove trees or shrubs that grow from the high water mark of spring tides to just above mean sea level. Mangroves are limited to the area between the Tropics of Cancer and Capricorn and occupy an estimated 60 to 75 per cent of the tropical coast lines of the world. Mangrove species are classified into 11 families, 4 of which are distributed throughout the tropics and contain 41 of the 55 most common genera. Mangroves reach their best development in the brackish water of estuaries, but they are also well developed in protected regions dominated by sea water or along rivers or streams where salt water is occasionally present.

# Development of Fishing in the World

Recent history of fishing and its future prospects enable to appreciate to what extent fisheries utilize the production of life in the seas. The history also tells us how research problems have evolved both in time and according to the level of exploitation.

Towards the end of 19th century, in the wake of the industrial revolution, conditions became ripe in the Atlantic and Northern Pacific for fishing industry to industrialized. At that time certain technical innovations were made that greatly increased the power and efficiency of the industry at every stage of production. They were in the field of catching of fishes (otter trawls, steel hulls, steam engines), preservation (ice and canning processes), distribution (railways) and commercialization (big outlets in the main industrial and urban centers).

Up until the second World War, this expansion was limited to the industrialized countries in the Northern Hemisphere. The demersal species were then most sought after and production of these greatly surpassed that of the pelagic species.

Starting at the end of the 1940s, two development occurred. The extension of industrial fishing all over the globe as a result of the greater number of participants (USSR, Indonesia, Peru, Thailand etc) and the use of long range ships capable of freezing and treating their catches on board, far from the traditional centers of consumption.

The intensification of fishing for pelagic species (coastal and oceanic), which was facilitated by several technical innovations. Some of these improved the methods of capture (improvement to surrounding nets, refinements of pelagic trawls and acoustic detection). Others opened up new outlets (the use of fish meal to fatten pigs and chicken).

The result was that by 1970, catches of pelagic species were twice that of demersal species and 90 per cent of the pelagic fish catch and half the total catch went for processing into fish meal.

The series of innovations enabled the fishing industry to expand at a rapid rate. From 1900 to 1970, world fish production went from 4 to 70 million tonnes, which means that it doubled approximately every ten years. This was the highest growth rate of any food production sector and it is one of the few sectors, in which the production grew faster than world population.

Since 1972, however, the total catch has leveled off, mainly because of the decline in the catch of a single stock, the Peruvian anchoveta. Presently, for the world as a whole, the fishing industry supplies about 10 per cent of the animal protein consumed by man as food. The proportion is several times greater than this in the majority of developing countries, particularly, in Africa and Asia, where fish is the basic source of protein in the human diet.

There are a number of prerequisites to fishery development (resources, means of capture, the ability to operate and manage the equipment, labor, systems of processing and preservation, distribution net works and markets), as well as, the establishment of adequate working relations among research institutes, industry and the administrative authorities. Without such working relations, in fact, even the most basic programs and facilities can not be exploited to their full potential. A comparison of the recent performances of various countries show that neither in the most developed nor in the least developed countries are all the conditions mentioned above as requirements of a healthy fishing industry fully satisfied. On the whole conditions appear to be more favorable in the group of countries that are at an intermediate stage of development, *e.g.* Spain, Korea, Cuba, Indonesia etc.

In most areas the fishing industry has developed in three stages, intensified fishing of traditional stocks (the most abundant, the easiest to catch and sell, those found nearest to existing markets), sometimes till a point is reached, when fishing there is no longer profitable. Fishing of unconventional species on the traditional fishing grounds (i.e species that were of no commercial interest when traditional stocks were still abundant). Extension of fishing activity to areas progressively farther away from the original bases (and in these areas the first two stages are repeated).

The steady extension of fisheries to new species and areas has brought about a dramatic change in the overall pattern of the world's fishery resources .Whereas formerly, despite isolated cases of over exploitation, the resources of the various regions were not fully exploited, now a days in most regions the exploitation of most species is very intense, even excessive, which calls for the urgent implementation of more and more serious measures of restraint.

## Nature and Distribution of Fishery Resources

For exploiting resources, certain conditions must be satisfied. Densities must be high enough (at least temporarily) to provide profitable catch rates. Stocks and potential yields must be sufficiently large to justify investments and to allow catches to be maintained at a reasonable level. The product must be marketable. This is a condition which up to now has eliminated species at the lower trophic levels, although these are the most abundant and productive.

Due to the wide dispersal of living matter in the ocean, these conditions only occasionally coincide. To appreciate this it is only necessary to compare, on a world scale, primary production (which is in the order of 150 X 1000000000 tonnes per year) with the volume of marine catches (about 60 X 1000000 tonnes per year). In fact, fishing is presently viable only at a small number of productive 'traps", where the production of the seas is concentrated. To illustrate the highly selective nature of fishing, it is sufficient to compare the catches of the different elements of the flora and fauna to their respective biomasses. Thus as regards the flora, exploitation is very unevenly spread geographically and basically applies to just a few species of macroscopic algae, of which the harvest accounts for only 1 per cent of the total harvest of living matter of aquatic origin. Of more than 20000 species making up the world's fish fauna, a mere 100 species account for over 70 per cent of the world fish catch. In 1971, a single species, the Peruvian anchoveta, accounted for more than one-fifth of the world's fish catch, while the 7 species of anchoveta then being exploited accounted not more than a quarter of the total. This comparison does not take into account the potential of the Argentine and the Californian anchoveta stocks whose biomasses amount to millions of tonnes.

The increase in the proportion of pelagic fish in the total catch since the last world war is a measure of intensified fishing at the lower levels of the food chain this phenomenon can even be seen in the composition of pelagic catches, where the weight ratio of phytoplankton feeders to zooplankton feeders has gone from 4/96 to 39/61 over the past thirty years. This development is the result of the greater productivity of the lower levels of the food chain. It was estimated that the oceanic production of zooplankton alone (ie not including phytoplankton) as being 13 to 15 times greater than that of the benthos consumed by the exploited species while the total weight of plankton feerders directly fished or eaten by predators that are fished, is only 10 to 12 times greater than the total weight of exploited demersal species which feed on benthos.While the complexity of the predator-prey relationships prevents any direct comparisons, these figures do suggest that pelagic stocks are less intensely exploited than the traditional demersal stocks. This view is supported by the results of stock assessments that show coastal pelagic resources throughout the world could supply about another 15 million tonnes per year.

The geographic distribution of fishing is also highly selective. Almost the entire catch is made in waters over the continental shelf (in 1971 almost the entire demersal catch and 94 per cent of pelagic catch) which accounts for the importance of the extent of the continental shelf as a factor in the fishery potential of a region. For example, the Atlantic and North Pacific (where the continental shelf is particularly extensive and half the North Atlantic is less than 1000 m deep) supply half of the total world catch. The proportion is even higher for the demersal fish catch.

Even among neretic waters, fishery resources are unevenly spread. Upwelling regions account for around half the total potential (of conventional species) in the seas i.e 40 to 60 million tonnes out of total which is in the order of 100 million tonnes. In fact, up to now, man has only been skimming off the cream of the ocean's total production. To improve the performance in near future, prospects can be considered in three groupings.

1. As regards traditional stocks, production will not increase more than 50-100 per cent. Considering the previous rate of expansion in world fishing, such a position can be reached within a decade. In many regions and for the more sought after and easily utilized stocks the achievement of this objective already depends more on the implementation of suitable management schemes than on the intensification of fishing.

2. The development of new resources is now technically possible in some cases. Krill- (potential possibility in the region of 50-100 X 1000000 tonnes) Common and oceanic squids (potential possibility between 10 and 100 X 1000000 tonnes) Bathy pelagic fish (potential> 100 X 1000000 tonnes).

It is likely that the development of these resources will depend less on perfecting adequate fishing and treating processes than on the possibilities of finding new outlets that are suitable both as regards quality (new products) and above all as regards quantities (their potential is comparable to present world production). There is no way that one can further define these prospects since the utilization of the lower trophic levels will depend on other factors that can not yet be quantified in the relationship between the cost of the catch and the value of the products (increased energy costs on the one hand due to greater dispension in the marine environment and on the other the generally lower market value of new types of products), the effects that exploiting these stocks may have on the productivity of traditional stocks.

3)There is some potential in marine fish farms, which at present produce little over 5 per cent of the world catch and could produce two folds within 10 years creating job opportunities Even if marine fish farming and fishing are in competition in certain markets for certain similar products, these two types of industry will remain independent for a long time yet as regards their source of supply (i.e its geographic distribution).Since the ocean and its stocks are very difficult to control fishing will remain for a number of decades, the most suitable method of exploitation in the open areas. Marine fish farming will be concentrated especially in the narrow land/sea interface that can be more easily managed. But here it will be in conflict with other uses of the environment, notably town planning, tourism, industry and agriculture, either directly because they are competing for the similar sites or indirectly because of environmental changes brought about by these different types of activity.

## Characteristics of Fishing and Fishery Resources

The fishery resources are living. The importance of knowing their biology and ecology are necessary to stress the fact that they are renewable and thus exploited for ever, but not at any rate we like (as opposed to non-renewable resources).

Above all, they are wild and thus free. Stocks in their distribution and migrations are unaware of the frontiers drawn by man (all marine species, even sessile species have at least one period in their life when they move freely). In general therefore, they can not be owned by individual exploiters. The latter can only enjoy the benefits of exploitation generally in groups (however, the groups may be defined). Within these groups, the fishermen compete directly for shares of the yield of the stock, which is generally limited (such a stock is often referred to as a freely accessible resources).

For these resources, it is not possible to catch fish, for example, at only a certain age and a certain predetermined size. Thus, it is not possible to catch all the members of a particular year class at the age when the weight of the year class is its maximum, as can be done in the case of domestic animals raised for meat. Further more, in the open sea, just as in inland waters above a certain size, the environment can not be controlled. Physio-chemical conditions, nutrient salts, the composition of associated flora and fauna (food, predators and competitors etc) are beyond man's control. Even in case of extensive cultivation there can be only partial control of the nature and degree of environmental conditions. These difficulties connected with controlling the marine environment, its inhabitants and their yield mean that the comparisons, such as fruit picking versus settled agriculture, hunting versus stock breeding (i.e between the land environment and the sea environment) are not really justified. They also explain why even though fish farming has been in existence for a long time, it was in practice limited to immobile shell fish species and had to be confined to the narrow land/sea interface where at least partial contol could be exercised.

Given the living and wild nature of fish stocks, the optimum rate of exploitation (and even the method, since that may determine the average age and size of individual fish taken) can not be chosen arbitrarily. In the long term the highest yield will be attained by maintaining the rate of exploitation at a level corresponding to the maximum rate of natural replacement of the stock, above this rate and below it there will be some decrease in the yield. The objective of stock assessment is to determine, for the various stocks, what is the maximum rate of replacement and what the pattern of exploitation should be to realize it. The object of this course is to see how this can be done.

## Investigation and Assessment of Resources

In fact, the kind of information required and its precision, change with the intensity of exploitation of a stock.

### Development of a Fishery

The first step, when exploitation is still light or nil, consists of identifying those resources which are most likely to support an expansion of the industry and meet the deemed market.

Among research tasks at the various stages of fishery development, distinctions can be made according to the nature of the information being sought.

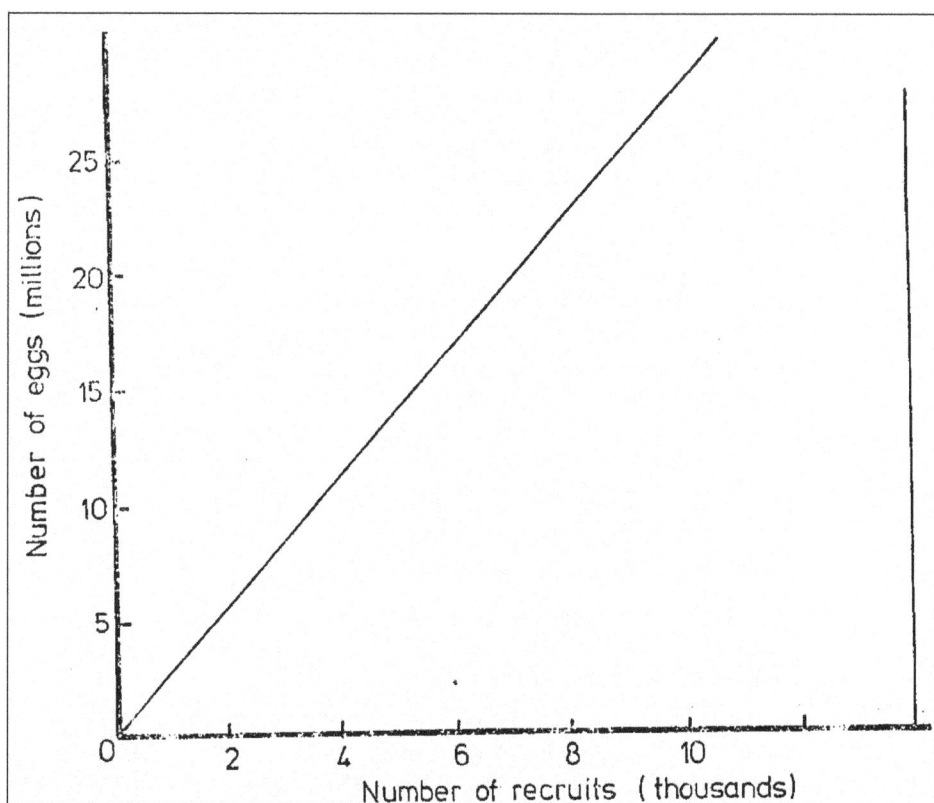

**Figure 4: Number of Eggs Produced by different Numbers of Recruit.**

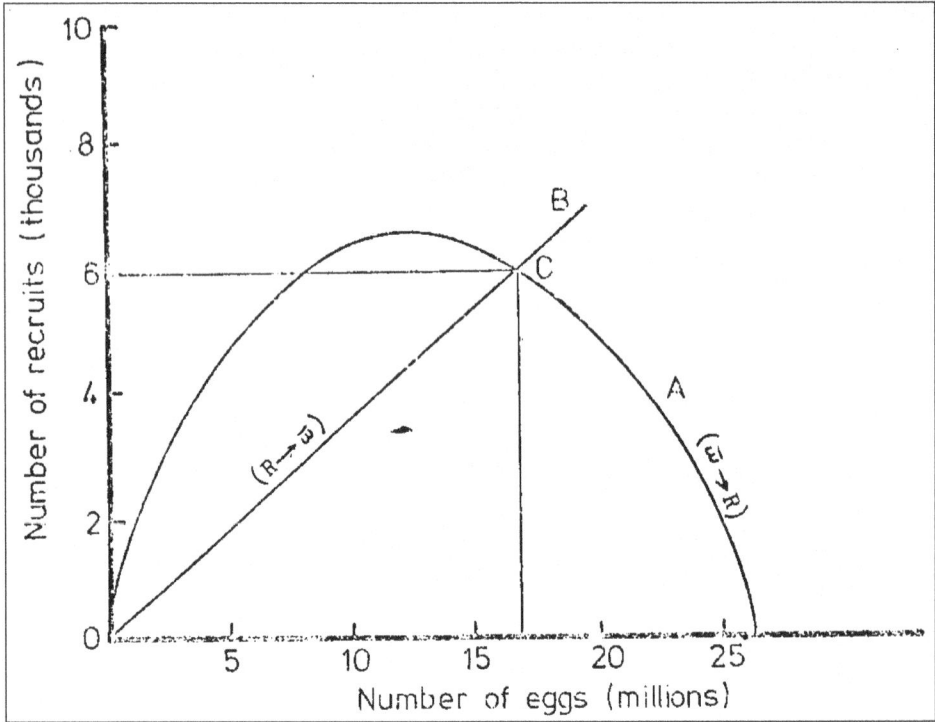

**Figure 5: Determination of Population Equilibrium given.**
**(A) An egg to recruit relationship and (B) A recruit to egg relationship.**

1. Surveys aimed at directing the industry to the more interesting stocks (bearing in mind the needs and capacities of each country) so as to develop fisheries on the various stocks in the most appropriate order. This has not always been the case since fishing often develops on the basis of borrowed attitudes or methods which only rarely conform to actual requirements. Thus on the west coast of Africa trawling for demersal fish developed before seine fishing for coastal pelagic fish which better suits the needs of the region. The main goals of these surveys are to establish,

   – an inventory of potentially usable stocks;

   ☆ the commercial possibilities of the corresponding catches;

   ☆ an approximate order of magnitude of potential catch, or at least a minimum limit of these potentials which can be used as a temporary ceiling for development plans.

   Moreover, to arouse the interest of potential investors, it is necessary to get the figures on, (a) estimated catches and revenues for various types of vessels and method of fishing; (b) the seasonal and a real variations in catch rates (particularly by localizing in time and space the most dense concentrations).

2. Monitoring the state of stocks at different levels of exploitation. All fishermen know that when the number of boats exploiting a stock increases, the catch rates and individual catches decline progressively until, at a certain level, the total catch levels off. Any new investment will then lead to a lowering in the long term of stock abundance and catches. Since increasing fishing efforts will not produce an increase in the total catch indefinitely, proper planning requires a prediction of the effects on the size and composition of the stock on the one hand, and on the yields and total catch on the other, of different increases in fishing effort.

In particular, answers must be found to the following questions; (1) what proportion does the current catch represent of the potential maximum catch? (2) what are the current catch rates and how will they change if fishing is intensified? (3) what size of the fleet is required to attain the levels of production that can be envisaged? and (4) what will be the effects on the stocks and catches of given changes in mesh size or more generally, in the minimum size of individual fish caught?

(c) Assessment of potential maximum catch – There are in fact, only too many examples of cases where over-optimistic estimates of potential have led to excessive investments and eventually considerable economic loss and where the failure to take decisions to control fishing has led to serious over-exploitation of stocks and collapse of certain fisheries. Since the control of fisheries can in the short term, result in real hardships (reduction of investments, loss of jobs), information on the state of stocks should be sufficiently clear and precise so as to convince the decision makers. Finally it should be noted that the potential catch rarely remain constant from one year to the next. In fact, the maximum surplus that can be fished is liable to vary from one year to the next depending on changing environmental conditions. These unpredictable fluctuations, like long term variations, can be quite considerable for certain stocks, e.g coastal pelagic fish. To derive the greatest benefit from them, it would be wise to take these fluctuations into account in management plans or at least, to be in a position to cut back on fishing in the event of an abnormal drop in stock abundance. Stock evaluation therefore, should be considered as an ongoing task where estimates are constantly being readjusted and refined.

# Transfer of Energy in the Food Web

One can approach the biomasses and the potential production of elements utilizable by man in an ecosystem by examining these quantities at successive trophic levels. These supposes that the trophic relationships between levels (or the components of successive levels being compared) are known both qualitatively and quantitatively and that these relationships are fairly stable over time. Such a procedure, which is essential in understanding how living matter is produced in the ocean, is still difficult to apply, owing to the complexity of trophic relationships in the marine environment; where successive levels of production intermingle according to ramified networks showing *anastomoses* and diversions in constant evolution.

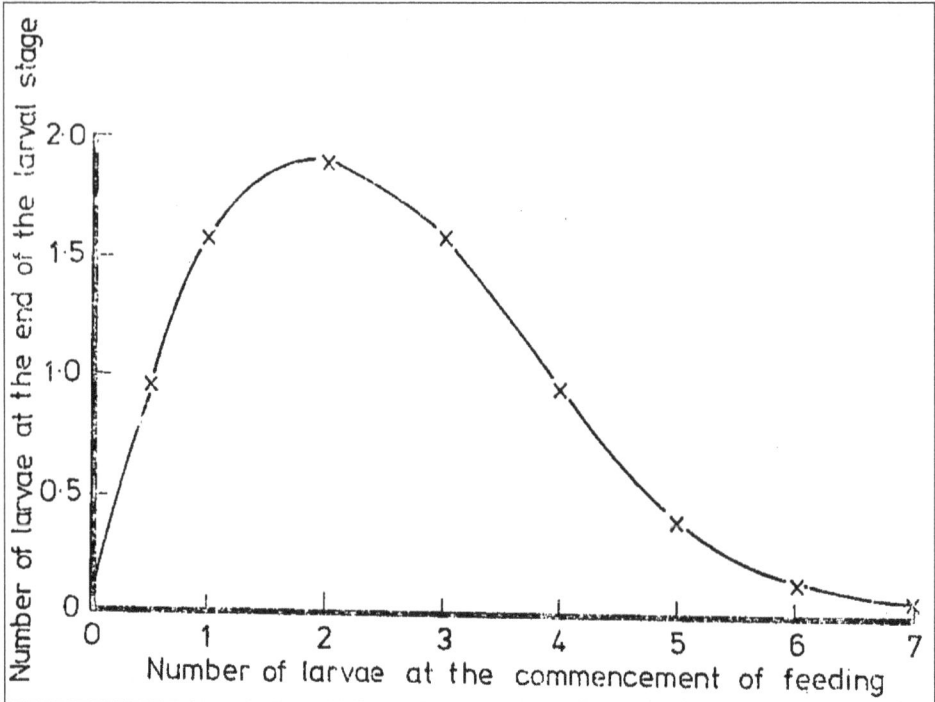

**Figure 6: A Domed Shaped Stock/Recruit Curve, Superficially Similar to a Ricker Curve, can also be Generated by Supposing that Larval Survival is Dependant on Larval Food Abundance.**

The most common applications bear on the evaluation of relationships between successive trophic levels taken as a whole (primary, secondary and tertiary production). Several attempts have been made to estimate by this method the potential resources that can be utilized by man. The range of results obtained (200-2000 m.tons) casts doubt on the usefulness of this approach, at least as regards the validity of results. In fact, much of the divergence among results is due to the criteria followed by the authors in defining utilizable resources. As noticed in fishing and assessment of stocks, the lower limit of the levels utilizable by man depends on artificial factors (available technology, market conditions, cost of energy for capture etc) that are destined to change with time.

An illustration of the calculations and difficulties that are implicit in this approach can be found in the work of Cushing (1969) on the assessment of the fisheries potential in the upwelling regions. According to these assessments half the world's fisheries potential (40-60 m.tons) lies in the yield of upwelling zones. If primary and secondary production can be assessed with relative security, the energy transfer co-efficient between successive levels are still little known because, on the one hand they differ among the organisms involved and on the other hand, the higher the level does not always use all the energy available to it from the lower level.

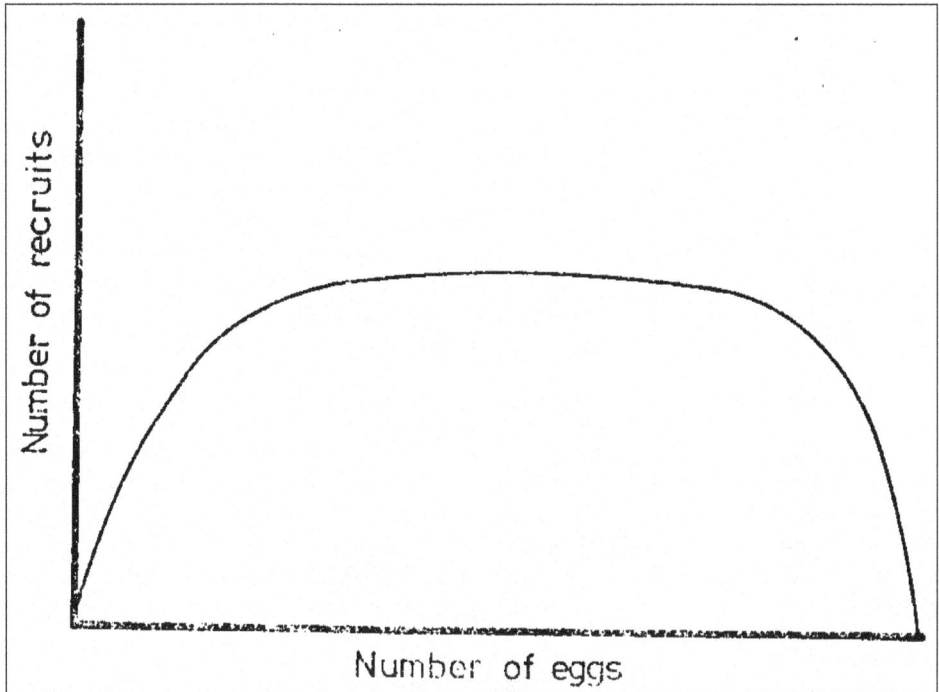

**Figure 7: Shape of Stock/Recruit Curve that might be Expected if Predation (or living space) Tended to Reduce the Density of Juveniles to some Critical Level.**

The approximate nature of this type of assessment can be illustrated by the comparison made by Pauly (1972) between estimates calculated for the same region (Peru current) by two different authors. Cushing estimated the total annual carbon fixation. He considered that this phytoplankton production was consumed by the zooplankton and by the anchovy stock, the young of which are supposed to feed on copepods and phytoplankton, and the adults mainly on phytoplankton. He assumed an energy yield of 10 per cent per transfer. He arrived at similar conclusions by starting directly from secondary production.

Ryther, following the same procedure, but with slightly different hypotheses and reasoning, arrived at final results that are practically identical. Furthermore, the two results coincide to a remarkable extent with those obtained through the classic methods of assessment which gave a total annual production of 20 m.tons (10 ton for fishing, 9 ton for natural death and marine predators and 1 ton for consumption of guano birds) before the collapse of the fishery in 1972 and 1973. However, if we compare the successive stages of the calculations of both authors, the agreement between the results is less reassuring. The figures used by Cushing and Ryther for the area and total energy yield are quite different.

Taking different areas need not be serious in itself- in taking a smaller area Ryther could have neglected a peripheral zone of low productivity. But in that case his figure for carbon fixation should have been proportionally higher than that of

Cushing. So if the estimates agree in the end, this is because the authors are using quite different values for the total energy yield.

Since the anchovy is the main user of the plankton production, in the Peruvian upwelling zone, it was possible by this method to assess a well defined stock. More often, in fact, the complexity of the trophic relationships between successive levels is such that these assessment processes can only be applied to groups of fairly heterogeneous resources. Finally, it should be noted that these methods are not used exclusively for estimating the productivity of the higher levels in the food web. It has been calculated, for example, that in the virgin state whale stocks (1.0-1.5 m.tons) consumed yearly around 50 m.tons of krill. As whales are not the only consumers of krill, this figure already gives a lower limit of the potential of this resources.

## Evaluation of Potential Yield Starting from Biomass Measurements

A third approach that is more commonly used is to deduce the potential yield of a stock from an estimate of its biomass, which can be obtained from specially organized survey. This method has the advantage that it does not require a series of data gathered over a long period of the fishery's history. An estimate of the biomass only requires the time needed to do a survey. On the other hand, quantitative surveys often requires highly specialized material and human resources that are not available everywhere. Several types of surveys can be used.

Of course, only surveys which lead to estimates in absolute terms are useful here. Basically the methods listed below are used.

1. Direct census (sessile or slightly mobile animal, such as, shell fish, salmon, whales etc.)
2. Surveys of eggs and larvae from which the number of spawning females can be deduced and thus the size of the parent stock.
3. Trawling surveys, to the extent that one can learn the true efficiency of the gear, *i.e.* the proportion (F) of the biomass present in the area swept by the trawl, that is caught by it.
4. Quantitative acoustic surveys (especially for coastal pelagic species).

## Stock and Recruitment

Relationships between the size of a fish stock and the numbers of individuals that recruit to it annually.

Though many studies has focused attention on particular parts of the life history only, such as the larval stage. In general, however, any factors responsible for controlling the size of a population and maintaining its stability under a wide range of environmental conditions is relevant. In this context, stability does not necessarily mean the maintenance of population size at a particular level. The population that exists to day are those that have not been eliminated during an extremely long time period. One is therefore dealing with biological systems that are not so much stable in the mathematical sense, as ones in which the probability of elimination (at least by natural cause) has been extremely small indeed.

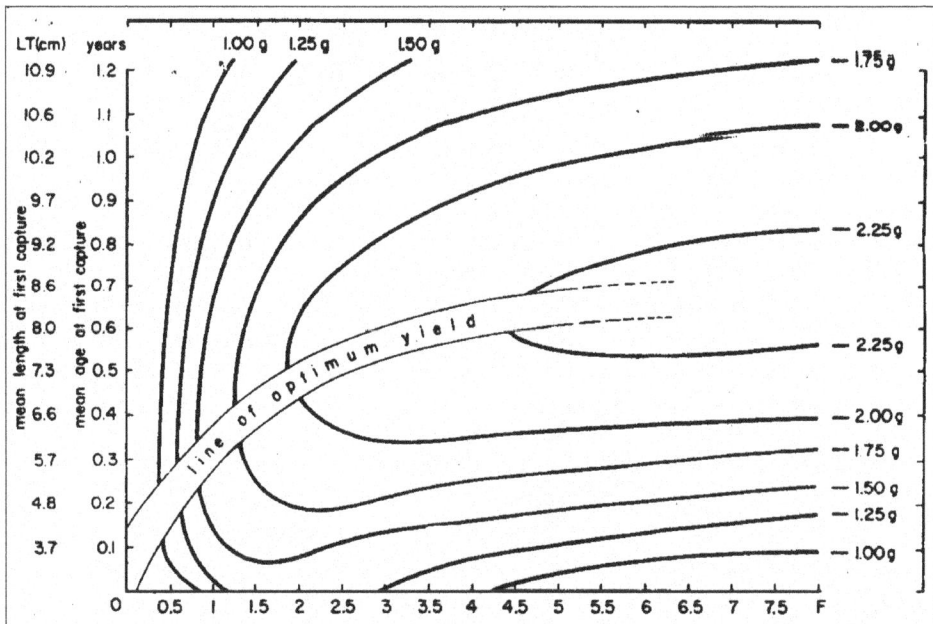

**Figure 8: The Yield/Recruit in Relation to Size or Age at First Capture (Ordinate) and the Force of Fishing (Abcissa) of the Slipmouth *Leiognathus splendens*. The Beverton and Holt method was used to calculate the diagram.**

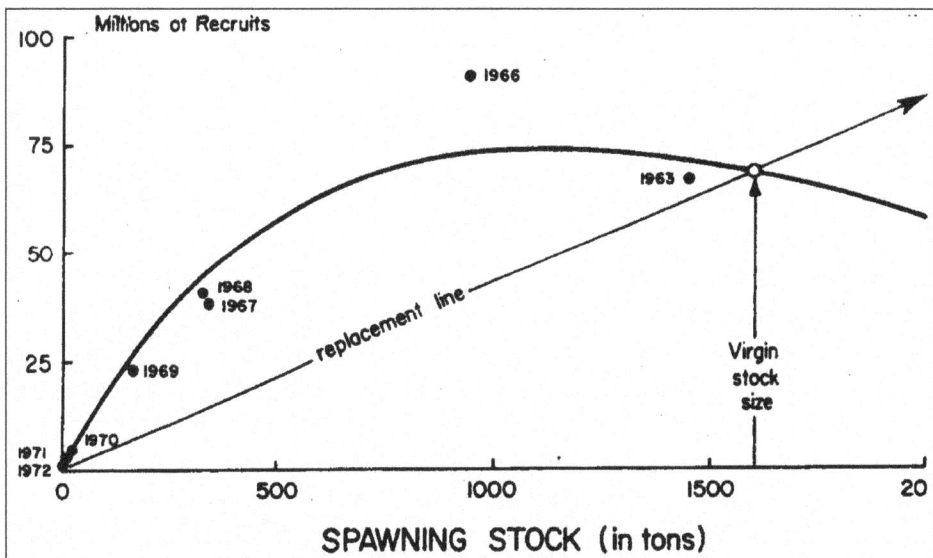

**Figure 9: Stock-Recruitment Relationship for the Stock *Lactarius lactarius* in the Gulf of Thailand.**

# Density-Dependence and Independence

The terms density-dependent and density-independent are frequently used in discussing stock-recruitment relationships.

Illustration shows various relationships between hypothetical initial numbers of individuals and the numbers surviving after a given time or at a given size. The relationship shown by the line A represents the situation where the number of survivors is some constant proportion of the initial number of individuals. This is referred to as a density-independent relationship. Curve B shows a situation where the number of survivors increases indefinitely as the initial number increases. However it is not a constant proportion of the initial numbers. Curve C shows a situation where the number of survivors increase initially, but eventually declines as the initial number is increased further. Both of the relationships B and C are referred to as density dependent relationships. It is implicit in any discussion of population control that there is at least one stage in the life history, where the number of survivors is not directly proportional to the initial numbers i.e, at one or more stages in the life history, a density-dependent relationship of some kind is inferred.

Biologically the factors most likely to prevent an indefinite build-up of population biomass are (a) food limitation, (b) predation and (c) disease. Of these the factors 2 and 3 may operate independently of food limitation or as a cause of food limitation i.e it is useful to distinguish between the situation in which an individual is eaten, because it is weakened due to lack of food and the situation in which healthy individuals are just as liable to be eaten as weakened individuals. In the first case the number eaten will tend to be a function of the food supply as well as of the number of predators. In the second case the number eaten will depend mainly on the number of predators.

# Sources of Food Energy

Of the various factors likely to influence the size of a fish population, food energy is one of the most important. Fish do not necessarily gather all their food energy from any one source, however, and some species exploit a series of food sources, often at various trophic levels.

A North Sea haddock eats food organisms from various trophic levels as it grows. Up to a length of about 5 cm (an age of about 80 days) the principal food is herbivores, such as, copepods.

From about a length of 5 cm to the end of first year of life the food comes mainly from the next trophic level (from primary carnivores, such as, amphipods, euphausiids, and some young fish).

During the second year of life the fish become benthic and the food consists mainly of smaller benthic organisms.

From a length of about 29 cm (about 2 years of age) and for the rest of life, the food consists mainly of the larger benthic organisms and primary carnivores, including euphausiids, sand eels and small fish.

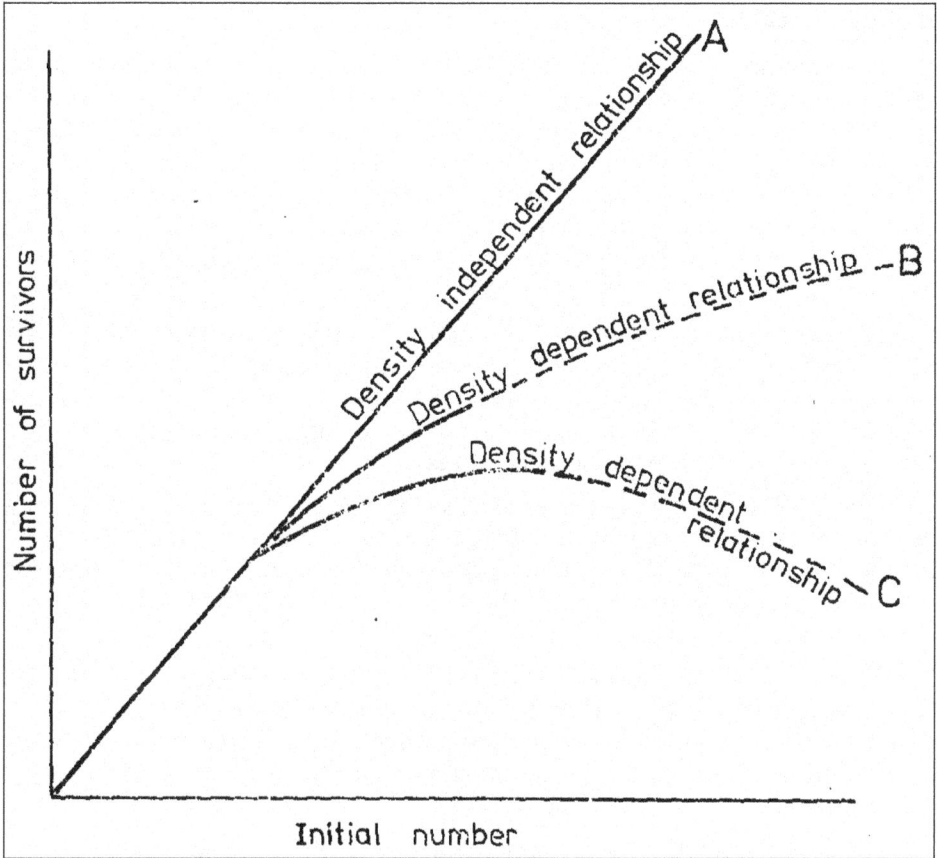

**Figure 10: Density Dependent and Independent Relationships.**

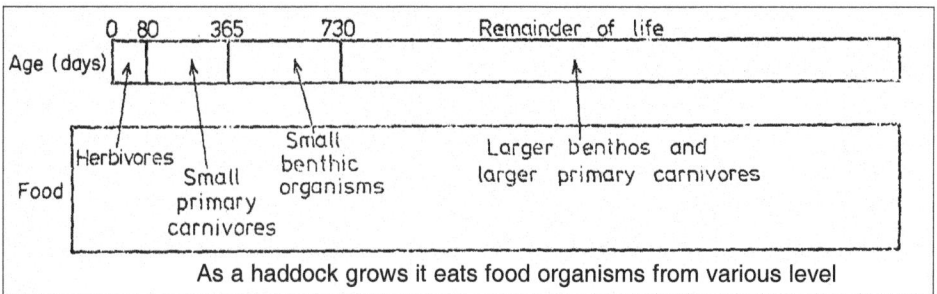

As a haddock grows it eats food organisms from various level

**Figure 11: Haddock Food Resources.**

It appears therefore, that juvenile haddock exploit a series of food sources before they are large enough to exploit the kind of food on which the mature biomass is largely dependent. There appears to be no reasons why the food from any one, or all of these sources might not be limiting.

## A Simplified Life History

To reduce the problem to its simplest form, it is convenient to consider the life history in two stages, each depend on a different sources of food energy. The individuals at the moment of transition from one stage to another are usually referred as "recruits" This term is frequently applied to the number of individuals aged one year. It might also apply however, to the number entering the exploitable part of the stock, or to the number attaining the stage of first maturity. Ecologically it would be appropriate to apply it to the number at one of the transition stages from one food type to the another.

However, the term "recruits" when defined, it is appropriate to consider at least two relationships. One is the relationship between the number of eggs produced by the mature stock and the subsequent number of recruits. The second is the relationship between the number of recruits and the number of eggs they can be expected to produce during the entire course of their lives.

Figure 12 shows a generalized density-dependent relationship between egg production and the subsequent number of recruits. It is assumed that somewhere between egg production and recruitment, food is limiting. If egg production is increased indefinitely, a stage would eventually be reached where all individuals are likely to die.

Figure 13 shows a comparable relationship between the numbers of recruits and the subsequent egg production from these throughout the remainder of their lives. Again it is assumed that food is limited so that an indefinite increasae in the number of recruits should eventually lead to a situation in which no eggs at all are produced. This relationship is given by curve B.

It is clear that equilibrium should occur at a value of egg production and a value of recruitment that satisfies both curve A and B.

Figure 14 shows a simple graphical way of finding this equilibrium point. Here both curves are combined a single diagram. Curve A is exactly as depicted in figure 12. Curve B is exactly depicted as in Figure 13, except that the axes have been interchanged. The result is two curves which diverge initially, but which eventually converges and cross over at the point marked C. The coordinates of this point define a level of egg production and a number of recruits that satisfy the relationships shown in Figures 12and 13.

The argument has been conducted in terms of number of eggs and numbers of recruits. To take account of growth, however, it would be appropriate to use other units, such as, the biomass of eggs and the biomass of recruits.

## The Effect of Fishing

Figure 15.1 shows the relationship between recruitment and subsequent egg production at two levels of fishing effort. Since it is assumed that there is relatively unlimited food for mature fish, changes in fishing effort would simply move the B curves up or down, *i.e.* for a given level of recruitment, a low level of fishing effort (curve B1) should lead to a higher egg production, than a high level of fishing effort

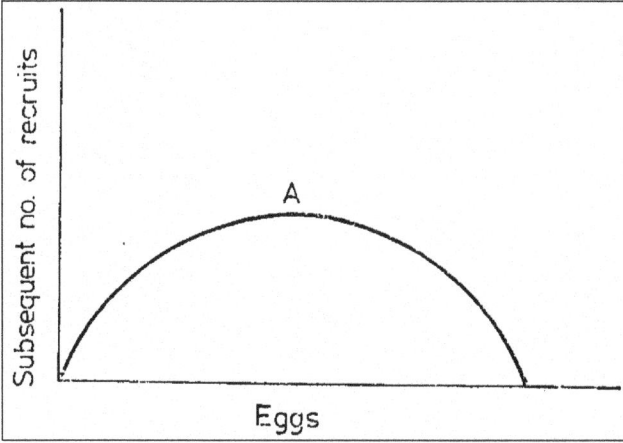

**Figure 12: Egg Production and Subsequent Recruitment.**

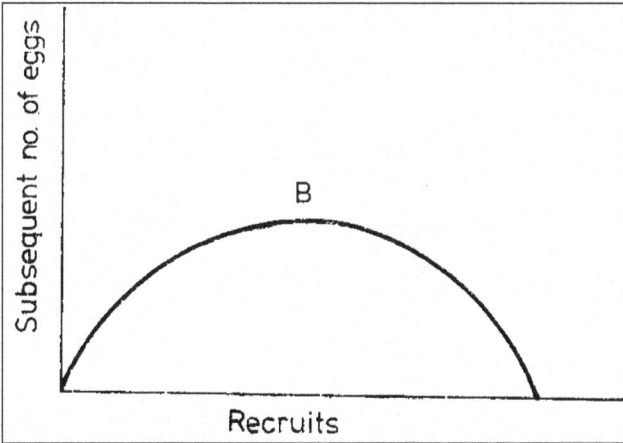

**Figure 13: Recruitment and Subsequent Egg Production.**

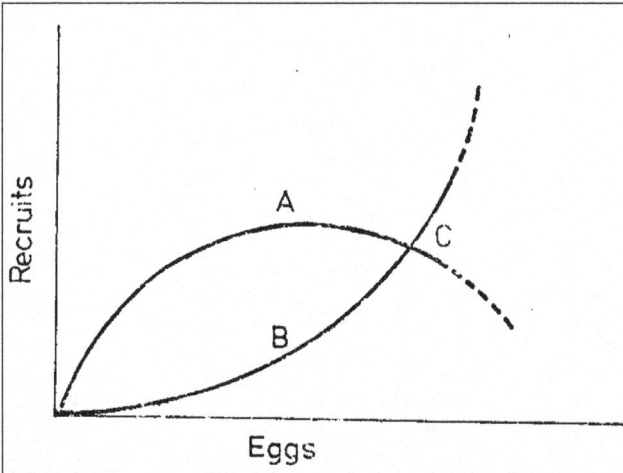

**Figure 14: Finding an Equilibrium Point (C) to Satisfy both Relationships.**

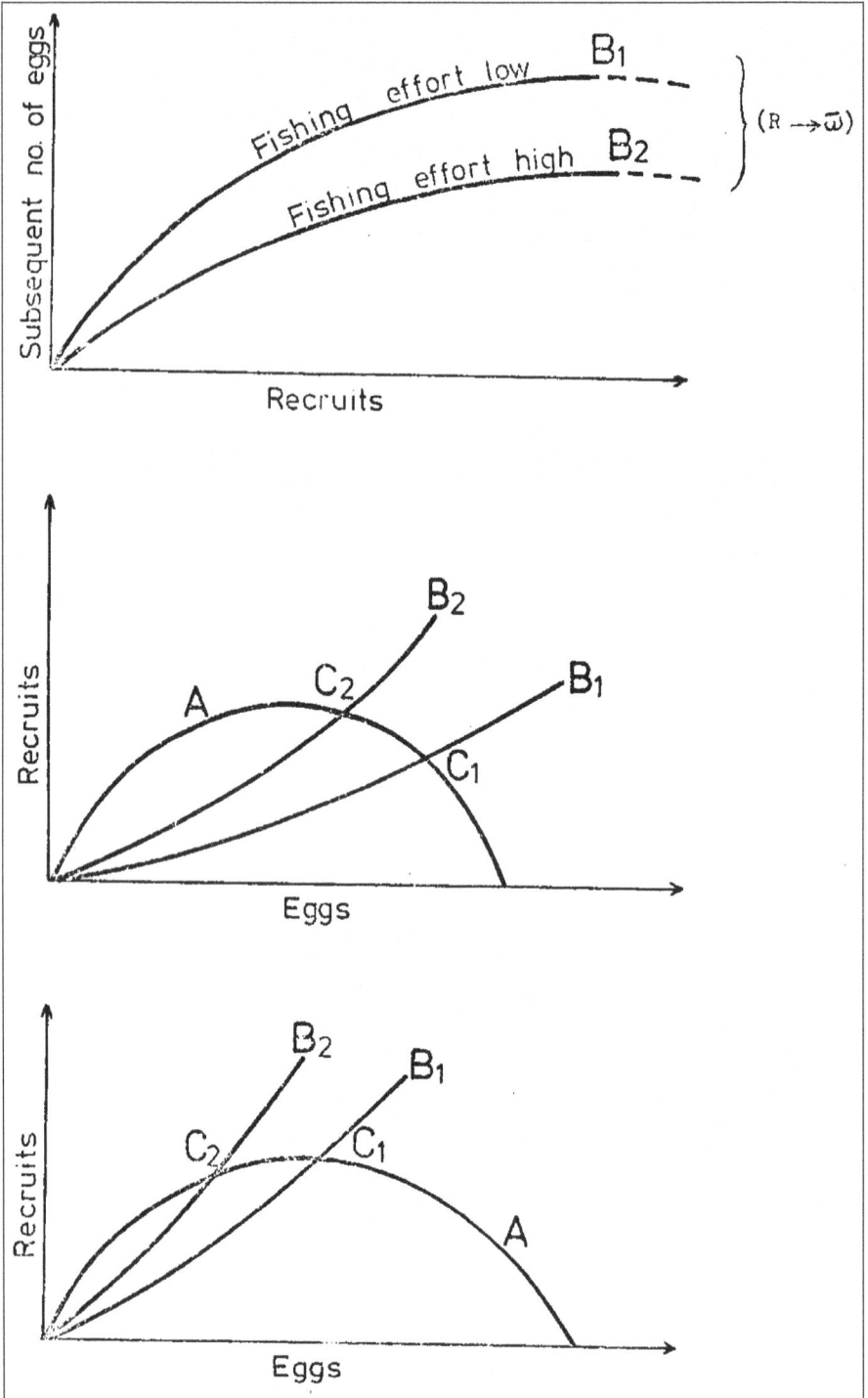

**Figure 15: Effect of Fishing I**

(B2). In general, the effect of fishing should be to cause the B curve to move down toward the recruit axes.

Figure 15.2 shows the combination of the two B curves with the A curve. C1 is the equilibrium position when fishing effort is low. C2 is the equilibrium position when

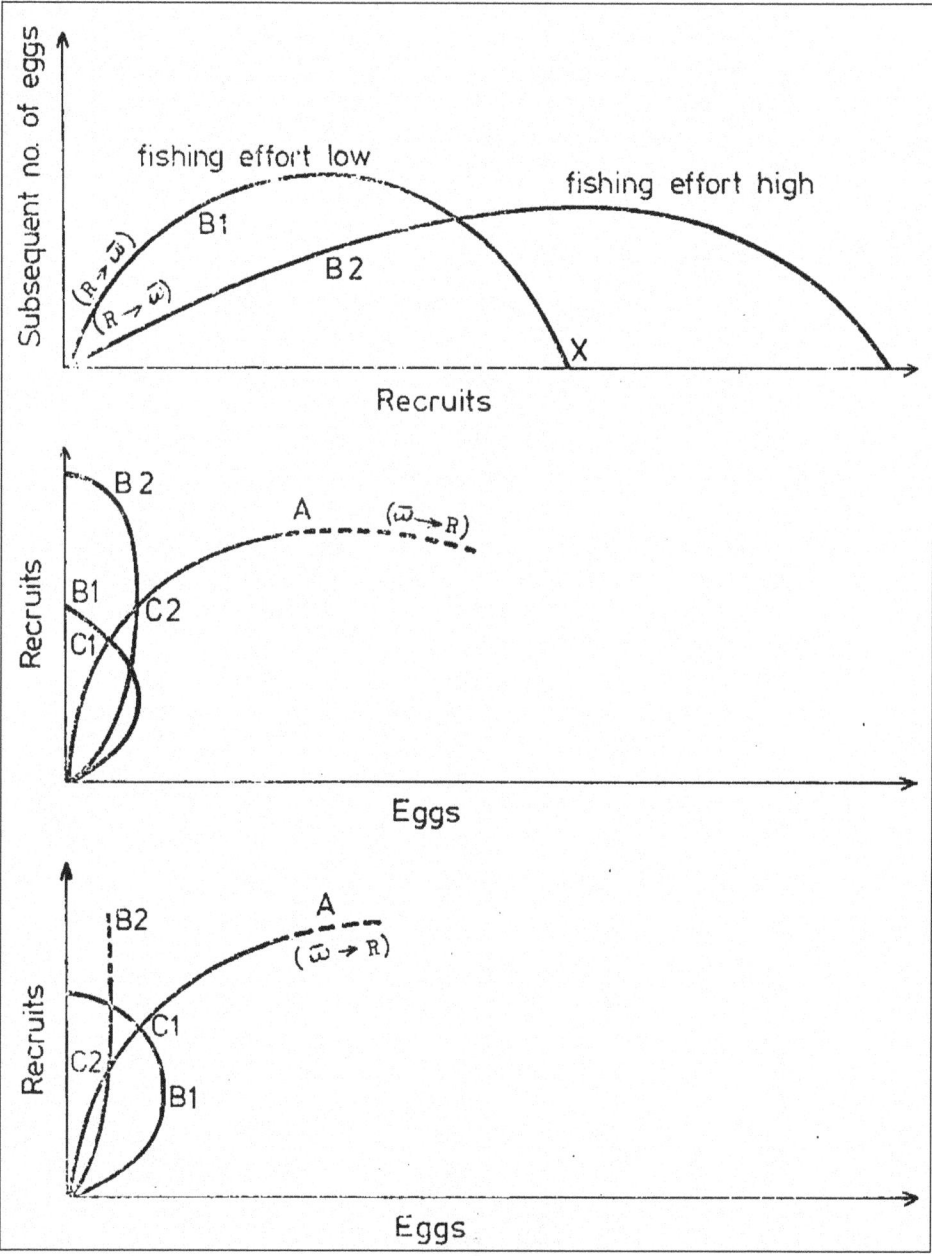

**Figure 16: Effect of Fishing II**

fishing effort is high. In general, it is clear that the effect of fishing should be to move the point of equilibrium along the A curve toward its origin. At the same time, this should be associated with a decline in egg production. The effect on recruitment depends on the relative position of the B curves in relation to the A curve. Figure 15.2 for example shows a situation where an increase in fishing effort should increase the mean level of recruitment. Figure 16 on the other hand, shows a situation where an increase in fishing effort should cause recruitment to decline.

It is possible that the situation depicted in Figure 15.2 is applicable to a stock in its early stages of exploitation, whereas Figure 16 is more likely to apply to a stock that is already intensively exploited. Clearly the higher the rate of exploitation and the closer the equilibrium point is forced toward the origin, the greater the ultimate danger of stock collapse.

## Implications for Management

The effect of fishing on levels of recruitment and egg production have important implications for management. There are three principal situations;

1. It may happen that over a certain range of fishing effort, recruitment is approximately constant. Within this range it is expected that yields could be maximized by maximizing the yield per recruit. Management measures intended to maximize the yield per recruit would then be appropriate.

2. In situations where recruitment is likely to change with changes in fishing effort it is more likely that maximum yields would be associated with a high level of recruitment rather than simply with high levels of yield per recruit. Management policy would then have to take recruitment, as well as yield per recruit, into account.

3. In the situation where fishing effort is so high that egg production is below some critical level, there is always the danger of a stock collapse. Management should be prepared for this possibility and if the situation warrants it, be prepared to stop fishing entirely until there has been an adequate recovery of the stock.

## Population Size at different Stages in the Life History

### The Larval Stage

For some species, the larval period has been regarded as the principal stage where population size might be limited. Biologically, important factors are; Larvae grow relatively rapidly. Their food requirements are therefore relatively large for their size, yet, being small, their capacity for searching for food is relatively small. Food limitation is therefore likely to be more critical for rapidly growing larvae than for slowly growing plankton organisms of the same size. For certain species (e.g, haddock) it has been calculated that the average density of the young stages of copepods on which the larvae feed is such that larval mortality could easily occur due to food deprivation. This species feeds on the young growing stages of copepods, the growth rate of the larvae being approximately the same as that of the copepodite. The net result is that each cohort of larvae tends to be limited for the first 1-2 months to about 3 weeks production of copepods. Copepods born earlier than this tend to be excluded as food as they tend to be too large to eat, and copepods born later tend not to be eaten, presumably because they would be so small that too many would be required to satisfy the food requirements of the larvae. A situation such as this, where individuals grow rapidly for a period on a fixed food supply, provides an effective way of limiting population size. Not all species of larvae grow at the same rate as their food however, so that limitation of numbers at the larval stage need not necessarily apply to all species. Also even for species such as haddock where it may apply, this does not preclude the possibility of limitation of numbers at other stages in the life history

Once haddock larvae are large enough to eat fully grown copepods, they should be able to exploit the entire production of copepods for the season, and the factors influencing survival are likely to be different.

Mortality rates are believed to be high, and death is probably due to predation. It is not certain however to what extent this is due to primary predation (i.e, consumption of healthy as much as weakened individuals) or to secondary predation (i.e, consumption of weakened individuals rather than healthy ones).

Many species of fish larvae appear to exploit food that occurs at a particular time in the productive cycle and sometimes mainly at a particular geographical location. It is important for survival therefore that, at the commencement of feeding, the larvae happen to be at the right place at the right time.

## The Stage of Maturity

After maturity, growth, survival and egg production are all factors that could be influenced by food production and the size of the stock. Each genotype is presumably adapted to partition energy for survival, growth and egg production in a particular way. However, if total food energy is reduced, any one of these three factors can only be favored at the expense of the other two. In particular, egg production is likely to then suffer;

(a) directly, because energy is used primarily to maintain growth and survival; or (b) indirectly, because of the reduction in growth and/or survival that would presumably occur if egg production were to be favored in the short term.

In the long term, food limitation in the mature stage ought therefore to limit egg production.

Evidence shows that a number of species have the capacity to limit egg production directly when food is scarce. For example, egg production can be reduced by a reduction in the number of oocytes starting vitellogenesis, or by the resorption of oocytes during the maturation period. This is a factor, however, that might be more important in virgin stocks than in stocks that are subject to high levels of exploitation.

## Intermediate Stages

In addition to a larval food "niche" and an adult food "niche' there may be one or more intermediate sources of food energy. Some of these may be similar to the haddock larval stage, i.e, they may represent transitory food sources only suitable for individuals of a certain size, and only available for part of a year. As fish approach maturity, however, their growth rate slows down and there may be an intermediate food source that is suitable in all times of the year. To a limited extent, a large year class may then be able to improve its chances of survival by growing more slowly than average. If growth is retarded too much, however, there would be the danger of a following year class catching up in size and competing with it.

In the long term therefore, intermediate food sources could be just as important as other food sources for limiting population size.

In addition to variations in growth rate with year class size, cannibalism also might be an important adaptation at an intermediate feeding stage, i.e;

1. It would be one way of reducing the competition from a following year class.
2. At the same time, it would be taking advantage of an additional source of food energy.

## Evolutionary Considerations

A detailed examination of the stomach contents of North Sea gadoids shows not only that these eat different individuals throughout the course of life, but that they do so in a way that appears to minimize a direct competition either with other gadoids or with other species in general. This may be done by feeding on particular organisms either in different geographical locations or at different times of the year or by feeding on different life stages of a particular species (i.e, possibly on the same species but on individuals of different sizes). It appears likely that at each stage in its life history, a gadoid is able to occupy an independent "niche" in the sense that competition with other species is avoided or reduced.

It might then be argued that in a perfectly stable environment, relationships such as, the situation in which there is more than enough food for the adults and juveniles should not occur. During the course of evolutionary time one might have expected so many sequences of feeding "niches" to have been tried by different genotypes that not only would all possible energy sources be fully utilized but that each species would fully occupy a niche at each point in its life history. This argument appears to favor egg/recruit relationships with high survival potential as the ultimate equilibrium form for all species.

In practice however, it seems more probable that the ecosystem is not in a state of perfect equilibrium in this sense, but cyclical changes can occur, causing some groups of species to increase whilst others decrease, i.e, there appears to be sufficient flexibility to permit variations in the energy flow to each feeding "niche". There seems no reason in principle therefore, why in the "short" term (i.e, periods possibly of the order of decades) individual species might not oscillate between alternatives, such as, egg production and recruitment.

If this were so it would help to explain the lack of success so far encountered in finding a single population control process for the marine teleosts.

# Marine Biodiversity in India

The marine ecosystem has a varying profile. The coastline encompasses almost all types of inter-tidal habitat, from hyper saline and brackish lagoons, estuaries, and coastal marsh and mudflats, to sandy and rocky shores. The sub-tidal habitats are equally diverse. Each local habitat reflects prevailing environmental factors and is further characterized by its biota. Thus, the marine fauna itself demonstrates gradients of change throughout the Indian coasts.

Out of total 32 animal phyla, 15 are represented by the taxa in the marine ecosystem. They may constitute either migratory or resident species. The former includes pelagic crustaceans, coelenterates (medusae), cephalopods, fishes, reptiles, birds and mammals. Amphibians are generally absent in estuaries. The benthic macro fauna comprises resident species of polychaetes, bivalves, gastropods, sipunculas and mud-burrowing fishes. Among invertebrates, the sponges, phoronids and echinoderms generally do not prefer an estuarine ecosystem. In the Indian estuaries, species diversity seems to be maximum in the mollusks. About 245 species belonging to 76 genera under 54 families have been catalogued. Other important taxa, polychaeta are represented by about 167 species belonging to 97 genera under 38 families. Maximum diversity has been reported in the much studied Hoogly-Matlah estuary (West Bengal). Macro organisms and meiofauna of Indian estuaries are not properly investigated. Estuarine mud may contain rich variety of bacteria, flagellates, ciliates, nematodes, ostracods, harpacticoid copepods, rotifers, gastrotriches, arachnids and tardigrades.

Free swimmers or nekton are important components of marine biodiversity and constitute important fisheries of the world. The dominant taxa in the nekton are fish, others being crustaceans, mollusks, reptiles and mammals. Out of the total 22000 finfish species, about 4000 species occur in the Indian Ocean of which 1800 species are reported in the Indian seas. A majority of the nektonic species is found in the coastal waters. It is estimated that 40 species of sharks and 250 species of bony fishes represented the oceanic species.

Among reptiles, sea snakes and turtles are important and represented world wide by 50 and 7 species respectively. These are generally oceanic forms but a majority of them visit the shore at some part of their life. About 26 species of sea snakes belonging to one family, Hydrophiidae, and five species of sea turtles were reported from seas around India. Oceanic islands seem to harbor more reptiles in their marine environment. All the sea snakes and four species of turtles in their marine environment are known from islands of Andaman and Nicobar. Nesting sites of an amphibious snake were reported from the shores of North Andaman Islands (Whitaker, 1985). Turtles visit the shore during breeding time to lay their eggs. The shore visit of these turtles, especially the olive ridley is a spectacular sight on the sandy beach at Gahirmatha near Bhitarkanika in Odisha. The Andaman and Nicobar Islands have the best nesting beaches for the leatherback, the hawksbill and the green turtle in addition to the olive ridley (Baskar, 1993).

Marine mammals belonging to three orders, Sirenia, Cetacea and Carnivora. About 120 species are estimated to occur in World Seas and of these 30 are reported from seas around India. But a majority of these is found in oceanic forms and occasionally a few individuals may get stranded on the shore. The sea cow occurs in near shore waters.

# Chapter 3

# Prospects for World Fisheries

The past decade has witnessed a profound change in the world fisheries. Although most projections made in 1960s were influenced by the diminishing number of stocks offering the possibility of sustained increases in catch, it was not foreseen that the rate of growth of world production would decline so soon and so sharply. Throughout the 1970s, in fact, the rate of growth of landings has been lower than that of world population with a consequent decline in the contribution of fish to human nutrition.

The growth and stagnation of the world fish catch during past five decades has been much influenced by the growth and decline of fisheries exploited largely for reduction of their landings to meal and oil. These fisheries accounted for 64 per cent of the rise in production in the period 1960/70. Likewise, since 1970, the fall of over four million tonnes in landings used for reduction has largely accounted for the slow growth in the world catch. Predominent among these fisheries was that for the anchoveta of the Peru current from which Chile and Peru combined increased their landings by 9 million tonnes between 1960 and 1970, but catches from which have since declined from a peak of 13 million tonnes in the latter year to about one million tonnes today.

In contrast to landings for reduction to meal and oil, production of fish for direct human consumption grew steadily throughout the 1960s and 1970s, and although since 1970 the rate of growth has declined. The increase in the landings of food fish in the developed world has come largely from a handful of countries, like, Japan, the USSR and the centrally planned countries of Eastern Europe and Spain.

The decline in the rate of growth of food fish production in developing countries has only become apparent in the past few years and is even now only seriously affecting a limited number of countries influenced by special factors, *e.g.* Ghana and

Thailand adversely affected by limit extensions. Until recently the increase in the production of fish for direct human consumption has been generally wide spread in the developing countries even if at various rates of growth, i.e slow in some middle eastern countries and fairly rapid in Latin America and Asia. The total food fish production in developing countries growing at a rate of some 4 per cent per annum has considerably more than doubled in the period 1960-1980 and with the concentration on high value export species, the real growth in monetary output will have been higher although this does mean that consumption in these countries has grown less rapidly than production.

Trends in trade in fishery products reflect closely changes in production. Thus the volume of exports of fish meal declined sharply in early seventies from a peak of 3.5 million tonnes in 1968 and continues to fluctuate at a level some 1.5 million tonnes below this. Fish oil has shared in this decline but trade in products for human consumption has, in most cases, increased. Shell fish exports in particular have increased steadily to the advantage of the balance of payments of many developing countries in Asia and Latin America. Trade in frozen fish has also grown with exports from developing countries playing an increasingly important role.

## Possibilities of Catch Increases

The growth in food fish production in the developing countries is one of the few trends in world fisheries continuing throughout 1960s and 1970s, but it has not been sufficient to prevent the rate of growth of total world catch from declining drastically, from around 5 per cent in the sixties to 1 per cent in the seventies. The basic cause of this decline is the diminishing number of stocks of conventional fish (*i.e.* those harvestable by existing types of gear and readily marketable in existing product form) which offer the possibility of sustained increases in catch.

The present level of exploitation compared with the commercially realizable potential of broad groups of conventional types of marine fish, crustaceans and cephalopods, indicates that marine catches can probably be increased by a further 20 to 30 million tonnes over 1980s levels. A part of this increase in catch is realizable through increased fishing effort, but a substantial part, as much as 50 per cent will be achieved only by better management.

This is particularly te case with pelagic species which offer considerable possibilities of catch increases and which well illustrate the divergent forms of action required to produce them. For those stocks such as the anchovy of the Peru current and the herring of the Northeast Atlantic, which have collapsed and are now yielding much lower catches. Careful management in the form of strict control of fishing effort is required if catches from these stocks are to increase to anything like their former levels. For other stocks of shoaling pelagic fish such as the herring of the Patagonian shelf or the sardine of the northwest Arabian Sea, increased yields will require an increase in fishing effort.

Less spectacular, but still significant increases in catch can be expected from better management of demersal species, particularly flounders and cod. Among the species for which increases in fishing effort will yield higher catches, the best commercial prospects are for hake and similar species off the southern coasts of South America and in particular for the hake on the Patagonial shelf. These stocks, however, are already attracting considerable attention and by this time are unlikely to have much potential remaining unexploited. Elsewhere and especially in the southern hemisphere and in tropical waters, there are unexploited resources, but as much of this potential consists of a wide variety of species and none in any great abundance, their commercial utilization will present, and in fact already presents, serious marketing problems.

For shellfish the possibilities of increased production are generally good and for many products future levels of output are likely to depend as much on market considerations as on resource availability. For example, cephalopods (squids, cuttle fish, octopus etc) are, in many areas of the world, only very lightly exploited but at the same time are regarded as conventional foods in only a handful of countries. Thus, without very considerable product development or consumer education, the full potential of this valuable resource seems unlikely to be realized even by the end of the century. Consumer acceptance is also a factor likely to govern the production of mussels, possibilities for the production of which by culture are very large indeed. Given the control of pollution and the availability of seed, good prospects exist for the cultivation of other mollusks, such as, oysters, clams and scallops.

Crustaceans generally are heavily exploited but some increases in catch can be looked for; *e.g.* from smaller crabs and from some shrimps including those in deeper waters and in some as yet rather under-surveyed areas, *e.g.* the northwest coast of Australia. In the long run however, it is clear that the supply of shrimp is likely to become increasingly inelastic and thus the consequent rising prices will give impetus to the culture of these animals. For many species the technical problems of culture have been solved and provided fry are available and the necessary environmental conditions (temperature, salinity etc) exist, the main determinant of increased output from culture will be the cost of inputs (mainly feed) in relation to the price of shrimp. Even though increasing and likely to double or treble, the amount of shrimp cultured by the end of the century is likely to remain small, *i.e.* less than 10 per cent of total production.

Although some growth can be expected from freshwater fisheries, the most interesting developments in this sector over the next 10 years are likely to be changes in the sources of production. Both for purposes of electricity generation and irrigation, interference with natural river basin systems seem likely to continue unabated with a consequent continuing decline in rivers and flood plains while output from reservoirs and intensive aquaculture can be expected to increase.

Fish are generally hardier animals than shrimps (and some mollusks, *e.g.* oysters) and food requirements for the culture of some species are less demanding, which in part explains the more rapid progress in the culture of fish compared with shrimp. Cultured fish presently represent about 6 per cent of the total world finfish supplies, a proportion which can confidently be expected to increase over the next decade.

# Future Trend in Capture Fisheries

The slow overall growth rate of world fishery resources is essentially a continuation of the trend in the seventies so far- results from the fact that conventional marine finfish, which account for some three quarters of the total production of living aquatic organisms, offer relatively poor prospects for increased catches. The situation is relatively more favorable in the developing countries where lightly exploited resources are somewhat more abundant than in the developed countries where technological innovation has (with some exceptions) led to the earlier heavy exploitation of stocks in adjacent waters.

Even within the developing countries, however, given a projected rate of population increase of over 2 percent, the rate of growth of production will on average be inadequate to maintain per capita levels of supply- notwithstanding the possibilities of diverting to direct human consumption some of the catches now used for reduction to meal and oil. Countries where significant declines in per capita consumption could occur include some of the least developed *e.g.* Mali and Chad, which depend on heavily or moderately heavily exploited flood plain fisheries and where the expansion of aquaculture is likely to do little more than offset the effect of possible interference with the aquatic environment

Other developing countries with fairly low projected growth rates include those distant water (or at least non-local) operations will be affected by the establishment of exclusive economic zones (EEZs). The latter are the offshore areas extending to a distance of 200 miles in which the coastal state has sovereign rights for exploiting the natural resources and thus the right to exclude the fishing vessels of other nations. Adjustment to an ocean regime of EEZs arising from the Third UN Conference on the Law of the Sea is likely to be a major influence on the changes in the pattern of fishing for most of the period to 2000. Within the developing countries, for example, the high growth rates for Argentina and some West African countries demonstrate the possibilities of production from abundant resources which have previously either been relatively lightly exploited or exploited by foreign vessels. Opportunities provided by extended jurisdiction explain also the relatively high rates projected for North America and for Oceania. The projected lack growth in Europe reflects the fact that the resources in most EEZs are already heavily exploited by the coastal state and few opportunities exist for the development of new fisheries. Implementation of policies with respect to EEZs will have little impact on the total catch, although in the short to medium term it is likely to depress yields as coastal states in many areas take action to protect their newly acquired resources.

# Chapter 4
# Current Rate of Exploitation

## Capture Trends of Oceanic Species

Out of 1205 species items, included in the FAO data base capture statistics, 120 have been recognized as oceanic, because they spend most of their adult life or are caught in the epipelagic, mesopelagic or bathypelagic zones. These species items were further divided into epipelagic (58 species items) and deep water species (62 items).

The epipelagic group consists of 45 fishes, 2 crustaceans (krill) and 7 cephalopods (family Ommastrephidae) species items. The two main groups of epipelagic fishes are tuna and tuna like species (24 species items) which belong to group 36 (Tunas, bonitos, bill fishes) of the International Standard Statistical Classification for Aquatic Animals and Plants (ISSCAAP) classification used in compiling the FAO fishery statistics and oceanic sharks (17 species items). The deep water group consists of 55 fish and 7 crustacean (shrimps and crabs) species items. Several families and orders are represented among the fish species, but the most significant group, both in terms of number (15 species items) and economic importance is that of the Gadiformis.

## Global Trend

Global catches of oceanic species have been steadily increasing (except for a small decrease in the early 1980s) during the 50 years (1950-1999) for which data are available in the FAO data base and reached about 8.6 million tonnes in 1999. The share of oceanic catches in global marine catches ranged between 4 and 8 percent from 1950 to 1989. In recent years the contribution of oceanic catches to total catches increased and exceeded 10 per cent in 1998 and 1999.

Until 1975, catches of deep water species were relatively small, ranging between 2 and 10 per cent of the total oceanic catches, but since the late 1970s their contribution has constantly been greater than 20 per cent, reaching 33 per cent of the total oceanic catches in 2001 and 2002 for which statistics were available.

Among the epipelagic species, catches of tuna and tuna like species have been increasing dramatically throughout the years. Since mid-1960s, the rate of increase in tuna and tuna-like catches has been much higher in comparison to other epipelagic species and tuna catches are still growing at a rapid pace, while those of the other species have decreased in recent years. Similarly, the deep water group is dominated by Gadiformes species (ISSCAAP group 32), but some differences can be noted; over half of the catches of the deep water Gadiformes in the 1955-99 period was constituted by a single species (*i.e.Micromesistius poutassou*, blue whiting) and the increasing trend of Gadiformes species was not as steady as that of tuna species and it experienced some drops (early and late 1980s). There is also a big difference in market value between tunas, which are amongst the most valued fishery resources and deep water species, which as in case of blue whiting are mostly processed into fish meal.

## Oceanic Catches of Distant Water Fleets (DWFs)

Total marine catches from distant water fisheries reported by DWFs increased from less than one million tonnes in the early 1950s to about 8 million tonnes in 1972, fluctuated around this value until 1991 and then declined rapidly to about 4.5 million tonnes, remaining stable in the most recent years. As a proportion of total marine captures, those reported by DWFs reached a maximum of 15.5 per cent in 1972 and then declined to about 5 per cent, a level at which they have stabilized since 1993. The starting points of the two marked decreasing trends of DWF catches coincided with two historical events; the oil price hike (1973) and the dissolution of the Former USSR (1991) whose fleets were actively fishing in all oceans.

Until the 1970s catches of oceanic species were a minor portion of the total DWF catches, but since 1993 oceanic catches of DWFs account for half or more of the total DWF catches. This remarkable change in the two fractions is due to the contemporaneous decrease of coastel species catches and increase of oceanic catches by DWFs. Following the declarations by an increasing number of countries of the Exclusive Economic Zones (EEZs), after the United Nations Convention on the Law of the Sea (UNCLOS) of 1982, distant water fishing nations had to negotiate access to the marine resources living within the 200 miles limit. This new situation together with the increasing price of fuel oil, led to an overall increase of costs for DWFs that progressively shifted to oceanic species which are both highly valuable (i.e tunas) and can be often caught in the high seas, outside areas of national jurisdictions.

However, in terms of quantities, the increase of oceanic catches in recent years is entirely due to the contribution of bordering countries whose catches of oceanic species have been steadily increasing since the early 1980s. The majority (always over 75 per cent) of oceanic catches by vessels of DWFs are of epipelagic species and the deep water catches exceeded 200000 tonnes only during the 1982-92 period.

# Fish Landing Trends as per FAO Fishing Areas

## Northwest Atlantic (FAO Area 21)

As a proportion of total marine catches in this area, oceanic catches have a limited importance, although there has been an increase in recent years (over 5 per cent since 1994). Another peak of oceanic catches was reached in the late 1970s (a maximum of 8.5 per cent on total catches in 1979) due to high catches (up to 90000 tonnes) of Northern short fin squid reported by Canada. The Northern short fin squid peak is paralleled by an increase in the same years of molluscan catches in general. After this peak, catches of deep water species have always been greater than epipelagic catches reaching 85 per cent of total oceanic catches in 1999. Most of the catches classified as deep water in Northwest Atlantic are Canadian landings of queen crab (*Chionoecetes opilio*), which have been progressively increasing in the 1990s and reached more than 95000 tonnes in 1999.

The percentage of oceanic catches taken by DWEs after the 1970s is very low, but previously it reached two noticeable peaks in 1966 and the 1971-75 period. Major fishing nations targeting oceanic species in those years were Former USSR, Japan Spain and Poland.

Catches of tuna and tuna-like species are not very high in this cold water area and reached two peaks in the mid-1960s and early 1980s of approximately 17000 tonnes. Since 1993, total catches of tunas never exceeded 10000 tonnes.

## Northeast Atlantic (FAO Area 27)

In the Northeast Atlantic area, the peak marine catches was reached in 1976. In the same year catches of oceanic species started to increase considerably mostly due to the catches of Blue whiting (*Micromesistius poutassou*) reported by the Former USSR. This confirms what has been suggested by Cannon (1997) that when catches of historically valuable or traditional species, such as, cod, haddock and herring began to decline, they were progressively replaced by oceanic deeper water species, formerly not economically viable to exploit.

Since 1978, catches of blue whiting have contributed over three quarters of the deep water catches in the area. Besides the Former USSR, Russian Federation major countries fishing deep water species in the Northeast Atlantic are Norway, Denmark and Iceland. However, the marked decrease in recent years of the catch per unit effort (CPUE) for some deep water species (*e.g.* blue ling, *Molva dypterygia* and round nose grenadier, *Coryphaenoides rupestris* in this area) has prompted the Advisory Committee on Fishery Management (ACFM) of the International Council for the Exploration of the Sea (ICES) to recommend immediate reduction in deep water fisheries unless they can be shown to be sustainable (ICES, 2002) and lead the European Commission to propose extra measures to protect vulnerable deep water species.

Catches of epipelagic species are not negligible in this area, but appear very low when compared to total marine catches. This is because the Northeast Atlantic has always been one of the most productive fishing areas in the world, together with the Northwest Pacific and the Southeast Pacific due to the high productivity of its continental shelf. Catches of the two most important species, albacore and northern bluefin tuna peaked in the early 1960s at around 65000 tonnes and since 1968 have ranged between 27000 and 42000 tonnes. DWF catches in this area are very low, usually lower than 2 per cent of the total oceanic catches.

## Western Central Atlantic (FAO Area 31)

Oceanic catches in this area consist mostly of epipelagic species since catches of deep water resources appear to be negligible all along the time period. Over 75 per cent of the total catches of epipelagic species are from tuna and tuna-like species. The remaining catches are mostly dolphin fish (*Coryphaena hippurus*) and oceanic shares of the family Carcharhinidae. Catches of tuna reached a peak in the mid-1980s of about 75000 tonnes. In the five years analyzed (1995-99), these catches have stabilized around 47000 tonnes. Overall oceanic catches represent a minimal portion of the total marine catches ranging mostly between 2 and 4 percent.

A comparison between the oceanic and total marine catches reported by DWFs shows that an average DWF oceanic catches represent 74 per cent of all DWF catches, indicating that DWFs in this area target mostly oceanic species. The share of DWFs in the total oceanic catches has been considerable before 1980 with peaks in 1958 (61 per cent), 1964 (78 per cent) and for most of the 1970s. After 1980, the share of DWFs remained below 30 per cent and has exceeded this value only in 1999 with increased tuna catches by Asian countries. It should be noted that about half of the 1994-99 tuna catches taken by DWFs in this area is included in the FAO data base as caught by "other nei (other countries not elsewhere identified)" and not assigned to a specific country. FAO derives most of the catch statistics for tunas in the Atlantic Ocean from the data provided by the International Commission for the Conservation of Atlantic Tunas (ICCAT). In the ICCAT data base, catches classified as "other nei" are mostly illegal, unreported and unregulated (IUU) catches estimated from trade data (ICCAT, 2001). This means that in this area an alarming quantity of tunas are illegally caught or not reported officially.

## Eastern Central Atlantic (FAO Area 34)

This area, which extends along the west coast of Africa from Morocco southwards to the Democratic Republic of Congo is characterized by a share of oceanic catches above the global average and by an historical presence of DWFs. Oceanic catches reached their peak in 1991 (402000 tonnes) and since then, they have ranged between 320000 and 380000 tonnes. About 95 per cent of these quantities are composed of tuna and tuna-like species, the deep water portion of oceanic catches always being rather small with a peak value of 43000 tonnes in 1980 (approximately 28000 tonnes of which constituted catches of snipe fish, *Macroramphosus scolopau* reported by Former USSR).

The bulk of oceanic catches in this area is constituted by three species, skipjack, yellowfin and bigeye tunas. The main countries fishing tunas in recent years are Spain, France, Ghana and Japan. As for the Western Central Atlantic, a great and increasing quantity of tuna catches are included in the data bases of international organizations (i.e ICCAT and FAO) as taken by vessels of unknown nationality ("other nei"). In 1990, the "other nei" tuna catches were one quarter (36000 tonnes) of the total tuna catches caught by DWFs, but in 1999 they reaches the 40 per cent .

The share of DWFs in oceanic catches has always been very significant in this area. Spain and Portugal are classified as bordering countries because part of their territories (i.e Canary and Madeira Islands) lies in this area. Absent until 1954, oceanic catches by DWFs reached almost 88 per cent of total oceanic catches in 1961 and remained at around 80 per cent for the whole of the 1960s. From the early 1970s until 1987 they slowly declined to 33 per cent, but in the 1990s the dwfs share of oceanic catches increased again to about 55 per cent .

## Mediterranean and Black Sea (FAO Area 37)

In FAO Area 37, oceanic catches represent a small portion of total marine catches, but they nevertheless have considerable importance due to the high commercial value of some tuna and tuna-like species. Catches of all epipelagic species together have stabilized around 50000 tonnes since 1984 and, after the highest ever peak of 69000 tonnes in 1996, they decreased to 52000 tonnes in 1999. Bluefin tuna and sword fish are the main target of tuna fisheries, mostly conducted by bordering countries, while Asian countries are catching only a small portion of these very valuable species. Apart from tunas, other epipelagic species of some importance are dolphin fish (*Coryphaena hippurus*) and the European flying squid (*Todarodes sagittatus*).

The practice of fattening of wild-caught bluefin tuna in captivity is booming in the area from 1996 to 2001. There was at least twenty fold increase in the number of cages in the Mediterranean. This practice aims mainly at increasing the fat content of the flesh, which strongly influences the price of the tuna meat in the Japanese *sashimi* market. The development of bluefin tuna farming has statistical, biological, management, environmental and socio-economic effects that need to be addressed urgently by international and national institutions

As for the Northeast Atlantic area, the bulk of catches in deep waters are constituted by a single species, the blue whiting (*Micromesistius poutassou*). Landings of this species increased by 50 per cent in the 1990s in comparison to the previous decade, mainly due to catches reported by Turkey.

The Mediterranean and the Black Sea are semi-enclosed seas and environmental threats, such as, increasing coastal population, heavy shipping traffic and introduction of alien species are more serious than in open ocean areas. In this area, extended (up to 200 miles) EEZs have not been implemented because of geographical (i.e complex coastal configurations and the presence of islands) and political circumstances i.e long standing maritime and territorial disputes are historically present and the whole sea would be subject to the jurisdiction of coastal states for a through analysis). Since national jurisdiction extend much less far than the other areas and the regional fishery management organization is still developing its management role, oceanic resources tend not to be managed and protected effectively.

## Southwest Atlantic (FAO Area 41)

The share of oceanic catches in total catches in this area is greater than the global average, exceeding 10 per cent since 1982. Oceanic catches started increasing during the late 1970s, they showed a maximum in 1983 as percentage of total catches (18.5 per cent) and in 1988 as absolute quantity (336000 tonnes). In the last five years total oceanic catches fluctuated around 250000 tonnes. Since the early 1980s, most of the oceanic catches have been composed of deep water species, such as, the southern blue whiting (*Micromesistius australis*), grenadiers (*Macruronus magellanices* and *Macrourus* spp) and recently by Patagonian tooth fish (*Dissostichus eleginoides*). Catch peaks of southern blue whiting and grenadiers show an asynchronous pattern; the former had peaked years in 1983 and 1990, the latter in 1988 and 1999. Until 1990, these species were caught mostly by DWFs (i.e those of Former USSR and other Eastern European countries) but immediately after these countries drastically reduced the activities of their DWFs. Argentina took over as the most important country fishing deep water resources in this area.

Catches of epipelagic species are mainly composed of tuna and tuna-like species and the fleets accounting for the main catches are from Brazil, Taiwan, Province of China, Spain and Japan. In the southwest Atlantic, there are very important fisheries for cephalopods operated mainly by Argentina and Asian countries, but these catches were not included in the oceanic data set object of this study as only one cephalopod species distributed in this area (*Martialia hyadesi*) has been classified as fully oceanic. Significant catches (23464 tonnes) for this species has been reported only in 1995 by Taiwan Province of China.

### Southeast Atlantic (FAO Area 47)

This area is characterized by intermittent regimes that affect quantitative fisheries, such as, those for small pelagics and this is reflected in the total marine captures, which had periodic peaks (1968, 1973, and 1987) along the time series. After the 1987 peak (2750000 tonnes), total catches have constantly declined and in 1999 they were reduced to less than half (1250000 tonnes) of the latest peak The general decline of marine catches has been associated to environmental changes (low oxygen levels in coastal waters) that led to the marked decrease of sardine stocks in the 1990s. Apparently, oceanic stocks were not affected by those environmental changes and their fisheries did not undergo any decline.

Share of oceanic catches was below 5 per cent up to 1993, a value around which it has stabilized in recent years. It should be noted, that in this area, there are only three coastal countries and that most of the oceanic catches are due to DWFs (Japan, Taiwan Province of China and before 1980, Former USSR). The DWFs portion of oceanic catches reached 93 per cent in 1975 and remained high (between 50 per cent and 80 per cent) for the rest of the time series. The DWFs harvested mainly tuna species (bigeye and southern bluefin) and *Geryon* crabs (caught mainly by Japan) among the deep water resources.

### Western Indian Ocean (FAO Area 51)

Total marine captures in this area increased continuously from 1950 onwards and have stabilized around 3.9 million tonnes since 1997. For the whole time series, the oceanic share has always been significant, reaching 20 per cent for the first time in 1995 and a maximum 22 per cent in 1999. Since 1983, more than 75 per cent of the oceanic catches have been from tuna species, while deep water catches have increased only in the latest years as compared to the quantities reported in the earliest years of the time series. The majority of the deep water catches are Indian catches of hairtail (family Trichiuridae), a group of fishes which could also be considered as epipelagic because it shows vertical feeding migration. A deep-water fishery that could possibly develop in future years is that for lantern fishes (family Myctophidae) in the Arabian Sea.

Since 1984, catches of oceanic tuna in this area have been increasing steeply and they exceeded 700000 tonnes in 1999. About two thirds of these catches are harvested by European (e.g Spain and France) and East Asian (Japan and Taiwan Province of China) fleets. In this area, as for the two tropical areas of the Atlantic Ocean, a great quantity of tuna catches (about 100000 tonnes in 1999) are attributed to "other nei" (not identified country) in the Indian Oceanic Tuna Commission (IOTC) and FAO data bases. Main tuna species caught are skipjack, yellowfin and bigeye tunas. Epipelagic species other than tuna represented in the fishery statistics are dolphin fish and sharks of the family Carcharhinidae.

## Eastern Indian Ocean (FAO Area 57)

Trends in both total marine and oceanic captures in the Eastern Indian Ocean are very similar to those in the Western Indian Ocean. In both areas, total catches have been progressively increasing along the entire time series and tuna catches constitute the bulk of oceanic catches. The major differences are that the steep increase of tuna catches in the Eastern Indian Ocean took place about 10 years later than Western Indian Ocean (in 1993 instead than 1984) and that DWFs have a more limited role in the Eastern area.

Main tuna target species are the same as in the Western Indian Ocean (i.e skipjack, yellowfin and bigeye tunas). Bordering nations with important tuna fisheries are Sri Lanka and Indonesia, while Japan and Taiwan Province of China are the main distant water fishing fleets. From 1960 onwards, Sri Lanka has been reporting considerable catches of silky shark (*Carcharhinus falciformis*). Since 1980, catches of this species ranged between 10000 and 25000 tonnes.

The share of deep-water catches is slightly higher (on average 18 per cent of the oceanic catches) in comparison to the Western Indian Ocean, with the highest quantities (mostly hairtail catches by India and Indonesia) recorded in 1976 and in 1999. Significant catches of orange roughy in the Eastern area were reported for 1998 and 1999 (4857 and 7553 tonnes respectively) by Australia, while in previous years catches of this species were mostly concentrated in area 81 (Southwest Pacific).

## Northwest Pacific (FAO Area 61)

Total catches in this area are strongly influenced by the trend of marine captures reported by China, which imply an average rate of 19 per cent increase per year in the 1984-99 period. If china is excluded, the sum of total catches of other countries has almost halved in the last ten years.

In contrast to other areas, oceanic catches in the Northwest Pacific have had a major importance both in terms of quantities and of share, in the first half of the time series (1950-74) than in the second one (1975-99). As for other temperate areas (e.g Nothwest Atlantic), the majority of the catches of epipelagic species are not accounted for by tuna and tuna-like species. The main epipelagic species caught throughout the years, mostly by Japan and secondarily by the Republic of Korea, are Pacific saury (*Cotolabis saira*) and the Japanese flying squid (*Todarodes pacificus*). Variations in the abundance of the latter strongly influence the general trend of oceanic catches in this area. Annual catches of Japanese flying squid depend largely on general environmental and ecological changes, such as, water temperatures and abundance of predators and/or prey, and have shown recovering and increasing trends in the absence of management regulations.

Deep water species represent only a small proportion of oceanic catches, with a single peak in the 1984-86 period due to catches reported by the Former USSR (silvery light fish and grenadiers). There is no oceanic species catches reported for DWFs in this area.

## Northeast Pacific (FAO Area 67)

As a proportion of total marine catches, oceanic catches in this area are negligible along the whole time series (percentage never exceeded 3.5 per cent). Oceanic catches had two peaks, the first and more significant one in the early 1970s and the second during the 1986-94 period. In both cases the bulk of the catches was represented by the deep water sable fish, *Anoplopoma fimbria*. However, while the first peak was due to catches reported by DWFs (mostly Japan), the second was attributable to bordering countries (USA and Canada).

Waters of area 67, which extend southwards as far as Cape Mendocino in northern California, should be expected too cold for tuna species but for an eleven year period (1968-78) and in a recent year (1997) catches of tuna and tuna-like species have exceeded 15000 tonnes. Most of these quantities are albacore catches reported by USA. In the latest years, Japan reported about 1000-2000 tonnes of catches of the neon flying squid (*Ommastrephes bartrami*) in this area.

## Western Central Pacific (FAO Area 71)

As for the two Indian Ocean areas, total catches in this tropical area have been progressively increasing throughout the years, with oceanic catches accounting for a significant percentage (10-20 per cent) of total catches in terms of quantity and much more in terms of value, and with DWFs always playing an important role. This is by far the most important FAO fishing area for catches of those tuna and tuna-like species classified as epipelagic (about 1.8 million tonnes in 1999, the second area in ranking, the Western Indian Ocean, totaled less than half of this).

The most important oceanic species caught in the area are skipjack (*Katsuwonus pelamis*) and yellowfin tuna (*Thunnus albacares*). Since 1970, catches of these two species have represented, without much oscillation, respectively 40-62 per cent and 18-28 per cent of the total catches of oceanic tunas. Distant water fleets took about half of these tuna catches throughout the whole time series. The main DWFs are from neighbouring Asian countries (*i.e.* Japan, Korea Rep. and Taiwan Province of China) and the USA. Among the bordering countries, Indonesia, the Philippines and the

Solomon Islands are the countries reporting higher quantities of tuna catches in recent years.

Deep-water species have a very limited importance in comparison to the epipelagic species. Only for hairtails (family Trichiuridae) have there been significant catches, and these have been continuously increasing since 1975, reaching about 34000 tonnes in 1999.

## Eastern Central Pacific (FAO Area 77)

Oceanic catches represent a stable percentage (33 per cent on average) of the total marine catches and showed a remarkable increase in the 1963-1985 period (up to 500000 tonnes in 1985), which subsequently stabilized or slightly decreased (444000 tonnes in 1999).

In the Eastern Central Pacific, as for the other tropical fishing areas, oceanic catches include mostly tuna and tuna-like species. Yellowfin, skipjack and bigeye are the most frequently caught species. Catches by DWFs have exceeded those by bordering countries in the 1985 and, since then, their share has been oscillating around 50 per cent with a decrease in recent years. Main DWFs are from Japan (which has considerably reduced its portion of tuna catches in the latest years), Republic of Korea and Venezuela. Tuna catches by bordering countries are mostly for Mexico and the USA, with a remarkable change in their shares: in 1970, Mexico was catching 5.4 per cent of the oceanic tunas by bordering countries and the USA 93.5 per cent while in 1999 the Mexican share rose to 74.8 per cent and that by of USA decreased to 14.9 per cent .

In recent years, significant catches have been reported for the jumbo flying squid (*Dosiidicus gigas*) and also a good portion of what was reported in previous years as "squids not elsewhere identified" were probably catches of jumbo flying squid. Catches of the family Carcharhinidae and of other oceanic sharks are also represented in the FAO database for this area. Deep-water catches are almost absent in this area except for some thousand tonnes of the deep-water sablefish, *Anoplopoma fimbria*, reported by the USA.

## Southwest Pacific (FAO Area 81)

This area has been characterized by increasing captures up to 1992 (when total marine catches reached over 900000 tonnes) and by a slight decrease in the latest years (780000 tonnes in 1999). This trend is closely matched by that of oceanic catches, mainly represented by deep water species, which increased from 1600 tonnes in 1950 to 498000 tonnes in 1999 after a peak of almost 600000 tonnes in 1992. The share of oceanic catches in total catches has been constantly increasing since the 1950s and in 1981 it exceeded that of coastal catches; in recent years it has stabilized at around 60 per cent .

The great importance of oceanic catches is due to deep water fisheries mainly targeting three species; the Gadiformes species blue grenadier (*Macruronus novaezelandiae*) and southern blue whiting (*Micromesistius australis*) and the orange roughy (*Hoplostethus atlanticus*). Up to the beginning of the 1980s, deep-water species were mostly caught by the Former USSR, while since mid-1980s Japan has been the main distant water fishing nation. New Zealand fisheries for deep water species started to catch significant quantities in 1979 and from 1992 they have exceeded the total catches of all DWFs which have been declining. Australia, the only other bordering country, has caught considerable quantities of deep water species only for a few years at the beginning of 1990s.

To better describe their trend, catches of epipelagic species can be divided into two time periods, before and after 1980-81. The first period was dominated by tuna catches, in particular those of southern bluefin tuna (*Thunnus maccoyii*). This species was so heavily fished in the 1960s that since mid-1980s the main fishing nations had to apply strict quotas to allow the stock to rebuild after a serious decline (CCSBT, 1997). In the second period, from 1981 onwards, fisheries for the Wellington flying squid (*Nototodarus sloani*) started developning. This species was targeted mostly by Japanese DWF vessels up to 1990, since when catches by New Zealand have progressively replaced those by DWFs.

## Southeast Pacific (FAO Area 87)

Trend of total catches in the Southeast Pacific is strongly influenced by the oscillations of the anchoveta (*Engraulis ringens*) and of other small pelagic species. Biomass of these species fluctuates in relation to the availability of upwelling nutrients, which is driven by the El Nino phenomenon. Total catches being extremely high in this area (the 1994 peak was over 20 million tonnes), the share of oceanic catches has been always quite low not exceeding 4 per cent up to 1997. In 1998, total catches were lower due to EL Nino, while oceanic catches increased and their share peaked at 8.1 per cent . In 1999, oceanic catches reached their maximum at almost 900000 tonnes but, with the total catches recovering, their share decreased to 6.2 per cent .

A significant increase of oceanic catches started in 1987. Since then, total catches of epipelagic and deep-water species grouped separately showed a series of asynchronous peaks, although the total catches of each group in the whole 1987-99 period have been very similar. Main species among the epipelagics are skipjacks and yellowfin tunas, which are increasingly caught by fleets of bordering countries (*e.g.* Ecuador and Colombia), while in the past DWFs played a major role. Catches of the jumbo flying squid by Japan, Republic of Korea and Peru had an extended peak in the 1991-97 period, collapsed almost to no catches in 1998 during El Nino, and recovered to a significant level (76000 tonnes) when El Nino was over in 1999.

Deep-water catches have been mostly composed of Patagonian grenadier (*Macruronus masellanicus*) and secondarily by southern blue whiting (*Micromesistius australis*) and Patagonian toothfish (*Dissostichus eleginoides*). Almost all these catches were reported by Chile and only very small quantities by DWFs.

## Arctic (FAO Area 18) and Antarctic areas (FAO Areas 48,58,88)

For the Arctic area, the Former USSR reported catches to FAO only for the 1967-70 period. For this reason, the Arctic area has not been considered in this analysis.

Reporting of data for the three Antarctic areas started in 1966, but up to 1973 no oceanic species were caught. Since 1979, the krill, *Euphausia superba*, an epipelagic species, has accounted for more than 70 per cent of the total catches in the Antarctic areas, with the only exception of 1983-84 when catches dropped. Great quantities of krill have been taken by the Former USSR (with peak of almost 500000 tonnes in 1982) up to 1991-92 when after the dissolution of the USSR, the new Republics drastically reduced their Antarctic fishing activities. In contrast, Japan has steadily caught krill since the 1980s ranging between 40000 and 80000 tonnes yearly.

Deep-water species are limited to an extended peak of Myctophidae (lantern fishes) caught during the 1988-92 period by Former USSR countries, and to catches of Patagonian tooth fish (*Dissostichus eleginoides*), mainly in area 58 (Antarctic Indian Ocean).

Decreasing total catches in recent years are due to specific causes, such as the distance from other major fishing grounds and the lack of demand for some Antarctic species, rather than to a depletion of the living resources, which are carefully managed by the Commission for the Conservation of Antarctic Living Resources (CCAMLR), although concern is rising for IUU catches of Patagonian tooth fish.

## Conclusion

The classification of the oceanic species items (either epipelagic or deep-water) included in the FAO capture fisheries database has allowed a description of the increasing share of oceanic catches in total global marine catches. In the 1990s, concurrent with a slightly declining trend in total coastal species catches (excluding Peruvian anchoveta) both groups of oceanic species have increased their catches by one million tonnes, epipelagics from 4.8 to 5.7 million tonnes and deep-water species from 1.8 to 2.9 million tonnes.

The majority of oceanic epipelagic catches (mainly tuna and tuna-like species) is from tropical areas whereas deep-water species are mostly caught in temperate regions. In the last decade, a continuous increase of epipelagic catches has occurred in the tropical areas of the Indian and Pacific Oceans whereas in the two tropical Atlantic areas they have been oscillating and in 1999 totalled catches similar to those of 1990. Deep-water catches have recently increased remarkably in the North Atlantic, probably due to shift of fishing effort to new target species after the decline of other marine resources in the area, although there have been signs of declining catches in other areas (*e.g.* Southwest Atlantic, Northeast Pacific and Southwest Pacific) where deep-water species have been caught in significant quantities during the 1980s and in the early 1990s.

However, due to the peculiar biological characteristics of deep-water species, concern is rising on the sustainability of deep-water fisheries and, in particular in the Northeast Atlantic, regional fishery commissions and related institutions are proposing action to protect the deep-water stocks. With regard to oceanic tunas and tuna-like species, differences in the life history traits between tropical tunas and temperate tunas may result in different responses to fishing pressure and partially explain why catches of tropical species are still growing whereas stocks of temperate blufin tuna species have shown serious declines in biomass and catches.

## Global Capture Fisheries for the Year 2011

The FAO capture database for inland and marine fisheries (1950-2011), the total global capture production in 2011 was the third ever, slightly after 1996 (93.8 million tonnes) and 2000 (93.5 million tonnes).

This result was mostly due to good catches of Peruvial anchoveta (which, however, in 2012 already decreased by about 3.5 million tonnes) but also to marine catches excluding anchoveta which grew for the third consecutive and in 2011 exceeded 74 million tonnes, a level that had not been reached since 2001.

Previous preliminary estimates of 2011 global total were lower as Japan's total catch was expected to reduce of about one third following March 2011 tsunami, but fortunately actual decrease in comparison to 2010 was only around 7 per cent .

As usual, recent and historical catches have been revised as new data became available from national sources and Regional Fishery Organizations. In particular in the Eastern Central Atlantic, data from coastal countries (*e.g.* Mauritania, Guinea-Bissau etc) on catches in their EEZ previously not reported by Distant Water Fishing Nations increased the annual total in area 34 by about 300000 tonnes in recent years.

Inland waters capture production slightly decreased in 2011 after the maximum ever reached in 2010, a year for which India reported an abnormally high production in inland waters. Inland catches of African countries as a whole increased by 0.1 million tonnes, whereas in the other continents remained stable.

Total number of species items in the database reached 1938. Out of 64 new species, 26 were from inland waters.

### Table 1: World Capture Production in 2010 and 2011.

|  | 2010 | 2011 | Variation |
|---|---|---|---|
|  | Million tonnes | million tonnes |  |
| Inland capture | 11.2 | 11.1 | -1.6 per cent |
| Marine capture | 77.7 | 82.4 | 6.1 per cent |
| Anchoveta | 4.2 | 8.3 | 97.8 per cent |
| Marine capture (excluding anchoveta) | 73.5 | 74.1 | 0.8 per cent |
| World total | 89.0 | 93.5 | 5.1 per cent |

### Table 2: World Captures for the Top 25 Fishing Countries (tonnes).

| Country | 2010 | 2011 | Variation |
|---|---|---|---|
| China | 15417011 | 15772054 | 2.35 |
| Peru | 4261091 | 8248482 | 93.6 per cent |
| Indonesia | 5380196 | 5707684 | 6.1 per cent |
| United States of America | 4425961 | 5153452 | 16.4 per cent |
| India | 4689316 | 4301534 | -8.3 per cent |

*Contd...*

**Table 2–** *Contd...*

| Country | 2010 | 2011 | Variation |
|---|---|---|---|
| Russian Federation | 4069624 | 4254864 | 4.6 per cent |
| Japan | 4069135 | 3761176 | -7.6 per cent |
| Maynmar | 3063210 | 3332979 | 8.8 per cent |
| Chile | 2679742 | 3063449 | 14.3 per cent |
| Viet Nam | 2414400 | 2502500 | 3.6 per cent |
| Philippines | 2611762 | 2363221 | -9.5 per cent |
| Norway | 2680187 | 2281429 | -14.9 per cent |
| Thailand | 1810620 | 1862151 | 2.8 per cent |
| Korea republic of | 1733310 | 1746998 | 0.8 per cent |
| Bangladesh | 1726586 | 1600918 | -7.3 per cent |
| Mexico | 1528945 | 1566365 | 2.4 per cent |
| Malaysia | 1433426 | 1378799 | -3.8 per cent |
| Iceland | 1060641 | 1138462 | 7.3 per cent |
| Spain | 971511 | 993457 | 2.35 |
| Morocco | 1136240 | 958907 | -15.6 per cent |
| Taiwan Province of China | 851384 | 903831 | 6.2 per cent |
| Canada | 936090 | 861388 | -8.0 per cent |
| Brazil | 785369 | 803267 | 2.3 per cent |
| Argentina | 811749 | 792505 | -2.4 per cent |
| Denmark | 828016 | 716312 | -13.5 per cent |
| Total 25 top countries | 71375522 | 76066184 | 6.6 per cent |
| Total other countries | 17594602 | 17428156 | -0.9 per cent |
| World total | 88970124 | 93494340 | 5.1 per cent |
| Share of 25 top Countries on total | 80.2 per cent | 81.4 per cent | |

**Table 3: World Captures of the Top 25 Species (tonnes).**

| Scientific Name | FAO English Name | 2010 | 2011 | Variation |
|---|---|---|---|---|
| *Engraulis ringens* | Peruvian anchovy | 4205979 | 8319597 | 97.8 per cent |
| *Theragra chalcogramma* | Alaska pollock | 2829570 | 3206513 | 13.3 per cent |
| *Katsuwonus pelamis* | Skipjack tuna | 2609920 | 2608578 | -0.1 per cent |
| *Clupea harengus* | Atlantic herring | 2203687 | 1778488 | -19.3 per cent |
| *Scomber japonicus* | Chub mackerel | 1633113 | 1714896 | 5.0 per cent |
| *Engraulis japonicus* | Japanese anchovy | 1199195 | 1321662 | 10.2 per cent |
| *Trichiurus lepturus* | Large head hairtail | 1341685 | 1258628 | -6.2 per cent |
| *Decapterus* spp. | Scads nei | 1207061 | 1231816 | 2.1 per cent |

*Contd...*

**Table 3–** *Contd...*

| Scientific Name | FAO English Name | 2010 | 2011 | Variation |
|---|---|---|---|---|
| *Thunnus albacares* | Yellowfin tuna | 1220812 | 1223907 | 0.3 per cent |
| *Gadus morhua* | Atlantic cod | 951934 | 1049666 | 10.3 per cent |
| *Sardina pilchardus* | European sardine | 1245956 | 1036708 | -16.8 per cent |
| *Sardinella* spp. | Sardinellas nei | 1034776 | 965431 | -6.7 per cent |
| *Scomber scombrus* | Atlantic mackerel | 887444 | 944748 | 6.5 per cent |
| *Dosidicus gigas* | Jumbo flying squid | 815978 | 906310 | 11.1 per cent |
| *Strangomera bentincki* | Araucanian herring | 750750 | 887272 | 18.2 per cent |
| *Sciaenidae* | Croakers, drums nei | 770868 | 860812 | 11.7 per cent |
| *Mallatus villasus* | Capelin | 506897 | 851472 | 68.0 per cent |
| *Sardinops caeruleus* | California pilchard | 696585 | 639235 | -8.2 per cent |
| *Trachurus murphyi* | Chilean jack mackerel | 686407 | 634173 | -7.6 per cent |
| *Srevoortia patronus* | Gulf menhaden | 438640 | 623369 | 42.1 per cent |
| *Cyprinidae* | Cyprinids nei | 747899 | 622260 | -16.8 per cent |
| *Osteichthyes* | Marine fishes nei | 10456562 | 10423369 | -0.3 per cent |
| *Osteichthyes* | Fresh water fishes nei | 5923353 | 6055890 | 2.2 per cent |
| *Natantia* | Natantian decapods nei | 755721 | 892834 | 18.1 per cent |
| *Mollusca* | Marine mollusks nei | 767021 | 738729 | -3.7 per cent |
| Total 25 top species items | | 45887813 | 50796363 | 10.7 per cent |
| Total other species | | 43082311 | 42697977 | -0.9 per cent |
| World total | | 88970124 | 93494340 | 5.1 per cent |
| Share of top 25 species on total | | 51.6 per cent | 54.3 per cent | |

**Table 4: World Captures by FAO Fishing Areas (tonnes).**

| Fishing Area | Name Code | 2010 | 2011 | Variation |
|---|---|---|---|---|
| Africa-Inland waters | 01 | 2603272 | 2703654 | 3.9 per cent |
| America, North-Inland waters | 02 | 179393 | 172972 | -3.6 per cent |
| America, South-Inland waters | 03 | 383848 | 383190 | -0.2 per cent |
| Asia-Inland waters | 04 | 7671520 | 7404762 | -3.5 per cent |
| Europe Inland waters | 05 | 384850 | 373975 | -2.8 per cent |
| Oceania-Inland waters | 06 | 16934 | 17832 | 5.3 per cent |
| Arctic Sea | 18 | 589 | 1 | -99.8 per cent |
| Atlantic Northwest | 21 | 2059676 | 1988840 | -3.4 per cent |
| Atlantic Northeast | 27 | 8723036 | 8021109 | -8.0 per cent |
| Atlantic Western Central | 31 | 1269670 | 1497487 | 17.0 per cent |
| Atlantic Eastern Central | 34 | 4382639 | 4217159 | -3.8 per cent |

*Contd...*

**Table 4–*Contd...***

| Fishing Area | Name Code | 2010 | 2011 | Variation |
|---|---|---|---|---|
| Mediterranean and Black Sea | 37 | 1434706 | 1440982 | 0.4 per cent |
| Atlantic Southwest | 41 | 1762721 | 1759192 | -0.2 per cent |
| Atlantic Southeast | 47 | 1316203 | 1248457 | -5.1 per cent |
| Atlantic Antarctic | 48 | 215216 | 183208 | -14.9 per cent |
| Indian Ocean Western | 51 | 4258232 | 4211857 | -1.1 per cent |
| Indian Ocean Eastern | 57 | 6858748 | 7211694 | 5.1 per cent |
| Indian Ocean Antarctic | 58 | 11074 | 10509 | -5.1 per cent |
| Pacific Northwest | 61 | 20965956 | 21436922 | 2.2 per cent |
| Pacific Northeast | 67 | 2436831 | 2949676 | 21.0 per cent |
| Pacific Western Central | 71 | 11769167 | 11521332 | -2.1 per cent |
| Pacific Eastern Central | 77 | 1925421 | 1912996 | -0.6 per cent |
| Pacific Southwest | 81 | 575528 | 570233 | -0.9 per cent |
| Pacific Southeast | 87 | 7761507 | 12253691 | 57.9 per cent |
| Pacific Antarctic | 88 | 3387 | 2592 | -23.5 per cent |
| World total | | 88970124 | 93494340 | 5.1 per cent |

# Chapter 5
# Marine Productivity in India

The Indian Ocean extending up to Antarctica has an area of 75 million square kilometers, which is roughly one-fifth of the world oceans. But the fish production from this ocean is only about 8 million tonnes, which is only about ten percent of the total marine fish production in the world. In terms of organic production and yield ratio the Indian ocean presents a miserably low percentage as compared to that of the Pacific and Atlantic Ocean .That means that the yield ratio, as a percentage of carbon, is roughly one-third of the Pacific and one-fourth of the Atlantic Ocean. This clearly indicates the wide gap in the potential harvestable stock especially in view of the fact that the average carbon fixation is almost similar for the Pacific, Atlantic and Indian Oceans with the western Indian Ocean indicating a slightly higher rate of fixation. The average annual gross production for all seas is estimated to be about 55-70 g/C/ sq.m. Assuming a 40 per cent loss through respiration and an area of 361 million square kilometer for all the oceans, the total net production per year for all the seas is estimated at about $1.2-1.5 \times 10^{10}$ tonnes of carbon. Ryther (1963) has subsequently modified this value to $2 \times 10^{10}$ tonnes. This value is practically the same as that estimated for the production on land. Of the 74917 square kilometer, which is conventionally taken as the Indian Ocean region, 3.1 million square kilometer is considered as coastal and near shore regions, which sustain the major part of the fishery and have an annual net production of $560 \times 10^6$ tonnes.

The harvest of marine fishery rsources doubled from a subsistence level of 0.5 million tonnes during 1950s to 1 million tonnes during 1970 as a result of research interventions. With the advent of gears and crafts a geometric progression during the 1970s, resource assessment studies stated radiating signals of potential dangers involved in unregulated fishery and management of Indian fisheries, which triggered new initiatives in resource assessment research. Estimated marine fish landings indicated an increasing trend in the marine fish production reaching 2 million tonnes by the beginning of 1990s and increasing steadily afterwards. For establishing a sustainable and enhanced productivity from Indian Seas there were lot of initiatives in the 1970s for rightly predicting the resources, regulating the fishery, introducing policy directives, enactment of legislations and development of stock assessment models for the diverse fishery in Indian waters. Heavy investment in harvest and post-harvest sectors in Indian fisheries during 1980s rendered vulnerable exploitation of many marine resources. Landing to the tune of 3.06 million tonnes, a record reckoning achievement was ensured by the end of this phase.

Total catch is an important indicator to monitor and assess the status of the fishery. The decline in the catch is a signal for appropriate interventions from the managers. Annual growth rate in marine fish production on a decadal average scale indicate that there has been a steady increase in marine fish production in the coastal waters of India. But globally the production has been in a retrogressive phase. There is a biological contrast in the fish available in Indian waters too. Unlike the abundant single species fish stock biomass of nearly 50 per cent replenishing the fishery in temperate waters; most of the multi-species fishery in the coastal waters of India is supported by fishes with high fecundity, continuous spawning ability, protracted spawning season and faster growth rates.

## Depleting Marine Fisheries Resources

In recent years, the marine resources too have come under the assault of greedy human beings the same way as other natural resources, such as, forest products, mining, ground water etc.

In the past, people were consuming premium varieties like, tiger prawns, pomfrets, kingfish lobsters etc. These varieties were available round the year. Many a times, these varieties were dried, salted and even used as manure to coconut trees during glut season.

But today these fishes have become food of rich people and the poor men are left with trash and thorny fish varieties as the premium varieties have gone scarce.

Till 1980s, the situation was very balanced. The fishing with mechanized boats just began and was co-existing with the non-mechanized ones. The fishermen were not very greedy at that time and this allowed fish breeding and facilitated natural replacement of whatever numbers/quantities caught.

Unfortunately, in late 1980s and early 1981 foreign deep sea trawlers started fishing in Indian waters. These deep sea vessels went on rampaging our waters by a method called Bull trawling, which totally destroyed the sea bed by sweeping and created imbalance in marine ecosystem.

After 5 to 8 years of fishing in Indian waters by these foreign vessels, the total stock exhausted and it become unprofitable for them also and they were forced to withdraw from fishing. During this period all the so called commercially important species like, shrimps, lobsters, pomfrets etc disappeared from our waters. Till date these varieties have failed to rejuvenate their population.

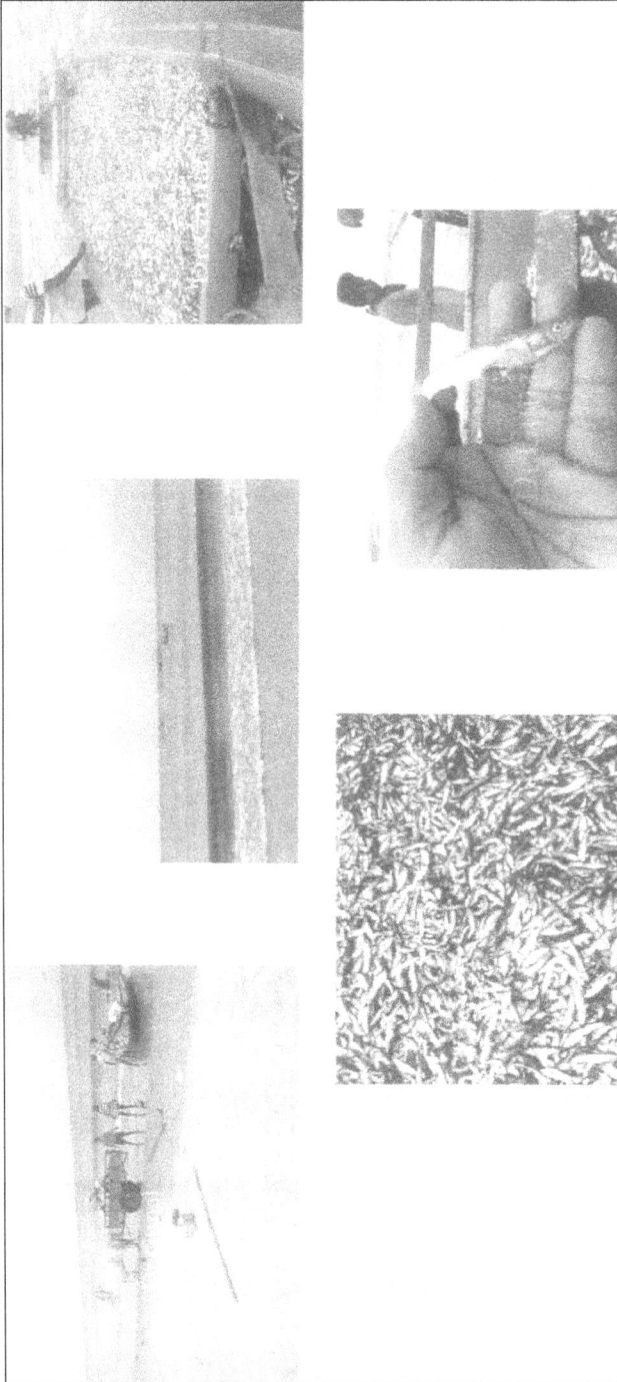

**Figure 17: Mass Exploitation of *S. longiceps*.**

This is a time when Indian fishermen began to explore/look out for unexploited stocks. But these had very limited commercial value, used to be dumped back into the sea. These are varieties like, pink perch, ribbon fish, lizard fish, horse mackerel scads, puffer fish etc. The fishermen continued their fishing business for their survival. These varieties too found export market later.

Meanwhile some of the fishermen became more ambitious and greedy, and replaced their existing 190 HP boat engines, with high speed 450 to 650 HP engines illegally without permission of the concerned authorities. These high speed boats resorted to bull trawling. This deadly method proved to be more destructive than the foreign deep sea trawlers. By this method they were able to catch pelagic, mid-water and bottom dwelling varieties. The result of this was clearly visible within a year of introduction of the illegal way of fishing with high speed engines. The abundantly available varieties, besides mackerel, tuna and sardines are fast disappearing from our marine waters. If this method is allowed to continue, mackerels and sardines too will meet the same fate of pomfret, kingfish and shrimps.

## History of Fishing and Export from Indian Seas

1. Till 1985 fishing and exports were based on high value shrimps, like tiger, white, pink brown, grey brown lobsters etc

2. From 1985-95 small and low value shrimps constituted a major share in landings and exports.

3. Till 1995 Japan was the major market for Indian sea food exports.

4. During 1990-95 squids and cuttle fish contributed for both fishermen and exporters. Europe being the major market.

5. From 1995 the shrimp catches declined drastically. Some of the exporters were forced to diversify for surimi by using pink perch, croaker, and other low value white meat fishes as raw material.

6. From 1995 onwards most of the exporters from the west coast were forced to modify their plants for exporting finfishes like king fish, pomfrets, ribbon fish, reef cod, mackerels etc.

7. From 2000-2010 both the fishermen and exporters struggled to survive with mackerels, ribbonfish mainly with some squids and cuttle fish, leather skin, scads, reef cod etc.

8. In 2010-12 the landings of most of the finfishes have reduced drastically and most of the major exporters had to export Indian oil sardines.

9. In 2010 some of the greedy fishermen have increased their engine power to 260 to 650 hp from 120 to 140 hp.

10. This change in engine power has directly resulted in the collapse of all the finfish fisheries in general and ribbonfish, sardines and mackerel fisheries in particular.

11. If continued in the same manner, what is ahead of 2013 is difficult to visualize.

According to provisional figures for half the year April to September 2012-13 there had been a decline in India's Marine Products Exports, compared to the same period in 2011-12.

The mechanized and traditional fishing were existing side by side in a profitable manner till late 1970s. During those days the seafood (marine resources) was mainly consisting of only premium species like shrimps, kingfish pomfrets etc.

Soon after introduction of deep sea Taiwanese fishing trawlers in early 1980s the landings of these prime species have declined drastically and almost gone extinct towards the end of 1980s.

Since then the decline in the catch and destruction of the sea bed continued, though the total figures of fish caught and exported have shown steady increase till 2011-2012. This is only because the fishermen and the industry exploited commercially unimportant and unexploited species like, pink perch, sardines, ribbon fish, horse mackerel etc, which were earlier dumped back into the sea or used as manure when landed in excess, prior to 1980s.

The damage and reduction in these low value varieties like pink perch, sardines, mackerels, ribbonfish etc was noticed after the introduction of high speed bull trawlers in 2010-2011.

In reality the fish landings of important varieties have steadily shown a decline from 1980s to till date. It is not just during April to September of 2012-2013.

The main reason for this rapid decline is the bull trawling. This could be of Taiwanese or Indian boats. This method of fishing is vulnerable selective and destructive. It destroys the entire sea bed which takes years to get back its normal flora and fauna.

To explain high speed bull trawling which sweeps and takes away whatever comes in its path. It is like exploding dynamite underwater. The entire water body becomes sterile and lifeless which takes years to restore normal ecosystem.

If continued in the same manner, within a year or two, even sardines and mackerels will not be seen in the market. The entire fishing industry and processing part of it also will callapse.

The decline in exports in the 1st half of 2012-2013 was not because of any temporary and passing phenomenon like climate change or cyclone etc. It was because of the deep sea bull trawling on the sea bed and degradation of marine ecosystem. Definitely there would not be any improvement in future till remedial measures are taken.

## Remedial Measures

It is just impossible to improve the damage caused in last three decades in a year's time. Irreparable damage must have been done already ti the entire marine ecosystem. This can be clearly understood and felt by analyzing the varieties and quantities caught and exported from 1970s to till date.

To improve the situation, some drastic and painful measures have to be implemented without any time lapse. They are as follows;

1. Deep sea high speed and bull trawling have to be suspended
2. Engine power of the fishing boats have to be limited;
3. Two ban periods in a year (1ˢᵗ May to 15ᵗʰ August and 1ˢᵗ December to 31ˢᵗ January) have to be enforced;
4. No new licenses for fishing boats to be given. No permission to have a new same kind of boat in place of scrapped one as the density of small boats is already in excess;
5. The mesh size of the nets should be allowed in such a way that no fingerlings are caught;
6. Catching of particular variety to be suspended once it is found with fully grown eggs;
7. There must be regular patrolling on land centers by authorities to monitor proper implementation of the measures.

These measures should be implemented for the entire coast right from Kanyakumari to Gujrat. For smooth implementation there must be a thorough discussion with participation of all stake holders of fishing, like Union/Cooperative societies of mechanized/traditional fishermen, prominent and progressive boat owners, representative of processing industries, representative of fisheries colleges and fisheries research institutes, representative of Government Fisheries Department.

From the introduction of mechanization and till mid 1980s the entire fishing and export from both the coasts were based on sea caught shrimps. The shrimps used to be available for almost 9-10 months in a year. The fishermen and the processors used to have enough catch and the business was very smooth and the nature too was able to reproduce the numbers to be caught to restore the balance. The damage to our marine resources started in early 1990s, when the government permitted Taiwanese joint venture boats to operate in our coastal waters. Within 3-5 years of the introduction of these monsters the entire marine ecosystem had undergone a drastic change.

The real fishery destruction has been stated with the replacement of high hp engines (350-600 hp), when these boats with high speed were sweeping the bottom of the sea covering the maximum area in terms of both width and depth. These boats land more than 20 tonnes of juveniles, larvae and eggs of exportable varieties of sea foods, such as, shrimps, squids, cuttle fishes, ribbonfish, pomfrets, mackerels, kingfish, horse mackerels, crabs, eels, soles, snappers, reef cod at a time.

This massacre is going on since 2010. For last few months this slaughter has been intensified. All the boats are engaged in this undesirable way of making money as no other fish is available.

It is pathetic and heart breaking to know, the landings in Malpe and Mangalore, on an average 2 lakh kg of these juveniles are massacred every day. If allowed to attain normal size these 2 lakh kg would have weighed over 50 lakh kg when harvested as grown up fish. Roughly it is estimated that in last two months 12 thousand tonnes of juveniles were massacred in Malpe and Mangalore alone. Because of their tender body most of them were fully damaged without skin and with bursting belly. Nothing went to fresh fish market. Instead they were supplied to fish meal plants and to cutting sheds for making surimi.

# Chapter 6

# Resources and Environment

The mult-species resources inhabiting the coastal waters of tropical seas are largely native species with some exceptions of cosmopolitan species widely distributed over the world's oceans. In case of sedentary species no intermingling with others takes place, while the highly migratory species does not always form part of the resources of the region. A large number of species are involved and their biological features differ greatly. These features determine (i) the species composition of the various fish communities harvested in specific waters, (ii) the amount of catch to be taken for each species and as a whole, and (iii) the fishing methods and the types of gear employed. Needless to say, variations in this framework of exploitable resources are determined also by environmental conditions in each of the specific waters in the region. Therefore, when the management strategy for multi-species resource in a specific water is planned, the environmental conditions of the water need to be taken fully into account.

The coastal waters are characterized by their highly favorable environmental conditions for biological and fisheries production benefiting from their geographical location and several prominent sea currents. A variety of stocks are available to the fisheries. The potential harvest of some stocks is huge, and various fish of high commercial value are also available, although the potential catch of some of them is small for each.

The combination of the available species and their catchability varies greatly according to local conditions of the fishing ground (latitudinal location, topographic and oceanographic conditions) annual and seasonal fluctuations in the environment. In some cases, the improvement or worsening of environmental conditions can result from activities entirely irrelevant to fishing. In short, the history of fisheries is that of the infinite adaptability of fishermen to various local conditions and their changes from one place/time to another.

Another peculiar feature of multi-species problems is the close relationship between so-called pelagic and demersal fish species. They are sometimes difficult to separate by habitat. These problem originate mostly from the eurybath nature of a few species and partly from the complicated inter-species relationships among them (prey predator relationships). For assessment and management purposes, therefore, the so-called pelagic and demersal fish species need to be dealt with together.

Furthermore, the neritic pelagic fish stocks show a strong multi-species nature within their habitat. Sardine, mackerel and anchovy have historically formed a complicated fish community in which inter-species relationships might have played an important role in the dynamic change in their abundance. The biological similarities between these species and the pelagic fish community means there is competition between them for space and food (as well as prey-predator relationships). Therefore, they also need to be dealt with together in some cases, especially for assessment purposes.

## Multi-Species Fisheries

The multi-species fisheries around tropical seas are multi-gear fisheries. They can, however, be roughly grouped into two categories according to their size and which fishing grounds they are permitted to use: (i) large to medium-type fisheries in offshore waters and (ii) small-scale fisheries in nearshore waters.

The structure of the first group is rather simple, being composed of a few types of highly efficient gear. These include offshore trawls (larger than 15 gross tons), larger one- and two-boat purse seines (over 40 gross tons), medium-type purse seines (5-40 gross tons), stick-held dipnet and squid-jigging fisheries. They may not be allowed to cooperate in nearshore waters. The second group is a complex of small scale fishing gear forming a highly complicated multi-gear fishery in each of the near shore waters where fishing is permitted. The fishing vessels employed in the second are mostly less than 5 gross tons except the small-scale mechanized trawls in defined sea areas and the boat seines in the inland sea (5-15 gross tons for each fishery).

It can be seen therefore, that these fisheries have a two layered structure. But if the situation is looked at in detail, especially that in near shore waters, the structure can be further divided and becomes multi-layered, with fisheries being defined and characterized by various fishing rights and licences. This includes not only capture fisheries but also aquaculture.

The structure of the fisheries and the deployment of their fishing operations in each of the defined sea areas are, of course, the results of the management decision. However, they are at the same time, the results of fishermen adapting to the natural conditions in each area throughout the long history of the development of the fisheries. In other words, they currently reflect the tradition and customs kept to throughout the history of each fishing community on the coast. These customs have been shared not only by fishermen but also by almost all social and economic sectors of the fishing communities. They are particularly strong in nearshore waters.

Japan is one of the traditional fishing nations in the world, where fishing has been one of the most important industries, providing not only subsistence for fishermen and a supply of animal protein for the nation but also a global improvement in the social and economic status of fishing communities and the entire nation. In this regard, tradition and customs have functioned fairly positively in maintaining social tranquility in each fishing community, and have been extremely effective in resolving conflicts among fishermen.

This deep-rooted philosophy is shared not only by the people in fishing communities but also by the nation as a whole. This is one of the reasons why, in establishing modern, democratic legal arrangements (laws and acts), those traditions and customs have had to be taken into account. This is also one of the main reasons for the success in organizing various fisheries co-operatives as autonomous co-ordinating bodies at a grass roots level.

## Change in Resources

The entire ecosystem of marine living organisms inhabiting the Inland Sea can be divided in to two sub-systems according to their food-web. The energy flow of each is schematically illustrated as follows;

**1. Piscivorous System**

Phytoplankton → Zooplankton → Fish → Piscivorous fish

**2. Omnivorous System**

Phytoplankton/detritus → Zooplankton/benthos → Invertebrates/fish → Carnivorous animals/fish

In addition to the above, various decomposers (bacteria, viruses, etc), which decomposes various resolvable organic items (*e.g.* carcasses of fauna and flora) into nutrient play an highly important role in the energy flow especially in the sea. This must have been critical when a substantial change in the biological productivity of the sea is taking place.

Some species bypass an intermediate stage of the flow, *e.g.* gizzard shad is a herbivorous fish so the energy flow is from "phytoplankton" to "fish" missing out "zooplankton" in this case. The fish is harvested by the shad fishery. In general, the fisheries harvest the animals or fish, as a commercial product, at various stages/ levels of the energy flow in each system. For instance, the catch of anchovy is product of the third level as planktivorous fish and amberjack (yellowtail) is at the fourth stage as a piscivorous fish in the first sub-system. Similarly, abalone and sea urchins are at the second level, shrimps and soles are at the third, and sea breams and octopuses are at the fourth level in the second sub-system. Howevr, these sub-systems are distinguished by the fact that the highest level is represented by piscivorous fish in the first and omnivorous animals and fish in the second.

Generally speaking, it is not easy to examine these two sub-systems through data observed in the field. Detailed statistics in terms of the species and area break down is required to examine changes in ecosystem of fishery resources in the Inland Sea.

It may be noted that the application of fishery statistics to such ecological concepts inevitably involves substantial bias and distortion caused by various factors. These factors include (a) the selective function of some types of gear employed, (b) species preference of fishermen, (c) the change in food items (feeding habit) of fish according to growth stage (almost all fish are planktivorous during their larval and fry stages, even those that acquire a piscivorous or omnivorous food habit in their adult stage), (d) the intermingling of fish to and from the region, etc.

However, it is worth examining the ecological concepts of the catch and exploitable resources, as far as possible, to clarify the biological features involved in a systematic way. Such examination could be carried out by analyzing tha data on a comparative basis, applying the same standards and rules within a defined framework.

The compilation of species caught, allocated to each trophic level by food item in each sub-system (photosynthesis, phytoplankton/detritus, zooplankton/various animals, fish/various animals) can be roughly regarded as representing the standing-state of the exploitable resources in the sea (the "state of organisms in a biomass pyramid at any one moment"). However, it should be kept in mind that thr total marine catch represents only a part of the biomass pyramid of the entire ecosystem. The mean value of the numbers of trophic level for the total catch, calculated by weighing the catch for each level, is an indicator of the "standing state" of the exploitable resources as a whole in terms of the center of gravity of the biomass pyramid of the entire catch or exploitable stocks (the mean value indicates the relative position of the catch in the trophic levels. However, it may not be strictly correct to call it an "average trophic level").

The annual change in the total catch for a period by sub-system and sub-region of the sea may show a steady increase over the years, which accords with the change in the total production of the sea. This indicates that the increase in the biological productivity of the sea applied to all resources and areas.

The rate of increase in catch may differ greatly by sub-region and sub-system. It may be the highest in the piscivorous catch in the some region, while it may be stagnant in other area, although the total increase may be doubled. In some area, the omnivorous catch may be stagnant over the years, while in other region they may increase steadily, the catch more than doubling. These facts indicate that large and various differences in the processes increasing biological production in the ecosystem occur depending on the structure of the system and, it is assumed, on the environmental conditions in each sub-region.

In conclusion, a change in the sea's ecosystem certainly did take place, in conjunction with the eutrophication of sea waters over years. But the changes in the structure of the ecosystem (biomass of each species and species-group, and supposedly, inter-species relationships etc.) are markedly different between the regions of the sea. These changes may result in differences in fisheries production between the two sub-regions as the final outcome of the enhancement in biological productivity. In other words, the fisheries of the Inland Sea are dependent upon two different ecosystems, that is, piscivorous system in one region and the omnivorous system in the other.

Major changes can also be observed in a few specific fish stocks in the sea. A few selected carnivorous species may be taken from the entire sea over years. They are of higher trophic levels, feeding intensively on fish and other animals at their adult stage, and are of high commercial value. They include red sea bream, bastard halibut, dagger tooth pike-conger, Japanese sea bass, Japanese Spanish mackerel, lizard fish and large head hairtail. The stock levels of all these show fluctuations over the years produced either by man-made or natural causes.

When the size of the fish of high commercial value decrease during decades and the loss of net economic return to fishermen harvesting these fish is serious caused by a decline in the catch rate coupled with a lower market price for fish of smaller size, these are apparently the typical symptoms of over fishing with respect to concerned species. It can be seen, however, that this over fishing occur while the substantial increase in the total biomass of exploitable fish was taking place in the sea.

Though these symptoms can be soon recognized in all seriousness, but there is no simple way to resolve the problem, because of the complexity of the fisheries and of the resources fished.

The recovery of these fish stocks may take place after about 10 years, 15 years and sometimes after 25 years after the initial decline provided strict and more comprehensive regulatory measures (protection of spawning stocks throughout their life and in particular spawning grounds and seasons, and the stronger protection of the nursery grounds of these fish, which are commonly distributed in the seaweed-bed area or under-water sea grass forests; limitations on fishing operations by efficient gears, such as mechanized trawls and surrounding seines, are taken.

The difference in the time-lag between decline and recovery may be chiefly a result of different biological features of these fish, especially as regards in life cycle. For instance, bastard halibut reach first maturity at the age of 2-3 years, while red sea bream do so at the age of 3-4 years and dagger tooth pike-conger at 6-7 years of age. The difference in reproductive potential (e.g spawning magnitude and natural mortality rate during early life stages etc.) would also have been important factor.

The increase in the prey biomass, would certainly have aided the recovery too. But the main trigger for the recovery must have been the employment of proper management, and not environmental factors. A serious decline in stocks of these fish would not occur in the future only by man-made causes, if the enforcement of proper management scheme is effectively maintained.

## Fishing and Assessment of Stocks

The assessment of fishery stocks can be seen as the application of the methods of population dynamics to stocks that are exploited by fishing.

## Exploitation and Future Prospect

The recent history of fishing and its future prospects enables to appreciate to what extent fisheries utilize the production of life in the seas. This glance at history also shows how research problems have evolved both in time and according to the level of exploitation.

Towards the end of the 19th century, in the wake of the industrial revolution, conditions became ripe in the Atlantic and Northern Pacific for the fishing industry to industrialize. At that time certain technical innovations were made that greatly increased the power and efficiency of the industry at every stage of production:

☆ Catches (otter trawls, steel hulls, steam engines),

☆ Preservation (ice and canning processes),

☆ Distribution (railways),

☆ Commercialization (big outlets in the main industrial and urban centers)

Up until the second world war, this expansion was limited to the industrialized countries in the Northern Hemisphere. The demersal species were then the most sought after and production of these greatly surpassed that of pelagic species.

Starting at the end of the 1940s, two development occurred:

☆ The extension of industrial fishing all over the globe as a result of the greater number of participants (USSR, Indonesia, Peru, Thailand etc.), and the use of long range ships capable of freezing and treating their catches on board, far from the traditional centers of consumption.

☆ The intensification of fishing for pelagic species (coastal and oceanic) which was facilitated by several technical innovations. Some of these improved methods of capture (improvements to surrounding nets, refinements of pelagic trawls and acoustic detection). Others opened up new outlets for the catch (the use of fish meal to fatten pigs and chickens).

The result was that by 1970 catches of pelagic species were twice those of demersal species, and 90 per cent of the pelagic fish catch and half the total catch went for processing into fishmeal.

This series of innovations enabled the fishing industry to expand at a rapid rate, identical to what was achieved during the first half of the century. From 1900 to 1970 world fish production went from 4 to 70 million tons, which means that it doubled approximately every ten years. This was the highest growth rate of any food production sector and it is one of the few sectors in which production grew faster than world population. Since 1972, however, the total catch has leveled off, mainly because of the decline in the catch of a single stock, the Peruvian anchoveta. Presently, for the world as a whole, the fishing industry supplies about 10 per cent of the animal protein consumed by man as food. The proportion is several times greater than this in the majority of the developing countries- particularly in Africa and Asia- where fish is the basic source of protein in the human diet.

Several points emerge from this brief historical survey. There are a number of prerequisites to fishery development (resources, means of capture, the ability to operate and manage the equipment, labor, systems of processing and preservation, distribution networks and markets) as well as, the establishment of adequate working relations among research institutes, industry and the administrative authorities. Without such working relations, in fact, even the most basic programs and facilities cannot be exploited to their full potential. A comparison of the performances of various countries shows that neither in the most developed nor in the least developed countries are all the conditions mentioned above as requirements of a healthy fishing industry, fully satisfied. On the whole, conditions appear to be more favorable in the group of countries that are at an intermediate stage of development (*e.g.* Spain, Korea, Cuba, Indonesia etc.).

In the most areas the fishing industry has developed in three stages, namely,:

☆ Intensified fishing of traditional stocks (the most abundant, the easiest to catch and sell, those found nearest to existing markets), sometimes till a point is reached where fishing them is no longer profitable.

☆ Fishing of unconventional species on the traditional fishing grounds (*i.e.* species that were of no commercial interest when traditional stocks were still abundant).

☆ Extension of fishing activity to areas progressively farther away from the original bases (and in these areas the first two stages are repeated).

The steady expansion of fisheries to new species and areas has brought about a dramatic change in the overall pattern of exploitation of the world's fishery resources. Whereas formerly, despite isolated cases of over exploitation, the resources of the various regions were not fully exploited, nowadays in most regions the exploitation of most species is very intense-even excessive-which calls for the urgent implementation of more and more serious measures of restraint.

## Exploitable Fishery Resources

For resources to be exploitable they must satisfy certain characteristics, such as,:

☆ The densities must be large enough (at least temporarily) to provide profitable catch rates.

☆ Stocks and potential yields must be sufficiently large to justify investments and to allow catches to be maintained at a reasonable level.

☆ The product must be marketable. This is a condition which up to now has eliminated species at lower trophic levels, although these are the most abundant and productive.

Due to the wide dispersal of living matter in the ocean these conditions only occasionally coincide. To appreciate this it is only necessary to compare, on a world scale, primary production (which is in the order of 150X1000000000 tons/year) with the volume of marine catches (about 89X1000000 tons/year). In fact, fishing is presently viable only at a small number of productive "traps" where the production of the seas is concentrated. To illustrate the highly selective nature of fishing it is sufficient to compare the catches of the different elements of the flora and fauna to their respective biomasses. Thus as regards the flora, exploitation is very unevenly spread geographically and basically applies to just a few species of macroscopic algae, of which the harvest accounts for only one percent of the total harvest of living matter of aquatic origin. Of the more than 20000 species making up world's fish fauna a mere 100 species account for over 70 per cent of the world catch. In 1971, a single species, the Peruvian anchoveta, accounted for more than a fifth of the world's fish catch, while the seven species of anchoveta then being exploited accounted for more than than a quarter of the total (this comparison does not take into account the potential of the Argentine and the Californian anchoveta stocks whose biomasses amount to millions of tonnes).

The increase in the proportion of pelagic fish in the total catch since the last world war was a measure of intensified fishing at the lowr levels of the food chain. This phenomenon can even be seen in the composition of pelagic catches, where the weight ratio of phytoplankton feeders to zooplankton feeders has gone from 4/96 to 39/61 over the past 30 years .This development is the result of the greater productivity of the lower levels of the food chain. Moiseev(1972) estimated the oceanic production of zooplankton alone (*i.e.* not including phytoplankton) as being 13 to 15 times greater than that of the benthos consumed by exploited species, while the total weight of plankton feerders directly fished, or eaten by predators that are fished, is only 10 to 12 times greater than the total weight of exploited demersal species which feed on benthos. While the complexity of the predator-prey relationships prevents any direct comparisons, these figures do suggest that pelagic stocks are less intensely exploited than the traditional demersal stocks. This view is supported by the results of stock assessments that show coastal pelagic resources throughout the world could supply about another 15 million tonnes per year, while demersal stocks could not supply more than an extra 5 to 10 million tonnes per year.

The geographic distribution of fishing is also highly selective. Almost the entire catch is made in waters over the continental shelf (in 1971 almost the entire demersal catch and 94 per cent of the pelagic catch), which accounts for the importance of the extent of the continental shelf as a factor in the fishery potential of the region. The Atlantic and North Pacific (where the continental shelf is particularly extensive, and half the North Atlantic is less than 1000 meters deep) supply half of the total world catch. The proportion is even higher for the demersal fish catch.

Even among neritic waters, fishery resources are unevenly spread. Upwelling regions account for around half the total potential (of conventional species) in the sea, *i.e.* 40 to 60 million tonnes out of a total which is in the order of 100 million tonnes (Cushing, 1972).

In fact, up to now, man has only been skimming off the cream of the ocean's total production. The prospects of improving the performance in the future can be considered in three groupings:

(a) As regards the traditional stocks, production probably will not increase more than 50 to 100 percent, *i.e.* perhaps to some 100 million tonnes. Considering previous rates of expansion in world fishing, such a position could be reached within the next ten years. In many regions and for the more sought after and easily utilized stocks, the achievement of this objective already depends more on the implementation of suitable management schemes than on an intensification of fishing.

(b) The development of new resources is now technically possible in some cases:

☆ Krill (potential possibly in the region of 50 to 100 million tonnes)

  Common and oceanic squids (potential possibly between 10 and 100 m.tonnes

☆ Bathypelagic fish (potential > 100.10 million tonnes)

It is likely that the development of these resources will depend less on perfecting adequate fishing and treating processes than on the possibilities of finding new outlets that are suitable both as regards quality (new products) and, above all, as regards quantities (their potential is comparable to present world production). There is no way that one can further define these prospects since the utilization of the lower trophic levels will depend on other factors that cannot yet be quantified.

☆ The relationship between the cost of the catch and the value of the products (increased energy costs on the one hand due to greater dispersion in the marine environment and on the other the generally lower market value of new types of products).

☆ The effects that exploiting these stocks may have on the productivity of traditional stocks.

## Fishery: A Living Resource

It may not be necessary to point out that fishery resources are living, except to emphasize the importance of knowing their biology and ecology and to stress the fact that they are renewable and thus exploitable for ever, but not at any rate we like (as opposed to non-renewable resources).

Above all, they are wild and thus free. Stocks, in their distribution and migrations, are unaware of the frontiers drawn by man (all marine species, even the sessile species, have at least one period in their life when they move freely). In general, therefore, they can not be owned by individual exploiters. The latter can only enjoy the benefits of exploitation, generally in groups. Within these groups, the fishermen compete directly for shares of the yield of the stock, which is generally limited. Such a stock is often referred to as a freely accessible resource.

For these reasons, it is not possible to catch fish, at only a certain age and a certain pre-determined size. Thus it is not possible to catch all the members of a particular year-class at the age when the weight of the year-class is at its maximum, as can be done in the case of domestic animals raised for meat. Furthermore, in the open sea, just as in inland waters above a certain size, the environment cannot be controlled. Physio-chemical conditions, nutrient salts, the composition of the associated flora and fauna (food, predators, competitors etc.) are beyond the man's control. Even in cases of extensive cultivation, there can be only partial control of the nature and degree of environmental conditions. These difficulties connected with controlling the marine environment, its inhabitants and their yield mean that the comparisons, such as, fruit picking versus settled agriculture, hunting versus stock breeding (i. e .between the land environment and the sea environment) are not really justified. They also explain why even though fish farming has been in existence for a long time (the Etruscans used to culture oysters), it was, in practice, limited to immobile species (shellfish) and had to be confined to the narrow land/sea interface where at least partial control could be exercised.

Given the living and wild nature of fish stocks, the optimum rate of exploitation (and even the method, since they may determine the average age and size of the individual fish taken) cannot be chosen arbitrarily. In the long term the highest yield will be attained by maintaining the rate of exploitation at a level corresponding to the maximum rate of natural replacement of the stock; above this rate and below it there will be some decrease in the yield. The objective of stock assessments is to determine, for the various stocks, what is their maximum rate of replacement and what the pattern of exploitation (pattern of exploitation means the combination of the rates and modes of exploitation) should be to realize it. The object of this course is to see how this can be done.

## Potentially Usable Resources

In fact, the kind of information required, and its precision, change with the intensity of exploitation of a stock.

The first step, when exploitation is still light or nil, consists of identifying those resources which are most likely to support an expansion of the industry and meet the demand of the market.

Among research tasks at the various stages of fishery development, distinctions can be made according to the nature of the information being sought;

(a) Surveys aimed at directing the industry to the more interesting stocks (bearing in mind the needs and capacities of each country) so as to develop fisheries on the various stocks in the most appropriate order. This has not always been the case since fishing often develops on the basis of borrowed attitudes or methods which only rarely conform to actual requirements. Thus on the west coast of Africa trawling for demersal fish developed befor seine fishing for coastal pelagic fish which better suits the needs of the region. The main goals of these surveys are to establish;

☆ An inventory of potentially usable stocks;

☆ The commercial possibilities of the corresponding catches;

☆ An approximate order of magnitude of potential catches, or at least a minimum limit of these potentials which can be used as a temporary ceiling for development plans.

Moreover to arouse the interest of potential investors it is necessary to get figures on;

☆ Estimated catches and revenues for various types of vessels and methods of fishing;

☆ The seasonal and areal variations in catch rates (particularly by localizing in time and space the most dense concentrations).

## Monitoring the State of Stocks

All the fishermen know that when the number of boats exploiting a stock increases, the catch rates and individual catches decline progressively until, at a certain level, the total catch levels off. Any new investment will then lead to a lowering in the long term of stock abundance and catches. Since increasing fishing effort will not produce an increase in the total catch indefinitely, proper planning requires a prediction of the effects on the size and composition of the stock on the one hand, and on the yields and total catch on the others,

In particular, answers must be found to the following questions:

☆ What proportion does the current catch represent of the potential maximum catch?

☆ What are the current catch rates and how will they change if fishing is intensified?

☆ What size of fleet is required to attain the levels of production that can be envisaged?

☆ What will be the effects on the stock and catches of given changes in mesh size or, more generally, in the minimum size of individual fish caught?

## Assessment of Potential Maximum Catch

There are, in fact, only too many examples of cases where over-optimistic estimates of potential have led to excessive investments and eventually considerable economic loss, and where the failure to take decisions to control fishing has led to serious over-exploitation of stocks and the collapse of certain fisheries. Since the control of fisheries can, in the short term, result in real hardships (reduction of investments, loss of jobs), information on the state of stocks should be sufficiently clear and precise so as to convince the decision makers. Finally, it should be noted that the potential catch rarely remains constant from one year to the next. In fact, the maximum surplus that can be fished is liable to vary from one year to the next depending on changing environmental conditions. These unpredictable fluctuations, like long-term variations, can be quite considerable for certain stocks, *e.g.* coastal pelagic fish. To derive the greatest benefit from them, it would be wise to take these fluctuations into account in management plans or, at least, to be in a position to cut back on fishing in the event of an abnormal drop in stock abundance. Stock evaluation, therefore, should be considered as an ongoing task where estimates are constantly being re-adjusted and readjusted and refined.

## Assessment of Tropical Fish Stocks

### Deck Sampling and Catch Recording Procedure

The following steps pertain to methods for sorting the catch of a fishery research vessel such that the catch composition, both by weight and number of each species (group) can be established.

1. Remove all sea snakes and other venomous or otherwise dangerous animals. Also remove turtles, and if alive return these to the sea. Record number and kind of animals removed.

2. Remove inorganic debris and plant material. Record type of material removed.

3. Remove the larger fishes that are readily visible and place them in a box.

4. Wash the remainder of the catch (of small fish) if necessary and mix with shovels.

5. Put the mixed catch in boxes, while continuing to remove larger fishes and putting them in the box. The boxes should be filled simultaneously, not one after the other, and it should be made certain that all boxes contain the same weight of fish.

6. Count the number of boxes with small fishes and record.

7. A rule of thumb is to take one box out of every five at random for sub-sampling.

8. The boxes taken for sub-sampling are then treated as follows;
   ☆ Weigh the total catch and record;
   ☆ Place fish of the box on a sorting table and sort to species level as far as food fishes and valuable crustraceans (shrinp) are concerned, and to taxonomic groupings as well-defined as possible (genus, family etc.) for the other groups (the non-edible fishes and miscellaneous crustaceans);
   ☆ Repeat the procedure, if appropriate for the other boxes.

9. If more than one box were sorted, compute for each species (or higher taxonomic group) the total weight and number in all sorted boxes.

10. Multiply the numbers and weight of fishes and invertebrate by species (or higher taxonomic group) by the ratio of the number of unsorted to sorted boxes.

11. Weigh and count the larger fishes by species (very large fish should be weighed individually and measured).

12. Add, when there is an overlap (when the fishes of a certain species occurred both in the sorted boxes of small fishes and in the large fish box) the weights and numbers obtained in step 11 to the weights and numbers in step 10.

13. Step 12 (as well as step 11, when there is no overlap) provide estimates of total catch, both in weight and number, by species or higher taxonomic groups. Record the totals, both in weight and number into an appropriate fishing log and convert to catch per hour if fishing time was less or more than one hour. During surveys, this step must be completed after each haul, or every evening at the latest, to preclude loss of information.

14. In addition to catch sampling, identifying and recording, the work of the fishery biologists generally includes among other things;
    ☆ Collecting length frequency data;

☆ Collecting miscellaneous biological information on the fish caught, *e.g.*, concerning their weight and maturity;

☆ Collecting and preserving specimens for further studies on shore;

☆ Collecting oceanographic data.

## Statistics: Regression and Correlation

Regression and correlation analysis are two very powerful statistical techniques are most common fields of application by fishery biologists.

### Linear Regression

Linear regression is a technique for quantifying the relationship that can be seen when a scatter diagram involving two variables is drawn, which relationship being summarized by a "best fitting" equation of the form:

$$Y = a + bx$$

In this equation, y represents the coordinate values along the vertical axis of the graph (ordinate), while x represents the coordinate values along the horizontal axis (abscissa). The value of "a" (which can be negative, positive or equal to zero) is called the intercept, while the value of b (which can be negative or positive) is called the slope or regression coefficient.

### Correlation

Correlation analysis is closely related to regression analysis and both can be viewed in fact as two aspects of the same thing.

The correlation between two variables, is, again put in the simplest trems, the degree of association between two variables. This degree of association is expressed by a single value called a correlation coefficient ®, which can take values ranging between -1 and +1. When r is negative, it means that one variable (either x or y) tends to decrease as the other increases- there is a "negative correlation" (corresponding to a negative value of b in regression analysis). When r is positive, on the other hand, it means that the one variable increases with the other (which corresponds to a positive value of b in regression analysis).

Values of r are easily computed for a set of x, y data pairs, using the same table and sums of the "regression". Thus r can then be obtained – indirectly – from the relationship, which provides a value of the coefficient of determination (= r square). All we need is then to take the square root of the coefficient of determination to obtain the (absolute) value of r, and then to add the sign (+ or -) depending on whether the correlation is positive or negative (which can be assessed by visual inspection of a scattergram or by computing the b value of the corresponding regression and using for r the sign of b).

When we compute values of r, we would also like to know, however, whether the correlation that was identified could have arisen by chance alone. This can be established by testing whether the computed value of r is "significant" that is whether the (absolute) value of r is higher than or equal to a "critical" value of r as given in a statistical table.

## Length-Weight Relationship

Both the regression and correlation analysis are based on the assumption of a "linear" relationship between the two variables involved (meaning that the best fitting line is straight). There are many cases in fishery biology, however, where the relationship between two variables is non-linear, and a well known example for this is the length-weight relationship, where the weight (W) is proportional to a certain power (b) of the length (L).

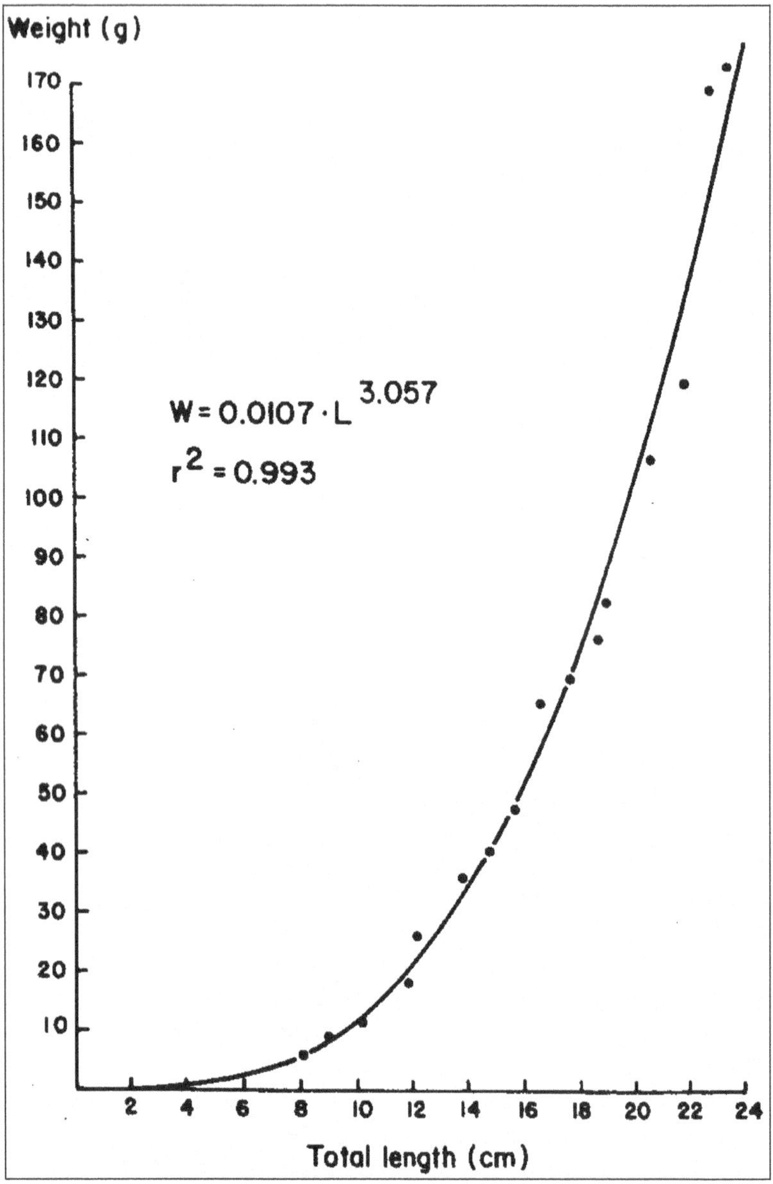


**Figure 18: Length-weight Relationship of *Nemipterus marginatus* in the South China Sea.**

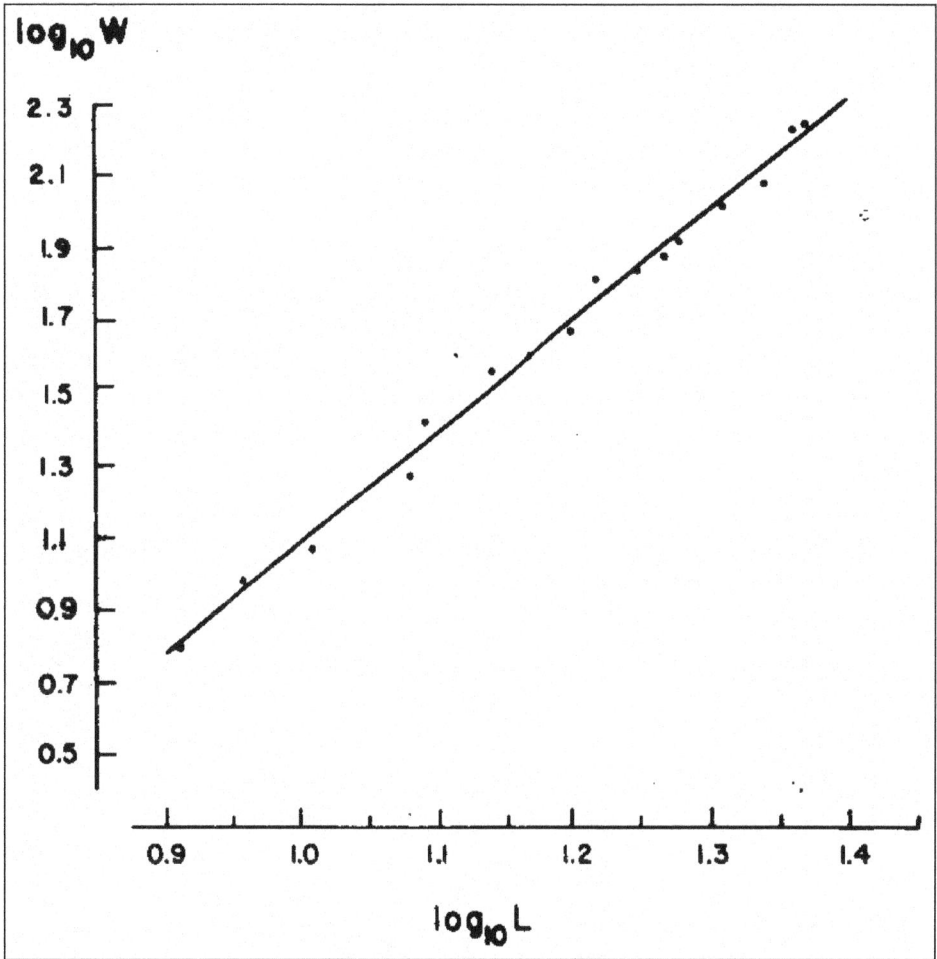

**Figure 19: Base 10 Logarithms.**

Length-weight data can, however, be fitted with a (linear) regression if logarithms are taken of both sides.

The logarithm of the length and weight are fitted extremely well by a linear regression, when the following steps are taken;

1. Take the logarithm of the length and weight values.
2. Compute the sums with x and y values as defined in the regression section
3. Compute a and b using equations
4. Take the antilogarithm of a to obtain alpha in equation 6.
5. Write your version of equation 6
6. Using the sums computed in step 2, compute the value of r square and r and check significance.

## Methods for Obtaining Growth Parameters from Length-Frequency Data of Tropical Fish

The study of fish growth and of phenomena related to growth such as maturation, migration, food and feeding habits is central to fishery biology. Indeed, it is largely with growth studies that fishery biology established itself as a field of its own by the end of nineteenth century.

Knowledge of how the fishes of a given stock grow is essential for most stock assessment purposes, both in the tropics and elsewhere, since it is the growth of individual fishes which provide from year to year the catch taken by a fishery.

For practical reasons, the available information on the growth of fishes of a given stock is generally reduced to and expressed by means of a single equation, such as the Von Bertalanffy Growth Formula (VBGF), the simplest version of which has the form

$$Lt + L \text{ infinity } (1\text{-}e\text{ } \text{-}K(t\text{-}to)),$$

Where L infinity is the mean length the fish would reach if they were to grow to a very old age (indefinitely, in fact)

K is a growth coefficient,

To is the "age" the fish would have had at length zero if they had always grown according to the equation (to generally has a negative value) and where,

Lt is the length at age t.

The biological data which can be used to obtain information ("growth data") from which growth parameters can be estimated are of three basic types :

1. Tagging-recapture data on (or direct observation of the growth of) individual fishes.

2. Period markings (annual, or daily) on skeletal parts such scales, otoliths, or other bones (or cartilage in elasmobranches).

3. Size-frequency data; most commonly length-frequency data (such data, it must be emphasized, never provide absolute age estimate, and hence no value of to).

Inspite of frequent criticism, the methods for the analysis of length frequency data have found, in the tropics, wider applications than the study of skeletal parts, while tagging studies have generally been under-utilized. The reason for this is that it is generally easier to analyse length frequency data than to study skeletal parts and that much less equipment is needed; this also applies to the comparison with tagging studies.

## Methods for the Analysis of Length-Frequency Data

The methods currently in use for the analysis of length-frequency data all find their origin in the work of Petersen (1892 and subsequent years). Traditionally, however, the name of Petersen has been associated with only one of the specific

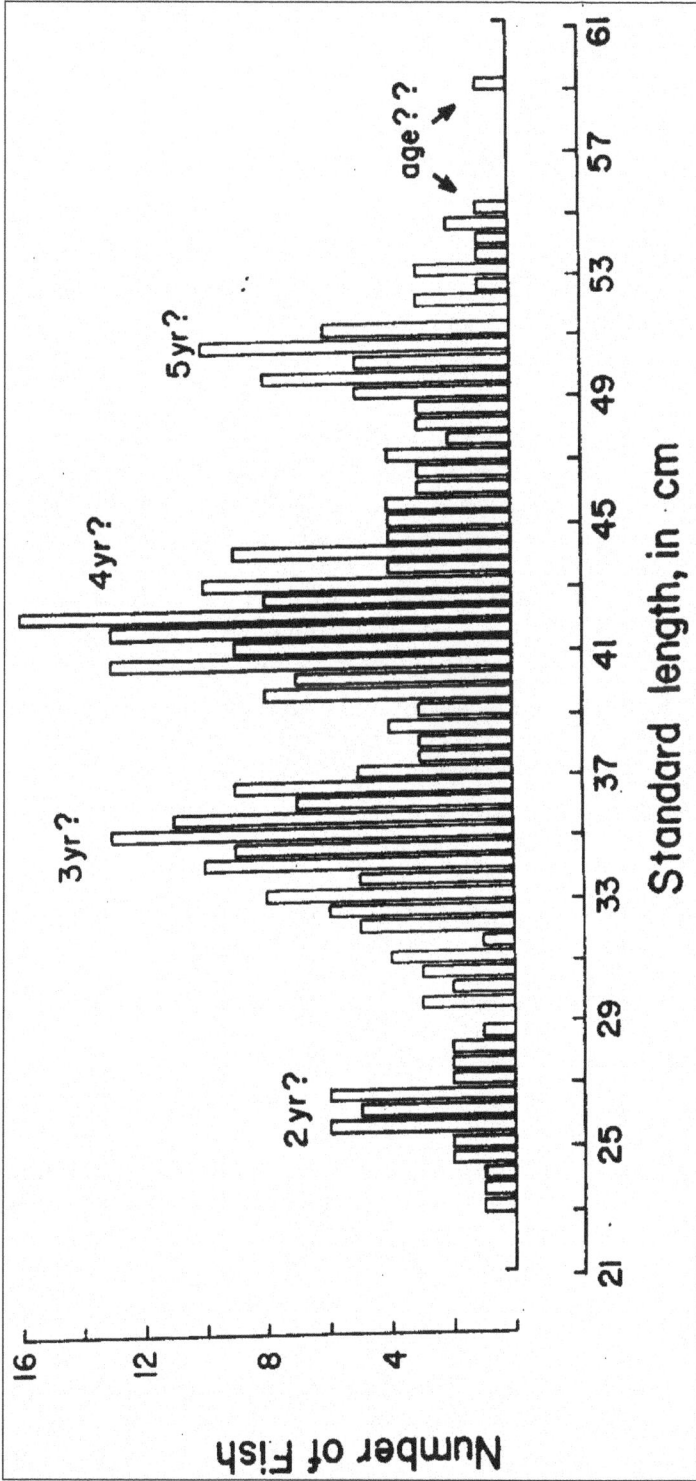

Figure 20: Length-frequency Data on the Coral Trout (*Plectropomus leopardus*) Obtained by Goeden (1978) from Heron Island (Great Barrier Reef, Australia) in October 1977. The "Ages" are from Goeden, with question marks added. N = 319.

approaches commonly used, such that we may distinguish three methods for the analysis of length-frequency data.

1. The "Petersen method"
2. The modal class progression analysis
3. A combination of methods 1 and 2 which may be called the "integrated method"

With the "Petersen method", assumptions are made as to the time interval separating the various peaks of one length-frequency sample, these peaks being assumed to represent distinct age groups.

With the second method, assumptions are made as to which of the peaks can be inter-connected that belong to various samples arranged sequentially.

The methods are quite subjective in the sense that several options are available for attributing ages to the various age groups or for inter-connecting peaks. Thus, both the "Petersen method" and the "modal class progression analysis" are often fraught with uncertainties. Some of these uncertainties can be overcome, however, by combining the two methods to an "integrated method" in which an attempt is made to draw a growth curve (*e.g.* with a curved ruler) directly upon the length-frequency samples sequentially arranges in time or onto the same sample repeated over and over along the time axis. . The method is based on the following tenets :

1. Length growth in fishes is at first rapid, then decreases smoothly and is, for the population as a whole, best approximated by a long continuous curve, rather by several, short straight segments.
2. A single, smooth growth curve interconnecting the majority of the peaks of sequentially arranged length-frequency samples is likely to represent the average growth of the fishes of a given stock.
3. The growth patterns repeat themselves from year to year (which is also assumed when the "annuli" of otoliths are counted).

Thus, the curve which interconnects most of the peaks of the 1957 *Leiognathus bindus* samples of Balan (1967) can be used to estimate the growth parameters of that species of slipmouth. An additional example for the application of the integrated method to length-frequency data of tropical fishes may be given here, pertaining to length-frequency data on *Sardinella sirm* from the Java Sea.

Note that the length-frequency data as presented by their original authors do not suggest any growth process, while the same data redrawn in the appropriated manner suggest a clear growth pattern and a single major growth curve which when drawn can be used to estimate growth parameters in this fish.

This example illustrates once more the major features of the integrated method;

1. The intervals on the time axis between the various samples must be proportional to the time elapsed between the sampling dates.
2. The original data must be plotted at least twice, or more along the time axis, which allows for longer, stabilized growth curves to be drawn and for all relevant age groups to be included in one single line.

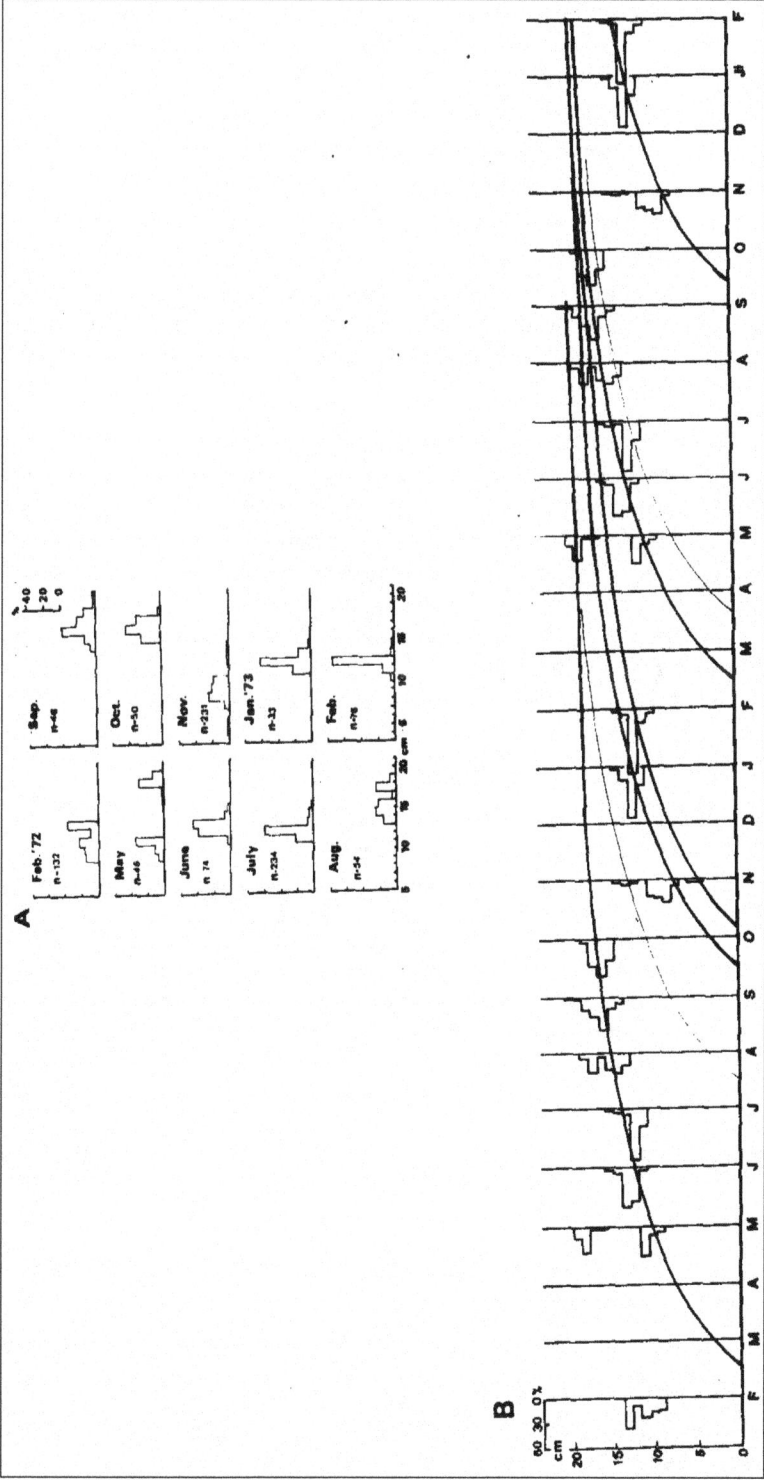

Figure 21: A: Length-frequency Data on *Sardinella sirm* as Presented by their Original Authors (Burhanuddin *et al.*, 1974); B: The Same Data, Redrawn According to the Integrated Method.

3. When several curves are drawn (reflecting the production of several broods per year) the various growth curves should have the same shape, and vary only as to their origin.

4. The scale of the ordinate (length) should start at zero, thus allowing approximate spawning periods to be identified.

5. Each growth curve must interconnect several peaks. The more peaks a curve inter-connects, the more likely it is to depict the actual growth of the population.

6. The modal lengths corresponding to various ages (starting from an arbitrary age) can be read off the curve at regular time intervals, and may be then used to determine the growth parameters with a method as simple as a Ford-Walford Plot.

The experience has shown that length-frequency data published in the literature or available in the form of unpublished manuscripts are generally under-utilized, especially in the tropics. More often than not, no attempt is made to extract growth parameters from length-frequency data even when these are eminently suitable to such treatment. It is also believed that the danger of obtaining completely erroneous growth parameters from length-frequency data is generally overstated, at least as far as small tropical fishes are concerned. In fact, the integrated method, makes it quite hard to trace "wrong" growth curves, and the parameters obtained from such curves will describe the growth of at least the exploited part of a population well enough for most purposes.

Methods for estimating total, fishing and natural mortalities

In fishery biology, the most useful manner of expressing the decay (=decrease) of a age group of fishes through time is by means of exponential rates. These rates, of which three are normally defined are given in the following two expressions :

$$N_t = N_o . e^{-Zt}$$

Where $N_o$ is the (initial) number of fishes at time $t=o$, and $N_t$ is the number of remaining fishes at the end of time t, Z being the instantaneous rate of total mortality. An advantage of instantaneous rates is that they can be added or subtracted. Thus we have

$$Z = M + F$$

Where M is the instantaneous rate of natural mortality and F the instantaneous rate of fishing mortality. Obviously, when

$$F = 0 \text{ then, } Z = M$$

Which means that natural and total mortality have the same value when there is no fishing (in an unexploited stock).

The fishery biologist, as far as mortalities are concerned, has two main jobs;

(a) To estimate the value of Z;

(b) To split, where appropriate, an estimated value of Z into its component parts M and F.

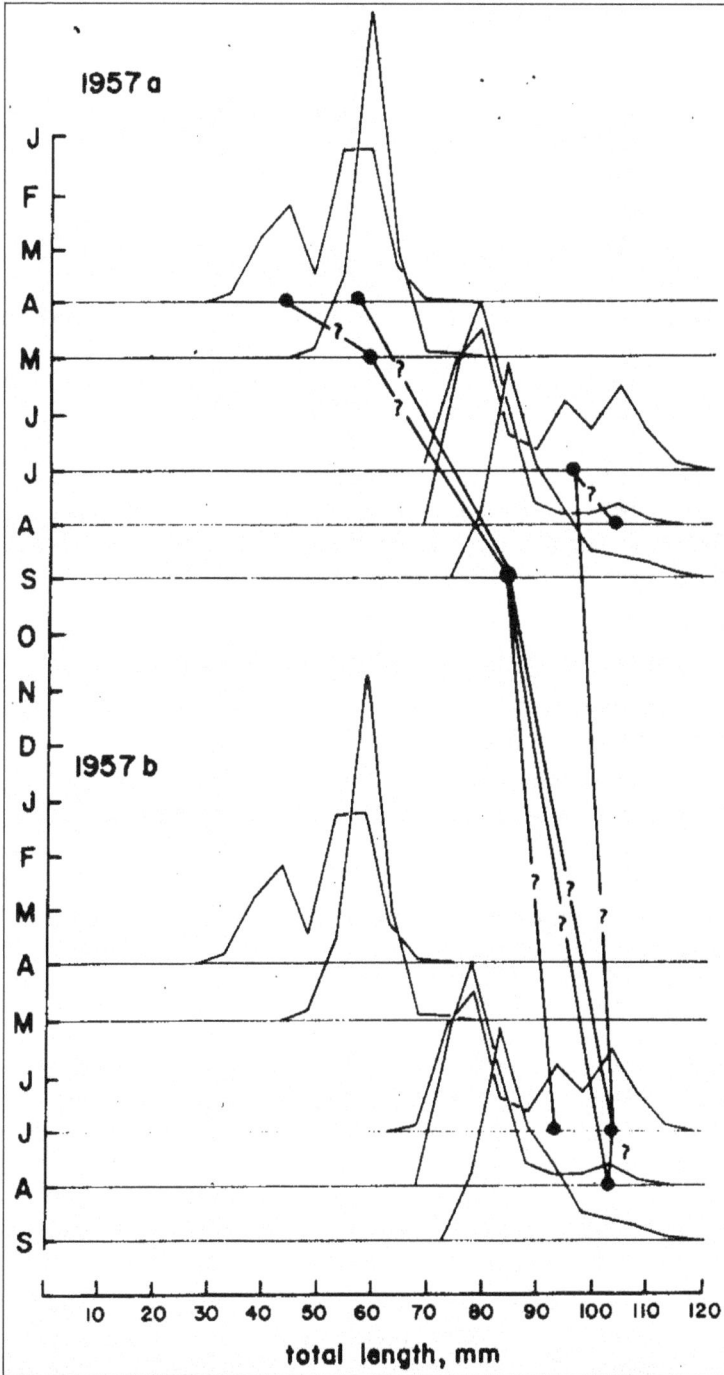

Figure 22: Showing that there are Several Options for Connecting Peaks when Using the "Modal Class Progression Analysis". Based on data of Balan (1967), for *Leiognathus bindus* caught in 1957 off Calicut, India.

## Estimating Total Mortality

Total mortality from the mean size in the catch

(a) When a large number of length-frequency data have been obtained from a given stock, by a given gear, Z can be estimated from the mean length (L) in the catch from a given population by means of

$$Z = \frac{K\,(L \text{ infinity} - L)}{L - L'}$$

Where L infinity and K are parameters of the von Bertalanffy growth equations, L is the mean length in the catch, and " L' is the smallest length of animals that are fully represented in catch samples" (Beverton and Holt, 1956).

## Estimating Z by Means of a catch curve

Another method of estimating Z consists of sampling a multi-aged population of fishes, then plotting the natural logarithm (loge) of the number of fishes in the sample (N) against their respective age (t) or

logeN = a + bt

where the value of b, with high changed, provides an estimate of Z.

Several requirements must be met for the values of -b to be a good estimator of Z. Among these, it may be mentioned :

(a) Only those values of logeN must be included which pertain to age group of fishes fully vulnerable to the gear in question (among other things, the fish must be larger than L'); This corresponds to using only the 'descending part" of a catch curve.

(b) Recruitment must have been constant within the period covered, or have varied in a random fashion only.

When suitable length-frequency samples are available, a catch curve may also be constructed through previous conversion from length to age by means of a set of growth parameters. Here, however, care must be taken not to include fish whose size is close to that of their asymptotic size, as this may result in their age being grossly over-estimated. This latter feature incidentally makes it imperative that a scatter diagram be drawn in order to properly identify the section of the catch curve which can be used to estimate Z. It will be noted also, that since Z is equal to the slope (with sign changed) of the catch curve the real age- which requires an estimate of to – can be here replaced by relative age *i.e.* by setting to = 0

Also, when converting a length-frequency sample to a catch curve, a problem must be considered which does not occur when fish have been aged individually. This problem is due to the fact that length growth not being linear, it takes an older fish longer than a younger fish to grow through a given size-group. Put another way, among bigger fish, a given magnitude of size interval (*e.g.*, a 1-cm length group) will contain more age groups than among small fish.

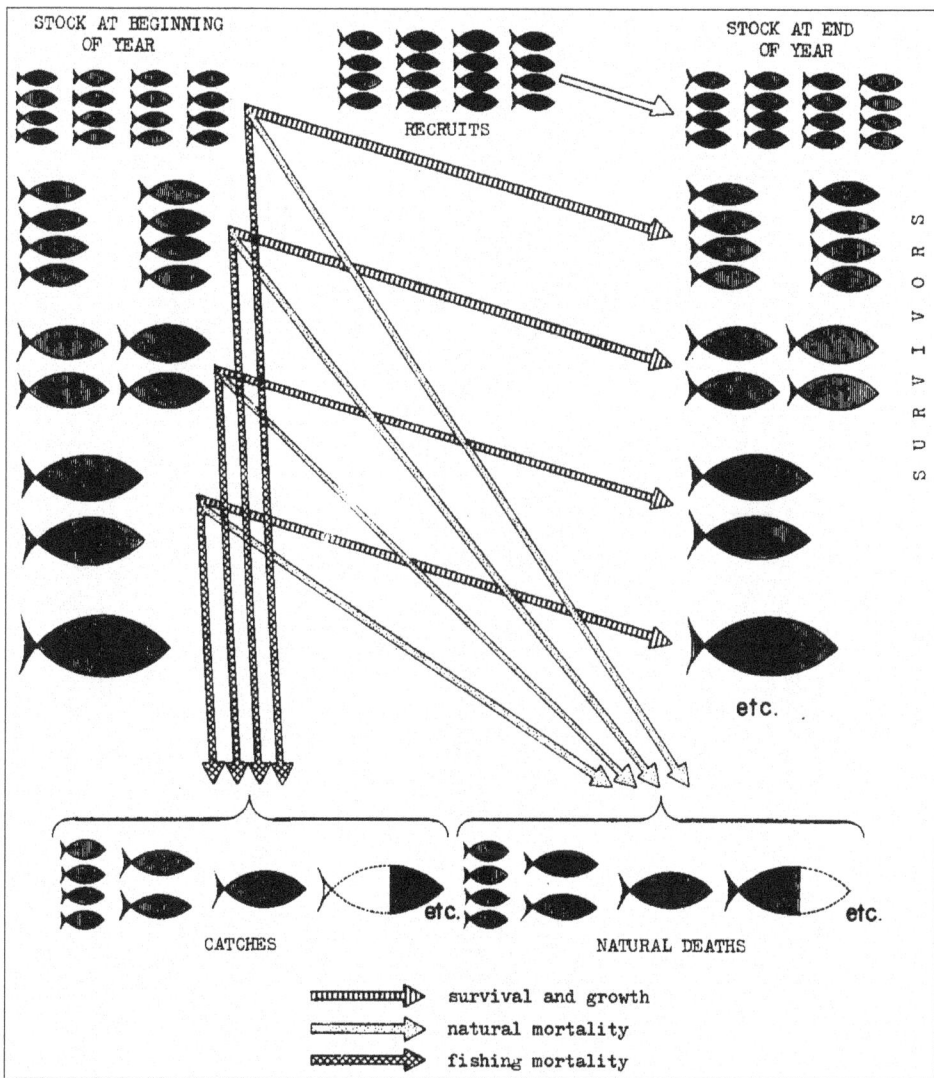

**Figure 23: Loss and Replacement of Biomass in an Exploited Population.**

Compensating for this "piling-up" effect is, however, quite straight forward and can be achieved, *e.g.* by rewriting the above equation as

Loge (N/delta t) = a + bt

Where delta t is the time needed to grow from the lower (ti) to the upper (t2) limit of a given length class, while t is the relative age corresponding to the mid-range of the length class in question.

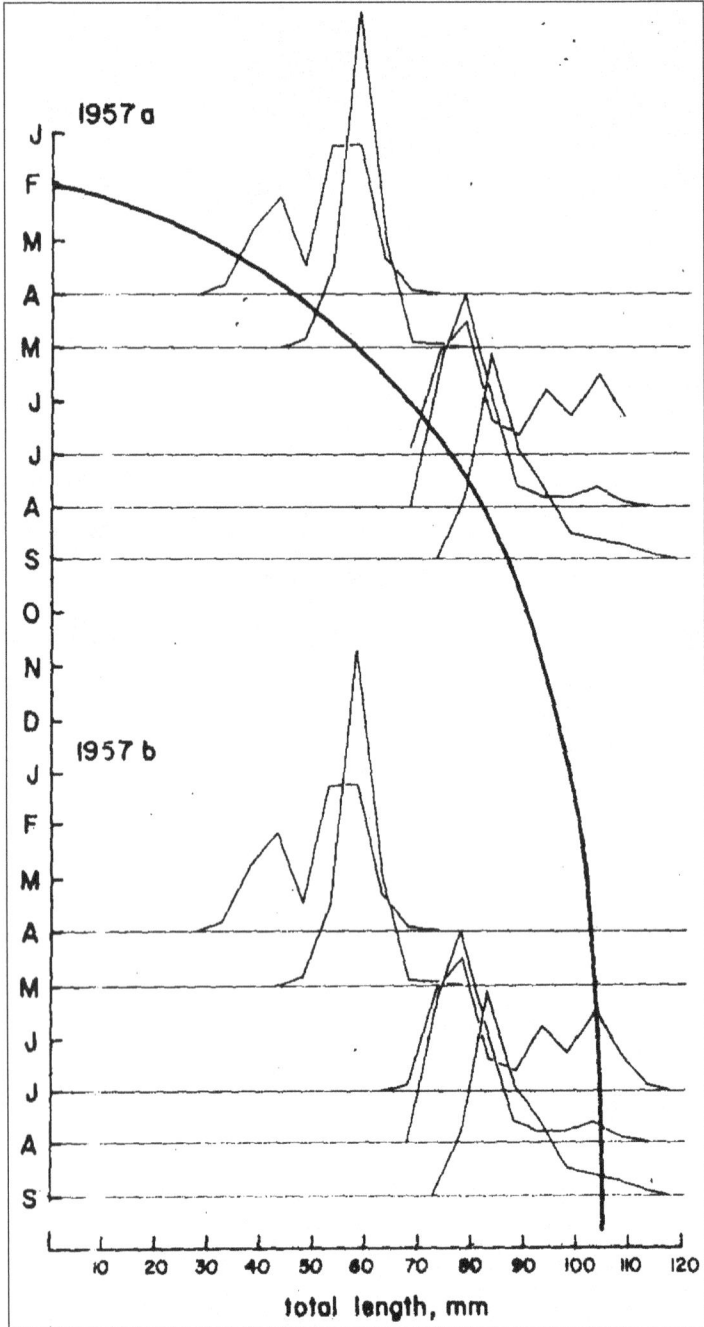

Figure 24: Showing how Drawing a Single, Continuous Growth Curve onto a Series of Samples Sequentially Arranged in Time Limits the Number of Available Options for Connecting Peaks to Only One Single, most Probable Option. Note repetition of sample sequence over two "years". Based on data of Balan (1967), for *Leiognathus bindus* caught in 1957 off Calicut, India.

## Splitting Z into M and F

Splitting Z into M and F by means of a plot of Z on effort

When values of Z are available for several years pertaining to different annual values of effort (f), the value of M can be calculated from

$$Z = M + qf$$

Where q is the "catchability coefficient", which relates f and fishing mortality (F) through

$$F = q.f$$

Thus a series of z (mean annual) values can be plotted against their corresponding values of f and a straight line fitted to the points by means of linear regression technique. This results in a regression line with the equation

$$Y = a + bx$$

Where $Z = y$ and $x = f$, the slope (b) of which provides an estimate of the catchability coefficient q while the intercept value (a) is an estimate of M in which values of Z based on equations

$$Z = \frac{K \, (L \text{ infinity} - L)}{L \, (\text{mean length} - L')}$$

have been plotted

Splitting Z into M and F by means of an independent estimate of M

When only one value of Z is available, or when the available values of Z and f cover too small a range of Z and f values for reasonable values of M and q to be obtained, the catchability coefficient (q) may be estimated through

$$q = \frac{Z - M}{F}$$

Where Z is the mean of the available values of Z (or a single value of Z) and f is the mean of the values of f (or a single value of f), M being an independent estimate of natural mortality.

## Stock Assessment

Stock assessment in the tropics is generally more difficult than in temperate waters. There are a large number of reasons for this, and two of them are given below.

 ☆ Tropical fisheries—especially demersal fisheries—often exploit a large number of species simultaneously, with the result that neither the commercial fishery nor the artisanal fisheries –even when relatively well monitored—can be expected to provide detailed catch and catch/effort statistics on a per species basis. For this reason, it is common in tropical fisheries to treat whole species assemblages as if they were single species.

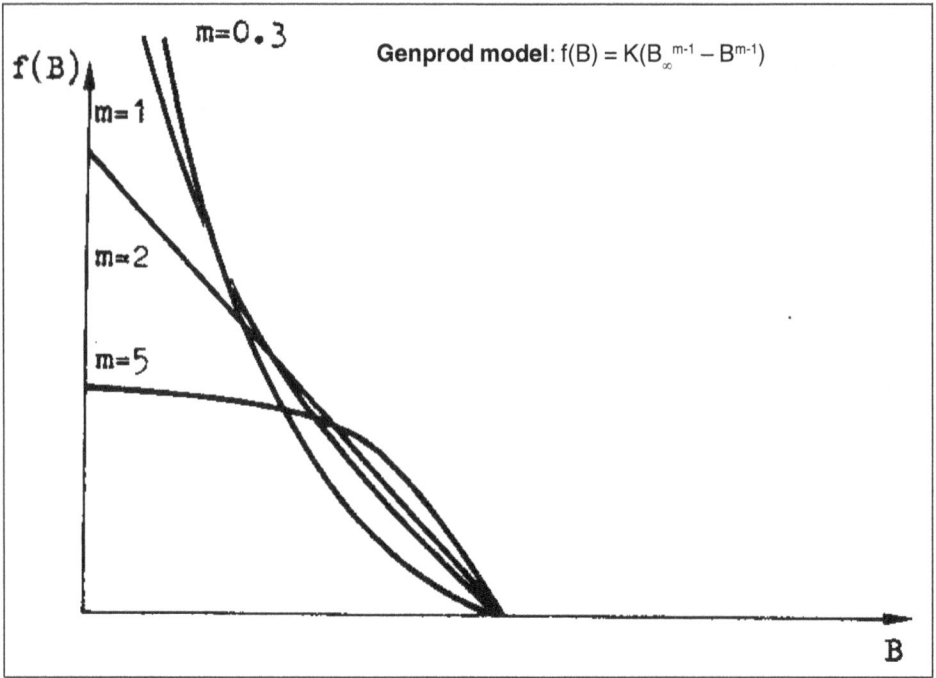

**Figure 25: Curves Showing the Theoretical Relationship between the Specific Rate of Natural Growth of Biomass and Total Biomass, for Selected Values of m.**

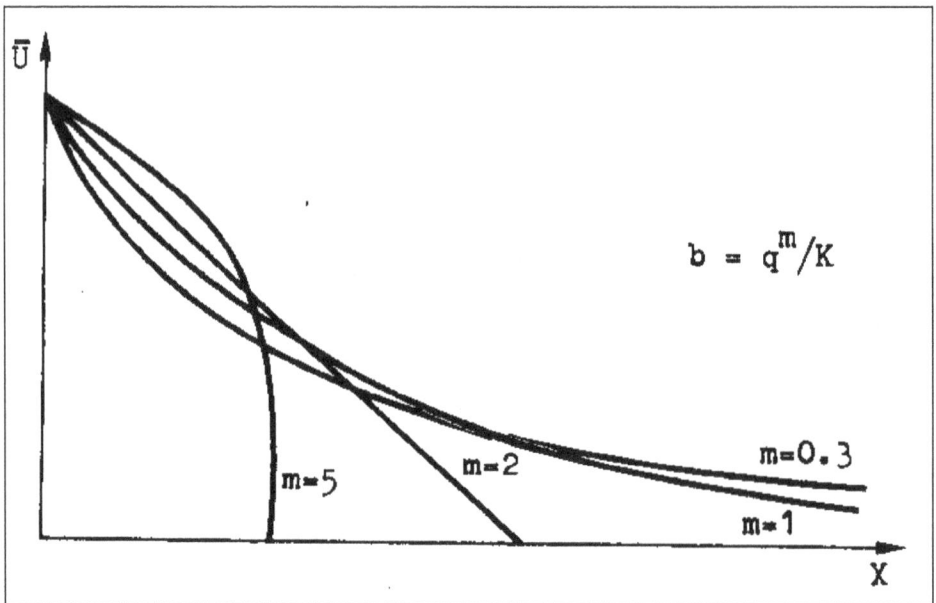

**Figure 26: Curves Showing the Relationship between the Index of Mean Biomass and the Index of Fishing Mortality, in Equilibrium Condition, for Selected Values of m.**

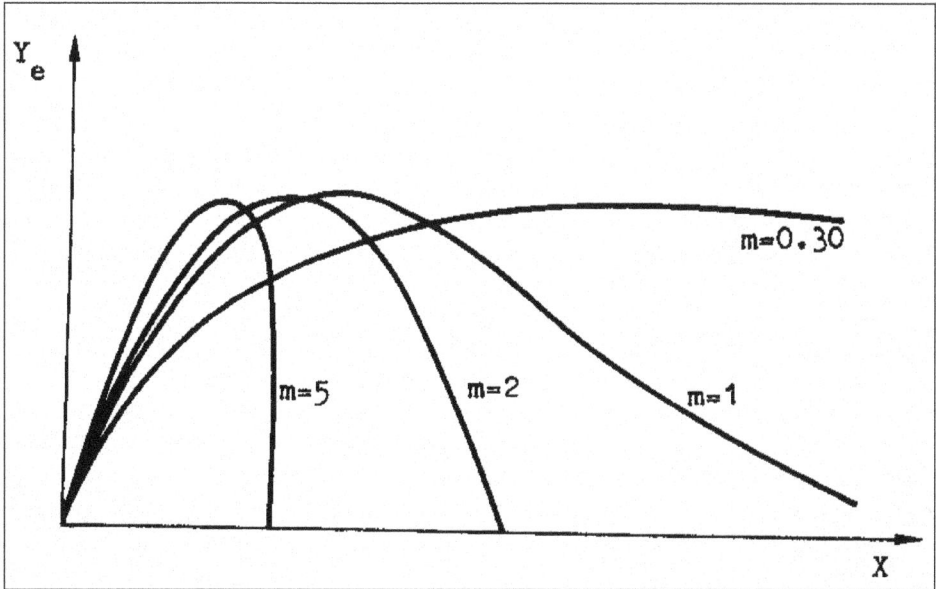

**Figure 27: Curves Showing the Relationship between the Equilibrium Catch and the Index of Fishing Mortality in Equilibrium Conditions, for Selected Values of m.**

☆ Tropical countries generally have a relatively limited research capability – as far as fisheries research is concerned – which often leaves most of the stocks sustaining their fishery completely uninvestigated.

Despite these and other problems, the fishery biologists working in tropical countries have been traditionally expected to provide (fast) answers to pressing questions such as;

☆ How much fish there is in a given area.

☆ How much should be taken annually.

☆ What gears should be used.

☆ How to accommodate various groups (*e.g.*, of fishermen) with diverging, or even conflicting interests.

☆ How to manage a fishery (what specific regulatory measures, how to enforce these, etc.).

In answer to some of these needs, several models and techniques have been developed which give (at least rough) answers to these questions.

## Estimating Stock Sizes

### Methods for Estimating the Stock Sizes of Pelagic Fishes

Stock sizes of small pelagic fishes are generally estimated by means of acoustic surveys. The methodology of such surveys is outlined in more or less detailed fashion in the following texts:

Forbes and Nakken (1972), Cushing (1973), Saville (1977). Results of pelagic acoustic surveys conducted in the Western Indian Ocean, south of equator, have been reviewed in Gulland (1979).

Estimating the standing stock size of large pelagic fishes such as tuna and other large scombroids is generally very difficult and the result obtained are often highly controversial (Sharp, 1978, 1979). Earlier surveys conducted in the Western Indian Ocean have generally concentrated on relative abundance (rather than absolute stock sizes) as indicated by the spatial distribution of the catch/effort of a standard gear (Williams, 1967).

## Methods for Estimating the Stock Size of Reef Fishes

Strangely enough, there is at present no generally accepted standard method for estimating the standing stock sizes of reef fishes and the wide variety of methods used (involving poisoning and SCUBA divers' direct count methods) as well as the different concepts of what actually belongs to a "reef" have led to widely differing standing stock estimates. This leads to the suggestion that estimates of yield per area be used, together with estimates of fishing mortality to estimate standing stock indirectly.

Thus, since we have

$Y = F \times B$

Which expresses the basic inter-relationship between annual catch in weight or yield (Y), mean standing stock size (B) and fishing mortality (F), we also have

$B = Y/F$

Which can be used to estimate standing stock sizes given reliable estimates of Y and F, the latter being obtained, for example from the average of several single values of F from different species, as obtained from the mean length in the catch and an independent estimate of M.

For obtaining more or less direct estimates of standing stock sizes in reefs are the methods for use in coral reef fish studies are those of Russel *et al.* (1978).

## Estimating the Biomass of Demersal Stocks

In areas where the sea bottom is smooth enough for trawling, standing stock sizes can be obtained from the relationship

$$B = \frac{c/f \cdot A}{A \cdot x1}$$

Where c/f is the mean catch per effort obtained during the survey (or for a given stratum) A total survey area (or the area of the stratum in question) and "a" the area "swept" by the net during one unit of effort (*e.g.*, one hour), x1 being the proportion of the fish in the path of the gear that are actually retained by the net.

In Southeast Asian waters, a value of x1 = 0.5 is commonly used and there is some evidence that this value might in fact be very realistic (Pauly, 1979a).

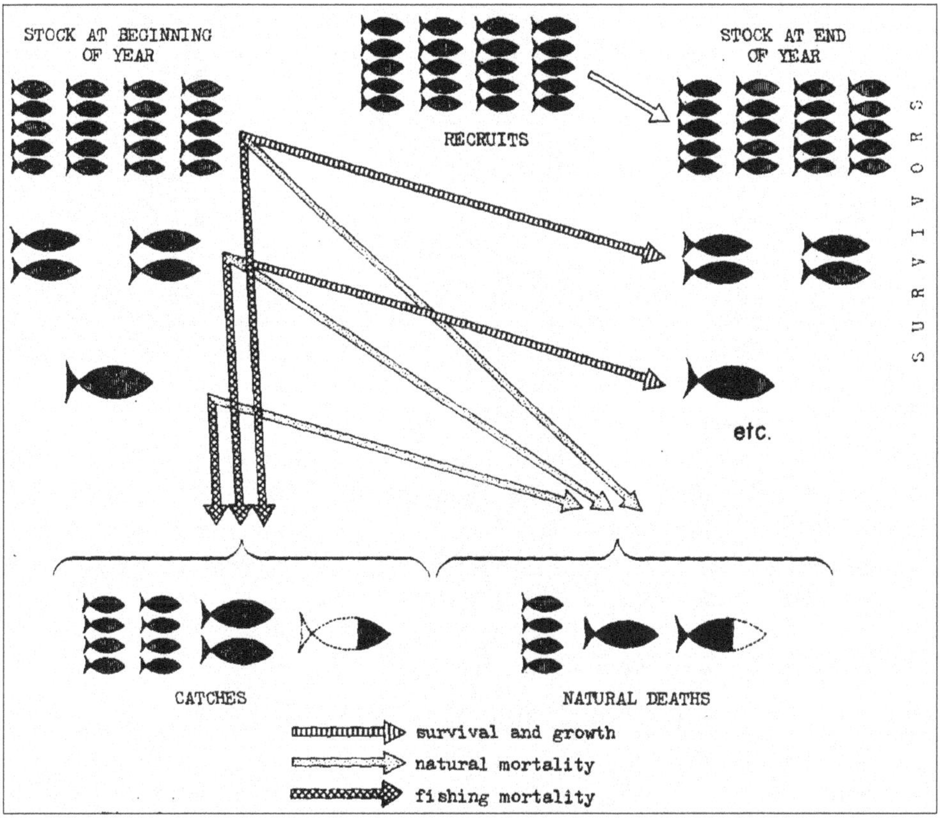

**Figure 28: New Eqiulibrium Resulting from an Increase in the Rate of Exploitation.**

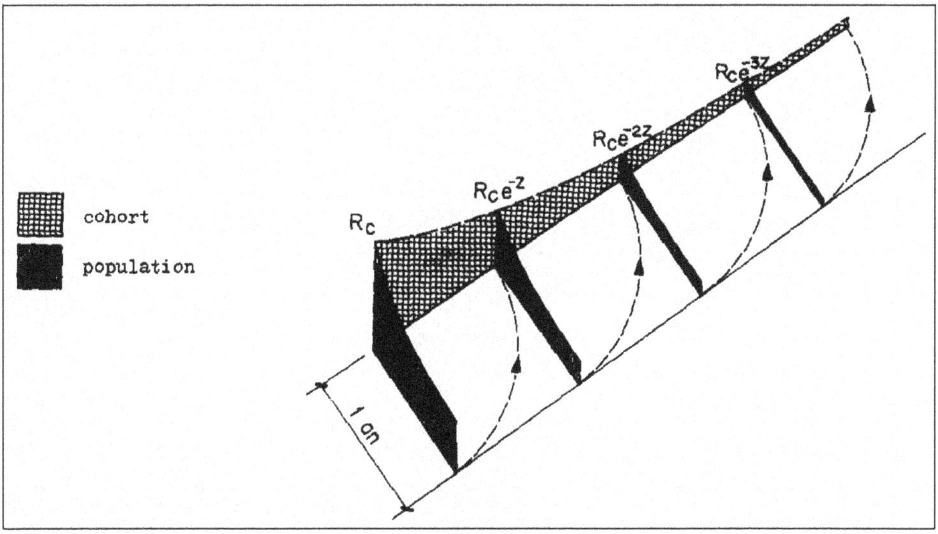

**Figure 29: Diagram Showing the Equivalence of Cohort Abundance as a Function of Time and Population Composition as a Function of Age.**

For the Western Indian Ocean south of the equator, it has been suggested, on the other hand, that all fish in the path of the trawl might be caught, which corresponds to

X1 = 1 (Gulland, 1979)

The surface swept by the gear during one unit of effort is computed from the expression

A = t × v × h. x2

Where v is the velocity of the trawler over ground when trawling, h is the length of the trawl's head rope, t is the time spent on trawling and x2 is a fraction expressing the width of the area swept by the net divided by the length of the head rope. In Southeast Asian waters, values for x2 ranging between 0.4 and 0.66 have been used, with 0.5 possibly being the best compromise (Pauly, 1979 a).

The above equations can be used to obtain standing stock estimates from commercial trawlers, provided their catch per effort, head rope length and trawling speed are known.

The "swept area" method, as the method presented above is called, has been adapted – using certain assumptions as to the behavior of fish – to line fishing over reefs (Wheeler and Ommaney, 1953) and this paper along with the comments of Gulland (1979) should be consulted for details.

## Estimating Maximum Sustainable Yield (MSY)

There are two basic models for estimating MSYs from fish stocks, namely " yield-per-recruit" model of Beverton and Holt (1957) and its variants and the "surplus yield" model of Schaefer (1954) and its variants.

Where suitable growth and mortality parameters are available, the model of Beverton and Holt (1957) or one of its simplified versions (*e.g.* Beverton and Holt, 1966) may be used to estimate yield-per-recruit, and if recruitment is known or assumed to be constant, to identify an optimal fishing strategy. This model, however, will not be reviewed here, both because its complexity would lead astray and because it tells surprisingly little about how to manage a tropical multi-species fishery.

The Schaefer model – in its simplest version at least – is quite easy to handle. Here is a stepwise approach to estimating MSY by means of this model :

1. Tabulate the catch and effort data and compute catch-per-effort figures.
2. Plot the catch-per-effort values against their corresponding value of effort, and estimate the intercept (a) and the slope (b) by the linear regression technique. Change the sign of b from minus to plus.
3. Compute MSY = a square/4b

   Optimum effort = a/2b

   Yield for a given effort = af – bf square

There is, finally, a third method for estimating maximum sustainable yields for a given fishery, and this is the comparative method.

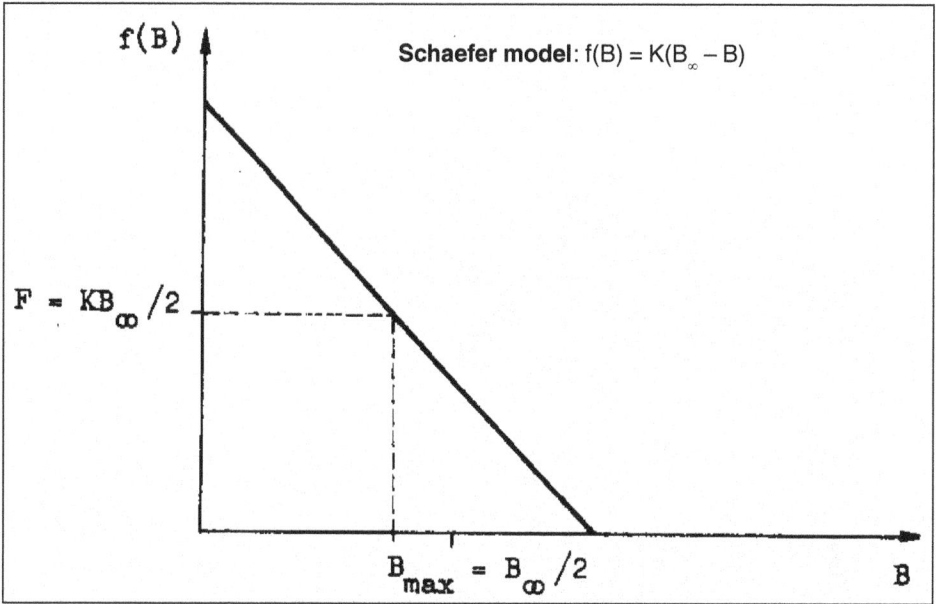

$f(B)$

**Schaefer model**: $f(B) = K(B_\infty - B)$

$F = KB_\infty/2$

$B_{max} = B_\infty/2$

$B$

**Figure 30: Theoretical Relationship between the Specific Rate of Natural Growth f(B) and Total Biomass B.**

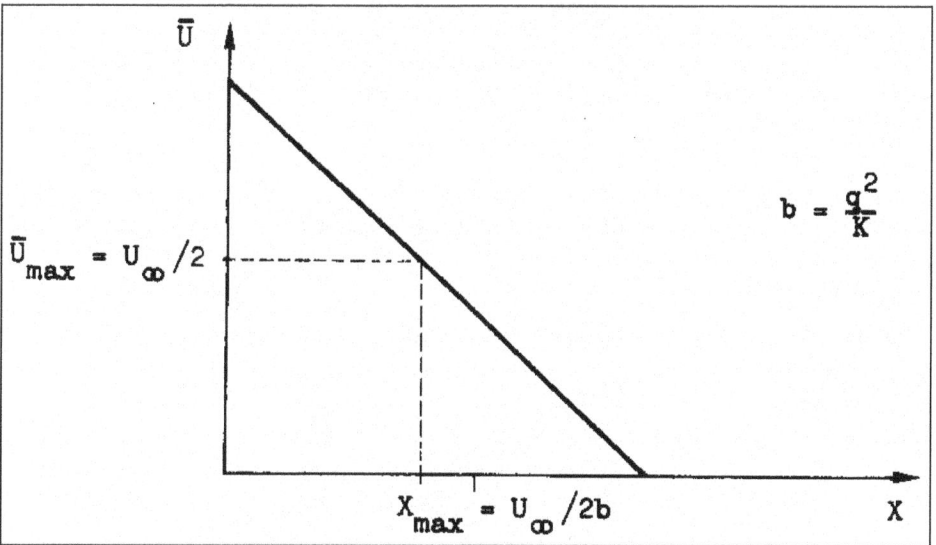

$\bar{U}$

$b = \dfrac{q^2}{K}$

$\bar{U}_{max} = U_\infty/2$

$X_{max} = U_\infty/2b$

$X$

**Figure 31: The Relationship between the Index of Mean Biomass and the Index of Fishing Mortality in Equilibrium Conditions.**

Certain ecosystems are extremely productive (*e.g.*, upwelling areas) or quite unproductive (such as deep oceans). As far as tropical, shallow water systems are concerned, however, a remarkable consistency of yields (when expressed on a per area basis) can be noticed, with yield ranging between 4 and 8 t/square km (all fish)

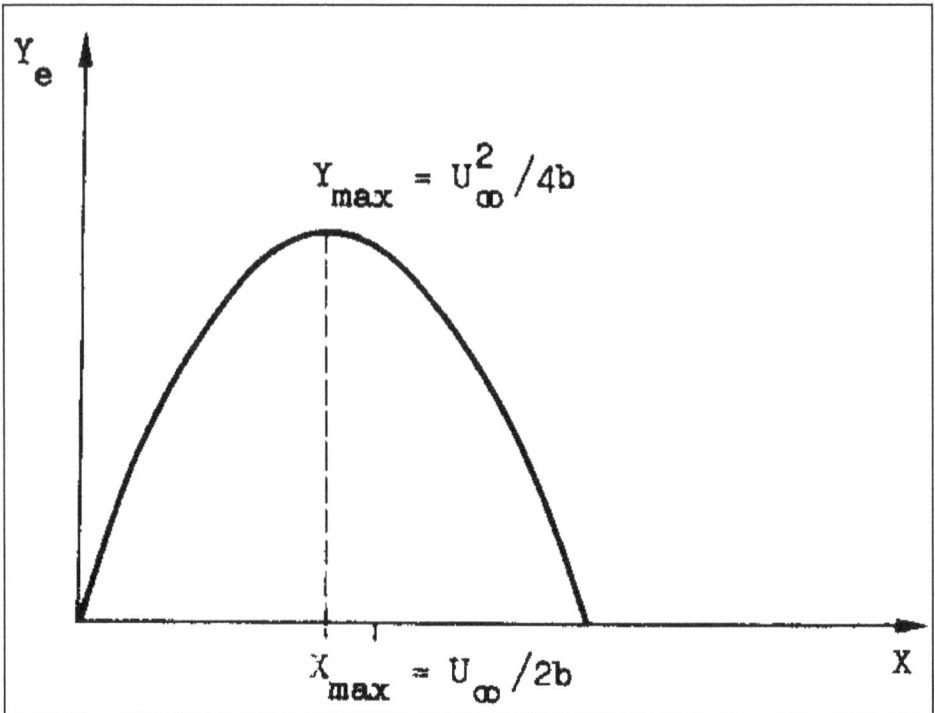

**Figure 32: The Relationship between the Equilibrium Catch and the Index of Fishing Mortality, in Equilibrium Conditions.**

in inshore areas (including reefs) with values in excess of 10 t/square km, where estuarine conditions boost productivity. These figures may thus be used to assess certain stocks and fisheries, *e.g.*, to assess if a certain stock is "under-fished", or "optimally exploited".

**Selected Values of Fish MSY per Surface Area for different Tropical Ecosystems**

| Ecosystem | Location | MSY (t/km sq.) | Source |
|-----------|----------|----------------|--------|
| Coral reef | Jamaica, Caribbean | 4 (all fish) | Munro (1975) |
| | Western Indian Ocean | 5 (all fish) | Gulland (1979) |
| Shelf | Gulf of Thailand (down to 50m) | 3.6 (demersal) | SCSP (1978) |
| Estuaries and | San Miguel Bay (down to 15m) | 15 (all fish) | Pauly and Mines |
| Lagoons | (The Philippines) | | |
| Shallow lagoons | Gulf of Mexico (Texas) | 12 (all fish) | Saila (1975) |
| (estuarine conditions) | Sakumo Lagoon (Ghana) | 15 (all fish) | Pauly (1976) |

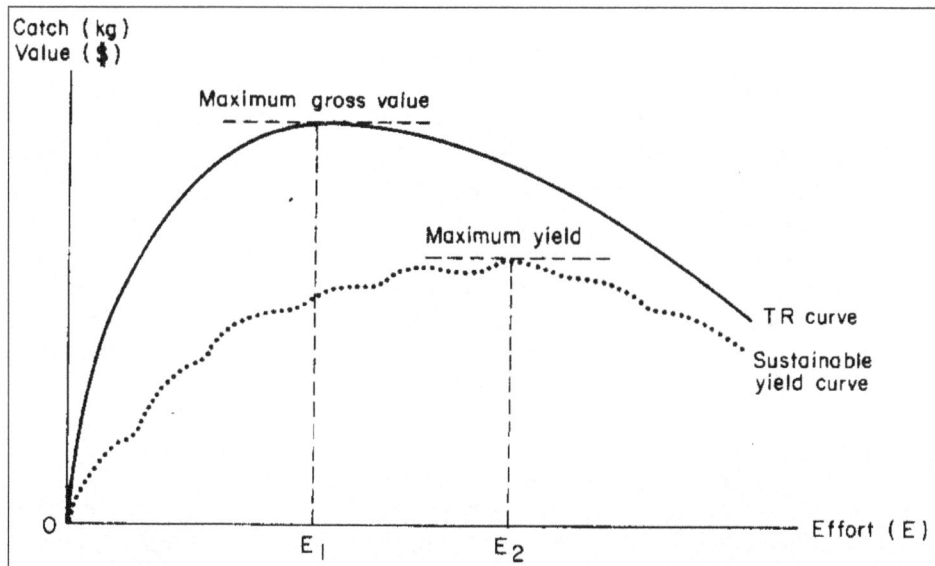

**Figure 33: The Gross Economic Yield or Total Revenue (TR) Curve of Multispecies Fishery Constructed by Multiplying the Catch of each Species by its Price and Summing Up over all Species, or by Multiplying the Aggregate Sustainable Yield Curve by the Average Price of Catch. Notice that the maximum value can be attained at a level of effort lower than that required for the maximum yield. At the maximum yield the value of catch is less than the maximum.**

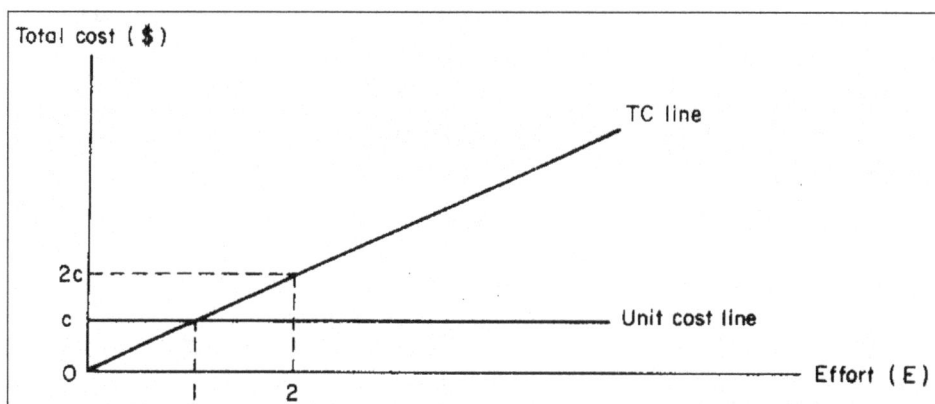

**Figure 34: Total Cost (TC) Line: A Proportional Relationship between Cost and Effort.**

## Stock Assessment of Small-Scale Fisheries in the Bay of Bengal

### Status of Exploited Coastal Fisheries in the Bay of Bengal Region

#### Annual Catch

The average annual catch during last half of 1970s was of the order of 128000 t, in Sri Lanka; 386000 t in India; 91000 t in Bangladesh; 246 t in Thailand and 308000 t in Malaysia. Except in Thailand, as much as 95 per cent to 100 per cent of the catches were credited to the small-scale fisheries, consisting of the traditional non-mechanized and small mechanized sectors. Fishing activities in the coastal fishery are carried out over distances of 12 to25 miles from the shore and upto depths ranging from about 20 meters in Bangladesh to the continental slope in Sri Lanka.

As regards year-to-year trends in the catches, they are reportedly on the increase in Sri Lanka due to increase in the effort of mechanized boats. In India, the landings have been fluctuation during the last five years of 1970s between 12 per cent and 13 per cent of the average. The data from Bangladesh were not adequate to draw any conclusions, although the catches were assumed to be on the increase due to increased motorization of traditional craft In Thailand, there is a general decline in the yield from demersal and some pelagic resources, particularly the mackerel resources. In Malaysia, the latest figures (1977) represent the heaviest recorded catch in the country, but this may be an exceptional year – the average of nine earlier years points to a fluctuation within 15 per cent of the average. One important feature noticed in recent years in Malaysia is the progressive decline in the "food" fish component of the trawler catches and an increase in the share of "trash" fish.

**Data on Fish Yield in the Bay of Bengal Region**

| Country | Annual Yield ('000 t) | Coast Line (km) | Exploited Area km (m/depth) | Active Fisher | Yield/km (t) | Yield/Fisher (t) |
|---------|------------------------|------------------|------------------------------|----------------|---------------|-------------------|
| Sri Lanka | 128 | 1200 | 24372 (0-200 m) | 58000 | 106.7 | 2.2 |
| India | 386 | 3010 | 88535 (0-75 m) | 151770 | 128.2 | 2.5 |
| Bangladesh | 91 | 480 | 32000 (0-24 m) | 156000 | 189.6 | 0.6 |
| Thailand | 246 | 740 | 44000 (0-100 m) | 11177 | 332.4 | 22.0 |
| Malaysia | 308 | 900 | 47420 (0-100 m) | 48690 | 342.2 | 6.3 |

## Craft and Gear

In Sri Lanka about 85 per cent of the total fleet are indigenous craft of which about 85 per cent again are non-mechanized, consisting mainly of dug-outs with outriggers and log rafts; the others are plank built boats and dug-outs without outriggers. The remainder are mechanized 28'-32' wooden and FRP boats and 17'-18' FRP boats. Fishing is largely done by gill nets, trolling lines and shore seines. In India, about 95 per cent of the boats are non-mechanized – mainly log-rafts, dug-out canoes and plank-built boats – operating mainly gill nets, boat seines, bag nets and hooks and lines. The small percentage of mechanized boats are trawlers. In Bangladesh, nearly 98 per cent of the boats are in the small-scale sector and are traditional non-mechanized craft – dug-out or plank-built boats, operating mainly gill nets, set bag nets and stake nets. The small percentage of motorized boats operate mainly gill nets. In Thailand, most of the fishing fleet consists of mechanized boats of which about 68 per cent belong to sizes less than 14 m. In Malaysia, about 83 per cent of the boats are mechanized, mostly with inboard engines. They employ mainly drift/gill nets, trawl nets and purse seines.

Thus on the western side of the Bay of Bengal, not less than 90 per cent of the total number of craft in the respective countries are non-mechanized – mostly log-rafts, dug-outs and plank-built boats – with gill net operation predominating. On the eastern side of the Bay of Bengal, most of the fishing craft are mechanized, operating trawl nets, gill nets and purse seines.

## Species Composition

In Sri Lanka, scombroids (tunas, Spanish mackerel, Indian mackerel); clupeoids (sardines, anchovies, wolf-herring), carangids (especially horse mackerel), and hair-tails are the important pelagic fishes, while snappers, croakers, groupers, elasmobranches and prawns are the important demersal resources. In India, the clupeoids (sardines, anchovies and hilsa), hairtails, carangids and Spanish mackerel are significant from the pelagic group, while in the demersal group, elasmobranches, catfishes, croakers, leiognathids, perches, pomfrets, prawns and crabs are the major items. In Bangladesh, the important pelagic fishes are hilsa, Bombay-duck, hair-tails, mackerel and scads; the important demersal fishes are elasmobranches, catfishes, threadfins, croakers, pomfrets, eels, snappers, grunts and prawns, In Thailand, mackerels, scads, carangids, sardines, anchovies, king nackerel and little tunnies dominate the pelagic group and elasmobranches, catfishes, threadfin breams, croakers, snappers and prawns are the important fisheries in the demersal sector. In Malaysia, the principal pelagic stocks exploited are those of mackerels, anchovies, sardines, mullets and scads, while the commercial food fishes from the demersal stocks include snappers, groupers, croakers, flat fishes, threadfin breams, cat fishes. Lizard fishes and prawns

Among the pelagic resources, the clupeoids, scombroids and carangids are the dominant groups in all the countries. In the clupeoid group, *Sardinella* and *Stolephorus* are important in all countries except Bangladesh. Hilsa replaces these species in the upper east coast of India and Bangladesh. Among the scombroids, *Rastrelliger* is important in all countries. The tunas and tuna-like fishes are exploited to a large extent in Sri Lanka and to some extent in the contiguous area of the Tamil Nadu coast of India. To a somewhat similar extent, this would apply to the Spanish mackerel also, whose importance however extends further north to the Andhra Pradesh coast of India. Carangids are represented by many genera, the most important of which are *Decapterus, Megalaspis, Carangoides* and *Caranx*. The hair-tails and Bombay duck are more of the sub-tropical importance, the former in Sri Lanka, India and Bangladesh and the latter in the upper east coast of India and Bangladesh.

Among the demersal resources, the snappers and groupers, croakers, elasmobranches and penaeid prawns are the important groups in all countries. Catfishes form a sizeable percentage in all the countries except Sri Lanka. The importance of leiognathids and pomfrets is confined to sub-regional pockets – the lower east coast of India for the former and upper east coast of India-Bangladesh for the latter, are the principal areas. Similar are the threadfin breams in Thailand and Malaysia and threadfins in the upper east coast of India and Bangladesh.

There is thus a general similarity in the important exploited varieties both from the pelagic and demersal stocks. There is also a general similarity in the species concerned, more so in the geographically contiguous waters.

## Stock Assessment in the Region

In Sri Lanka, the provisional estimates, from the results of the acoustic survey conducted by *R .V. Dr. Fridtjof Nansen* in 1978, indicated a potential yield of 250000 t comprising 170000 t pelagic resources and 80000 t demersal resources. The biological productivity data available in the literature appear to indicate a harvestable potential of 250000 to 300000 t. Considering the present state of exploitation, it would appear that the above estimated potential yield is a reasonable one to aim at for development purposes. However, it was also pointed out that the commercial sizes of tunas and prawns have declined, and that any increase in fishing effort for these species must carefully be considered.

In India, the estimates obtained from trawl surveys appear to indicate a harvestable potential of 343000 t from the demersal resources, as compared average production of about 192000 t. The catch and effort data pertaining to the period 1958-67 for individual groups of pelagic species or groups of species showed that the total maximum yield of these groups from the inshore waters of the east coast would be about 124000 t. As compared to this estimate, the average catch of these groups is 163000 t. Except *Chirocentrus, Stolephorus* and carangids, the yield of all the species/groups has exceeded the respective estimated maximum yield. The acoustic surveys conducted by *Rastrelliger* during 1973-75 mainly in the shelf area off Cape Comorin and in the Gulf of Mannar (7-9 degree N) indicated a high standing stock of fish biomass, mostly pelagic during the June-October period. It ranged between 127000 t and 970000 t with an average of about 624000 t. Of this *Stolephorus* stock was the mainstay, its abundance ranging from 55000 to 804000 t with an average of 509000 t forming 82 per cent of the general average standing stock of the total fish biomass.

From the organic productivity data, various estimates of exploitable potential yield from the continental shelf have been made, which range from 0.6 to 1.0 million t. From what has been exploited so far, it would appear that for the small-scale fisheries sector, there is good scope for higher catch in the southern-most region, as well as in the northern coasts of Orissa and West Bengal.

In Bangladesh, the estimate of exploitable yield is mainly confined to the trawl survey, which provided a figure of 175000 t of demersal fishes and 9000 t of prawns. No firm figure for pelagic stock is available. The recent acoustic survey by R.V. Dr. Fridtjof Nansen beyond 10 m depth indicated a provisional figure of 60000 t pelagic species, besides 150000 t of demersal stock. From the available provisional records on biological productivity in this and adjacent areas, a conservative figure of 354000 t and an optimistic figure of 770000 t of potential yield could be arrived at. Since the pelagic fishery stocks are assumed to be at least as large as the demersal resources, and since the present annual catches from both pelagic and demersal regimes are much lower than these figures, there is a distinct possibility of increasing the catches from the inshore region.

In Thailand, the estimates of MSY have been obtained largely from the logistic exponential model. The latest estimate indicates an optimum yield of 205000 t for demersal resources and 61000 t for pelagic resources, thus totaling 266000 t. The earlier estimates of MSY for exploitable demersal resources ranged from 85000 to 200000 t. The estimated maximum sustainable yield for mackerel, sardines and anchovies are 20000, 5000 and 7000 t respectively, and the actual yields have exceeded these estimates in different years during 1973-1976. The catches of these groups have since started to decline. There is evidence to suggest that the demersal stocks as well as the resources of mackerel have started declining due to over fishing. Available information on biological productivity indicates a tertiary production of about 370000 t and 280000 t for the shelf area up to 200 m and 100 m depths respectively, the latter being nearly 100 per cent of the estimated MSY from the catch and effort data of the corresponding exploited area.

In Malaysia, the MSY estimates based on simple statistical models are 160000 t of demersal resources and 88000 t of pelagic resources. Estimates of some individual pelagic species have also been made based on these models, which may be seen in the country's ststus paper. From the currently exploited situation, it appears that among the pelagic stocks, mackerel requires special management attention. The exploitation of demersal stocks has probably exceeded the optimum level; in the process, it has considerably reduced the component of food fish but increased the trash fish component in commercial catches. Among other records on estimates of potential yield, mention may be made of the 1965 trawl survey; its conservative estimate of the standing stock of demersal fishes within 100 m depth. Both these estimates are rather low when compared with the MSY estimates indicated earlier. The computed tertiary production for the area up to 100 m depth amounts to nearly 300000 t. As compared to this, the present fish production is about 378000 t and the estimated MSY of pelagic, demersal and prawn resources is 301000 t. Here again, as in the case of Thailand, it is interesting to note the absence of the conventionally assumed relationship between the tertiary production and the actual yield or potential yield. It is likely that the tertiary production has been under-estimated or that the efficiencies of energy flow are higher than presumed, or both.

It would generally appear that in countries bordering the western Bay of Bengal, there is a clear scope for increasing fish production, although initially the increase may be confined to certain pockets. This situation contrasts sharply with that in the eastern sector of the Bay of Bengal, where the fishery resources are heavily exploited.

## Measures for Proper Development/Management of Coastal Fishery of the Bay of Bengal

In Sri Lanka, mechanized boats have been kept out of certain areas where artisanal fishermen have been traditionally operating. In certain lagoons and bays, regulations permit only the use of traditional gears, *e.g.* cast nets and rod and line. There are also regulations relating to lobster fishing.

The Fisheries Ordinance bans the use of explosives in fishing. No licences are issued for foreign fishing vessels to operate in national waters. If any serious conflicts develop among the different fishing sectors, there is provision for legal action. An important indirect measure of conservation adopted recently is the ban on the export of lobsters.

There are indications of a reduction in the size of some commercially important fish species. If this is confirmed, conservation will be vitally necessary. "Closed season" or "closed areas" could be declared, mesh regulations could be imposed, but the snag lies in implementation. Although legal provision exists for enforcement, the required staff and facilities may not be available, and regulatory measures may also create socio-economic and political problems.

Demersal resources in Sri Lanka need to be better exploited. Experimental fishing/demonstrations and extension work are necessary.

In India, laws to protect small-scale fisheries exist in some of the coastal states. There are also some executive orders which stipulate that the first 5 km from the shore should be reserved for the traditional non-mechanized fisheries sector; beyond this limit, the small mechanized craft can operate; the larger-sized commercial fleet is permitted to operate only beyond 10 km from the shore. A model Marine Fisheries Bill has been circulated among the coastal states of India for their consideration.

An expert committee has been formed to examine the issue of prawn conservation. It is believed that the prawn resources of the northeast coast of India need conservation measures. Past experience indicates that enforcement of mesh size regulations is almost impossible and that any curbs on estuarine fishing to protect the nursery grounds of prawns are likely to adversely affect the livelihood of small fishermen who would have to be suitably rehabilitated. The only way to implement any legislative measure is to strengthen the coast guard or similar organizations. Indirect methods of conservation could include banning the export of certain sizes of prawns, removal of subsidies and incentives etc.

Regarding the development of under-exploited resources for small-scale fisheries, the *Stolephorus* stock of the Gulf of Mannar requires priority attention. It should be ensured, however, that any development measures taken do not impair the existing fisheries in the area.

In Bangladesh, no legislative measures exist to protect small-scale fisheries. There are also no data available regarding stocks that require conservation. The first 12 miles from the shore, however, have been reserved for national vessels, and extension of this area up to 30 miles is contemplated. In this connection, it was suggested that it would be preferable to prescribe different limits of depths and distances for different regions to ensure adequate exploitation of resources. The fishing boats should be registered.

The extensive clearing of mangrove forests for prawn culture was considered injurious to the prawn nursery grounds, besides causing ecological damage. It was suggested that embankments should not extend right along the coast and that provision should be made to allow migratory passage to the young prawns. The excessive capture of juvenile prawns in the estuaries and its drastic implications on marine fisheries is far reaching. The problems of the estuarine prawn fishery is also applicable to hilsa.

The demarcation of certain areas as sanctuaries, declaration of closed seasons, and regulation of mesh sizes were suggested. It was however recognized that the enforcement of such measures would be difficult. One way to solve the enforcement may be to provide alternative employment and income opportunities to people affected by such measures.

To assess the impact of the increased fishing pressure on the coastal fisheries in general, and on the prawn fishery in particular, special studies are considered desirable at some selected centers, such as, Cox's Bazar and Dubla Island.

In Thailand, the operation of trawlers and mechanized push nets within 3 km from the shore is prohibited. This regulation is meant to protect the resources rather than to help the traditional small fishermen operating non-mechanized craft. Certain areas, such as, Phang Nga Bay have been reserved exclusively for small scale fishermen. There are no other conservation measures on the Indian Ocean side of Thailand. In the Gulf of Thailand, however, closed areas and closed seasons for mackerel have been specified, and during the spawning season there are regulations governing the mesh size of gill nets. There is a need to regulate and conserve demersal stock and mackerel resources on the west coast of Thailand, where reduction of effort (number of boats) is considered necessary.

At present, conservation laws are being violated due to inadequacy of enforcement staff.

In Malaysia, the main existing legislation to protect small-scale fisheries is the Fisheries Act of 1963. Boats and fishing gear are licensed under the rules and regulations made under the Merchant Shipping Ordinance and the Fisheries Act. The bulk of the legislative measures are directed at trawl fisheries. Within three miles from the shore no mechanized fishing is permitted; mechanized boats larger than 25 tonnes and propelled by engines of more than 60 hp should operate beyond seven miles from the shore, and those larger than 100 tonnes and with engines of more than 200 hp should operate only beyond 12 miles from the shore.

The Department of Fisheries, the Marine Police and the Navy are authorized to enforce fisheries laws. The problems of enforcement, as elsewhere in the region, arise mainly from the inadequate size of enforcement staff. Although attempts have been made to educate fishermen, it has been found difficult to convince them of the need of conservation.

The consultation noted that complex and comprehensive studies are necessary to decide on mesh size regulations for conservation; determination of the best mesh size on a sound scientific basis and adequate rapport with the industry are essential if mesh size regulation is to be successful. In some place regulation exists on paper; they are not implemented because of stiff opposition from the fishermen. Those countries who are confident that mesh-size regulations can be implemented but have not made exhaustive studies for determining the right mesh size may utilize the studies relating to comparable or identical species in other areas.

There is an undisputed need for strengthening the extension set-up in the region. The problem encountered is that the fishermen seem apathetic and disinterested. To break this barrier, and to gain confidence of the fishermen, the dissemination of information has to be undertaken by technical/scientific personnel especially trained in extension techniques.

Measures are also considered necessary to project the importance of stock assessment studies to non-technical sectors. One way of doing so is to organize national seminars for administrators as well as various sectors of the fishing industry.

## Biological Over-Fishing of Tropical Stocks

In recent years there has been a large number of publications describing the growth and subsequent decline of tropical fisheries, with much being written about the relatively well documented stocks in Southeast Asian waters. Almost none of these publications failed to mention that several, mainly demersal, stocks of the region are "over-fished" ."Over-fishing" is indeed the primordial sin, the bankruptcy of fishery management. It is in fact, the worst epithet a fishery biologist can hurl at the fishing community.

In spite of all this, relatively few attempts have been made to "translate" and apply to tropical stocks those concepts of over-fishing that have been developed from considerations pertaining to temperate stocks. Some of these concepts are introduced here,together with some of their application to stocks in the region.

'Over-fishing" may occur as (a) Growth over-fishing; (b) Recruitment over-fishing, or, (c) Ecosystem over-fishing.

Growth over-fishing, which has hitherto received the greatest attention in the region occurs when the young fish that become available to the fishery (the "recruits") are caught before they can grow to a reasonable size. Thus, to the fishery biologist, the problem is to estimate the most suitable age (and/or size) at first capture and to suggest to the fishing community, *e.g.*, the mesh size which by allowing younger (smaller) fish to escape, optimizes the yield that can be obtained from a given number of recruits

The theory behind the computations used in estimating the optimal size at first capture and mesh size developed some 30 years ago by Beverton and Holt, also applies to tropical fish.

Thus theoretically it should be possible to prevent growth over-fishing in Southeast Asian waters except that at present no method can be conceived which would allow fishermen exploiting multiple-species stocks to catch the fish of each single species at their specific optimal size. This should ensure that we will have for the years to come quite a bit of growth over-fishing in the region, especially as demersal fisheries go.

Recruitment over-fishing is quite another matter. This is what occurs when the (parent) stock is reduced by fishing to the extent that not enough young fish are produced to ensure that the stock will maintain itself. Everybody knows that in any fish stock, there will be no young fish (= no recruits) if no parent fish are left by the fishery. These parents must mature, spawn, and fertilize eggs which to larvae, only a very small fraction of which eventually survive and become fully formed young fish (recruits).

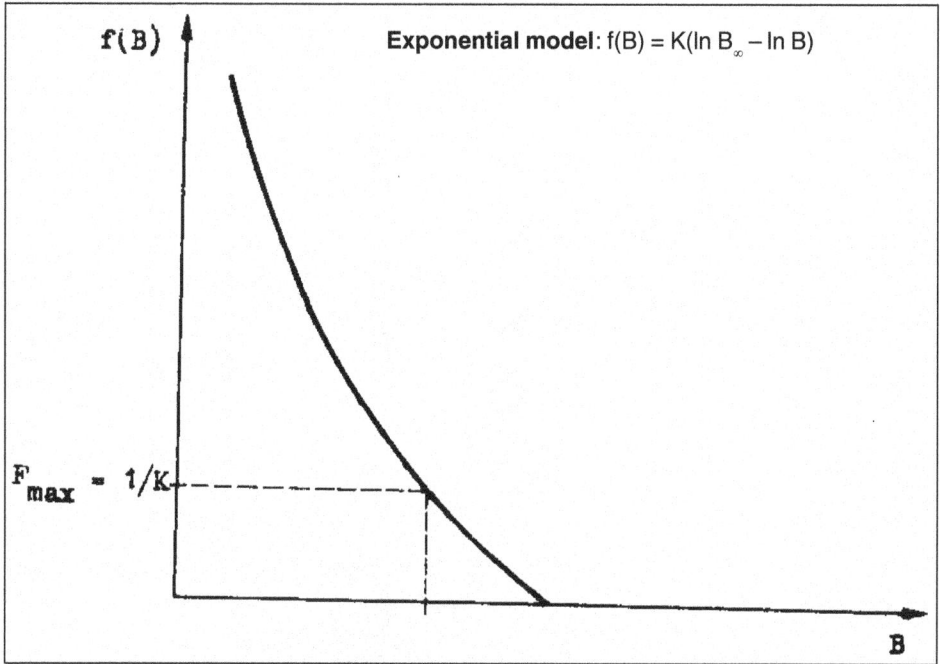

**Figure 35: Theoretical Relationship between the Specific Rate of Natural Growth f(B) and Total Biomass.**

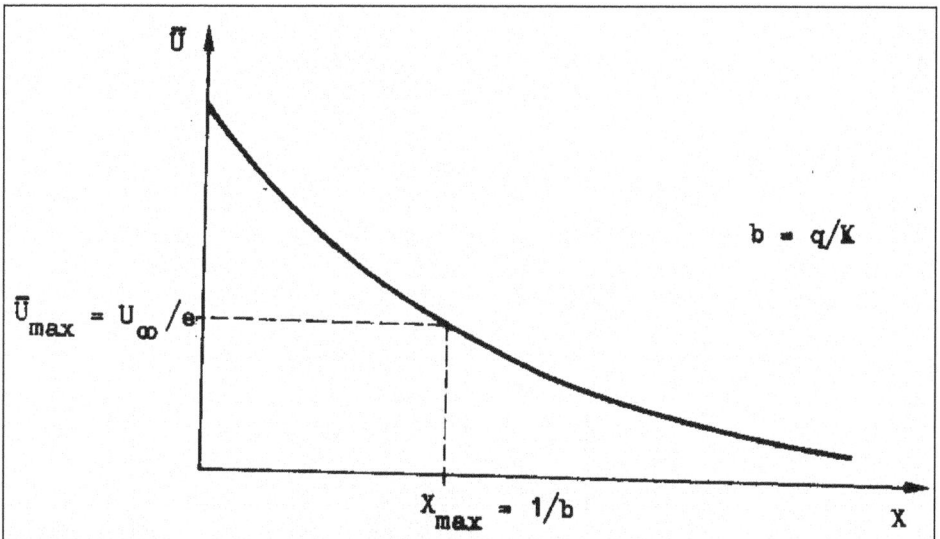

**Figure 36: Relationship between the Index of Mass Biomass and the Index of Fishing Mortality, in Equilibrium Conditions.**

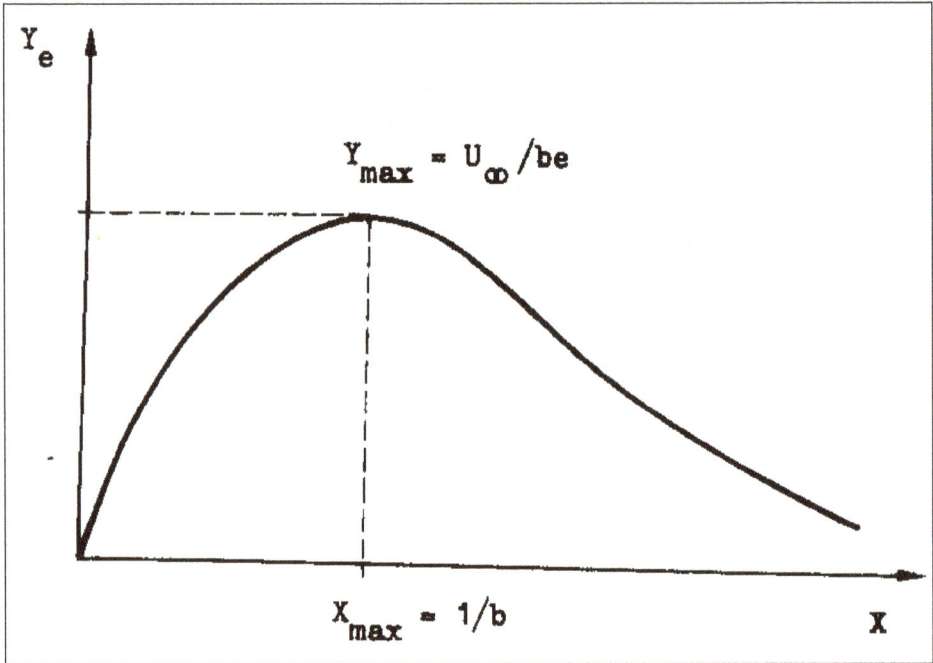

**Figure 37: Relationship between the Equilibrium Catch and the Index of Fishing Mortality, in Equilibrium Conditions.**

Generally the females of most fish species produce several thousands of eggs, sometimes even several millions as in the case of some commercially exploited species in temperate waters. To a certain extent this high fecundity has misled fishery biologists to assume that a very limited number of adult females would, in most fish stocks, be sufficient to replenish the number of recruits that eventually become available to the fishery.

Uncritically applied this assumption has been one of the causes of some of the most spectacular collapses in the world of fishing. Luckily this belief, that the lack of relationship between parent stock size and number of recruits should be the normal case in fishes is gradually replaced by its very opposite, namely, that most fish do display stock-recruitment relationships, the lack of such relationship being limited to a few groups such as the flatfishes and some gadoids. Strangely enough, apparently no attempt has been made to assess whether there is, in tropical stocks, an identifiable relationship between the size of spawning stock and the number of recruits produced by this spawning stock, although it is true that data which could be used for such a purpose are scarce.

Using rather conventional methods (swept-area method for estimating standing stock and fishing mortality, computation of yield-per-recruit and division of Y/R into catch to obtain recruit numbers, plus miscellaneous methods and assumptions for obtaining other parameters estimates and data standardization) and data from the Gulf of Thailand demersal trawl fishery, it has been established that stock-recruitment relationships in a number of species, one of which, pertaining to *Lactarius lactarius*, the curve is a very typical "Ricker-curve" depicts the general pattern in so far obtained for most of the stocks that have been investigated.

Only a few taxa showed no stock-recruitment relationships. Among these, are the flatfishes, one large predator (*Muraenesox*) and – by analogy (exact yield-per-recruit analysis was not performed) – the crabs, the shrimps and especially *Loligo*, whose spectacular increase in the Gulf of Thailand has been discussed by various authors.

Also, it appeared that in these taxa, there was a clear relationship between the number of their recruits (in any given year) and the standing stock size (for the same year) of their potential competitor and predators (as expressed by the biomass of all other taxa).

This last point – competition and predation between taxa – leads to the third form of over-fishing, namely, ecosystem over-fishing. Ecosystem over-fishing is a "soft concept", allowing much loose talk because it is not clearly defined. It may be described here as what takes place in a mixed fisheries when the decline (through fishing) of the originally abundant stocks is not fully compensated for by the contemporary or subsequent increase of the biomass of other exploitable animals.

Thus, as suggested by modern ecological theory, ecosystem over-fishing would be the transformation of a relatively mature, efficient system into an immature (or stressed), inefficient system. This, to a large extent, is what happened in the Gulf of Thailand where a (presumably) stable and efficient high biomass system dominated by teleostean fish was gradually turned into a (presumably) unstable and inefficient low biomass stock in which the role of invertebrates has markedly increased (note the reversal of the evolutionary sequence).

All three forms of over-fishing discussed here occur in Southeast Asian waters, and the theory of fishing could well benefit from a study of the experience gained in the region.

Also, as biological processes in the tropics often occur in "pure form", unmediated by strong fluctuations of the abiotic environment (as occur in temperate waters, which are temperate only on the average), it is even thinkable that the theory of fishing, especially as far as multi-species stocks are concerned, could make here in Southeast Asia one step or two into scientifically unexplored territory.

Furthermore, understanding the nature of over-fishing should considerably help solve resource allocation problems which have traditionally marred the relationships between artisanal and commercial fishermen in the region. It will, for example, become obvious that the catch, say of 100 t of relatively young fish by artisanal fishermen fishing close inshore has a radically different effect on a stock than the catch of 100 t of older and larger fish by a commercial fishery operating further offshore. This feature should indeed lead to the understanding that rather than having one single maximum yield, a given stock may have several "optimum sustainable yields" whose respective magnitudes depend mainly on the mode of operation of the fishing gear used as well as on the resulting age composition of the catch.

Finally, it is on the basis of the identification of such conflicting "OSYs" that fishery managers of the region can make sound decisions as to which segments of the fishing community should be encouraged or dissuaded from fishing.

## Characteristics of an Exploited Stock

### Effects of Fishing

In a fish stock, a number of fish is born each year. During the life of a year class, each year a certain percentage dies until, for some species after a few years, for others after a longer time span, all fish of that year class have disappeared.

**Table 1: Annual Survival of 1000 Young Fish at Successive Ages, for a Long Living Fish Species (Annual mortality 20 per cent) and a Short Living Fish Species (Annual mortality 70 per cent)**

| Annual Mortality Per cent | Age | | | | | | | | | | | |
|---|---|---|---|---|---|---|---|---|---|---|---|---|
| | 0 | 1 | 2 | 3 | 4 | 5 | 6 | 7 | 8 | 9 | 10 | etc. |
| 20 | 1000 | 800 | 640 | 512 | 410 | 328 | 262 | 210 | 168 | 134 | 107 | – |
| 70 | 1000 | 300 | 90 | 27 | 8 | 2 | 1 | | | | | |

A table can be drawn up giving the number of fish of a year class in the successive calendar years during its life. We can also include several year classes in a scheme as detailed below.

**Table 2: Number of Fish Surviving at each Age from 1000 Young Fish, for a Series of Successive Year Classes. Annual Mortality 20 per cent.**

| Year | Age | | | | | |
|---|---|---|---|---|---|---|
| | 0 | 1 | 2 | 3 | 4 | etc. |
| 1959 | I 1000 I | 800 | 640 | 512 | 410 | – |
| 1960 | (1000) | I (800) I | (640) | (512) | (410) | (–) |
| 1961 | 1000 | 800 | I 640 I | 512 | 410 | – |
| 1962 | 1000 | 800 | 640 | I 512 I | 410 | – |
| 1963 | 1000 | 800 | 640 | 512 | I 410 I | – |
| etc. | – | – | – | – | – | I – I |

**Table 3: Number of Fish at each Age, with Varying Year Class Strength.
Annual Mortality 20 per cent.**

| Year | Age | | | | | |
|------|------|------|------|------|------|------|
|      | *0* | *1* | *2* | *3* | *4* | *etc.* |
| 1959 | (1000) | 880 | 960 | 307 | 410 | — |
| 1960 | 900 | (800) | 704 | 768 | 245 | — |
| 1961 | 1300 | 720 | (640) | 563 | 614 | — |
| 1962 | 600 | 1040 | 567 | (512) | 451 | — |
| 1963 | 1000 | 480 | 832 | 461 | (410) | |
| etc. | – | – | – | – | – | (—) |

If we assume that 20 per cent of the fish die during each year of life, and that 1000 fish were born in 1959, the figures in parenthesis in the table show the numbers from that year class surviving at each age. If each year the same number of fish are born, it can be seen that the numbers of each age present in one year (encircled figures) are the same as the numbers of one year class at successive ages during its life span (figures in parenthesis). Hence the decline of numbers by age in the stock in a certain year also reflects the mortality of the fish (Tables 1 and 2)

Normally, the year class strength fluctuates from year to year. A table can be constructed as in Table 2. The age composition of the stock in any one year now depends on the year class fluctuations, but if these are not too large will still also reflect the average decline by the mortality (Table 3).

If a stock is exploited, each year a certain part of the fish is caught. Hence, the numbers decrease faster with age. If the numbers of survivors are set in the same scheme as the above tables, it can be seen that in any one year the stock is smaller than without fishing, and it will be smaller, the more intensive the fishery. The difference is most marked in the older fish. The heavier the fishery, the smaller the stock in the sea, and therefore also, the smaller the catch per boat. As the decrease is most marked in the older fish, the average size and age of the fish in the sea, and thus also in the catch, decreases with increased fishing. These are, in very schematic form, some of the principles of the effects of fishing on the fish stocks and the catches (Table 4).

The fish stock shown in table 4 has the same characteristic as that in Table 2 (annual natural mortality rate in the unfished state 20 per cent). The fish of this stock is now, however, subjected to fishing, from 3 years old onwards. The fishing effort is such that the number of fish caught at each age is equal to the number of dying by natural causes. At first glance it would seem that, thus, the number of fish caught during a year would also be 20 per cent of the number present at the beginning, and that the total mortality rate would be 20 + 20 = 40 per cent per year. This is however, not the case, because the effects of the natural mortality and of the fishing mortality are not independent. This can be easily visualized if it is realized that some fish which would have died by natural causes later in the year if no fishing took place, now will have been caught before that time. The heavier the fishery, the lower will therefore be the percentage of fish which will die each year by natural causes. It will be shown later during this course that if two causes of mortality and simultaneously on the same stock of fish and the number of fish caught is equal to 1, 2, 3, 4 ......., n times the number of natural deaths, the annual survival rate is equal to the survival rate in the unfished stock raised to the power 2, 3, 4, 5, ......, n + 1.

For the conditions in Table 4(a), where the number of fish caught is equal to the number dying by natural causes in the same time period, the annual survival rate is equal to the power 2 of the survival rate in the unfished stock (natural mortality rate 20 per cent) if this survival rate is expressed as a fraction rather than a percentage. Thus the total survival rate under these fishing conditions is 0.80 square = 0.64, and the total mortality rate 1.00 – 0.64 = 0.36 or 36 per cent . As the number of fish dying by fishing and by natural causes are equal, the number of fish dying by natural causes is therefore, 18 per cent . In the same way it can be calculated that in table 4(b), where fishing is more intensive and causes twice as many deaths as the natural mortality, the number of survivors at the end of a year as the result of the combined mortalities will be 0.80 cube = 0.51 of the initial number. Hence the total mortality is 0.49 or 49 per cent, of which two-thirds (33 per cent) due to fishing and one-third (16 per cent) due to natural causes.

**Table 4: Numbers of Fish at each Age in the Stock, and Numbers Caught, at different Levels of Fishing. The fishery catches the fish from 3-years old onwards.**

**(a) Total mortality rate 36 per cent, fishing mortality equal to natural mortality**

| Age | 0 | 1 | 2 | 3 | 4 | 5 | 6 | 7 | 8 | 9 | 10 | Total |
|---|---|---|---|---|---|---|---|---|---|---|---|---|
| Stock | 1000 | 800 | 640 | 512 | 328 | 210 | 134 | 86 | 55 | 35 | 22 | |
| Catch | | | | | 92 | 59 | 38 | 24 | 15 | 10 | 6 | 244 |

Average age 4.95 years

**(b) Total mortality rate 49 per cent, fishing mortality double the natural mortality**

| Age | 0 | 1 | 2 | 3 | 4 | 5 | 6 | 7 | 8 | 9 | 10 | Total |
|---|---|---|---|---|---|---|---|---|---|---|---|---|
| Stock | 1000 | 800 | 640 | 512 | 261 | 133 | 68 | 35 | 18 | 9 | 5 | |
| Catch | | | | | 167 | 85 | 44 | 22 | 11 | 6 | 3 | 338 |

Average age 4.65 years

The table also shows that the total catch in numbers increases with increasing fishing, but not proportionally. If fishing effort doubles, the numbers caught are less than doubled.

All these results are rather obvious. The more intensive the fishery, the more fish caught at a relatively young age, and less and less remain to become older fish, with the result that the stock declines. All this is reflected in the catches per boat. Furthermore, the more fish caught young, the less there are to die by natural causes before they are caught, and hence the total numbers caught increase with increasing fishery. Even though these principles are simple, it is most important that they are fully understood, because these are the effects of fishing, on which stock assessment is essentially based.

So far, fish in numbers only have been dealt. What is usually more important is the catch by weight. If known how fast the fish grows, and thus the weight is known at every age, we can convert the figures of catch in numbers into catch by weight.

From the curves obtained in these exercises, it appears that often the optimum catch by weight of a stock is obtained at an average level of fishing effort, and that at higher levels of effort the total catch does not increase, or declines again. The higher the mortality rate, the higher is the fishing effort at which the maximum catch is obtained. Again, this can be understood at closer consideration. With little fishing, the average size, and hence weight, of the fish is rather large, but few fish are caught and the total weight is low. With very heavy fishing, very many fish are caught, but all are very young when the weight per fish is low. Somewhere in between many fish are still caught, and many of fair size, resulting in a higher total weight. With high natural mortality, heavier fishing is needed to prevent too many fish dying by natural causes, and hence the optimum catch is at a higher level of effort. Similar considerations can be applied to understand the effects of changes in the age of first capture of fish.

The examples have been calculated for 1000 fish. It is easy to understand that what happens to these 1000 fish will happen to any other 1000 fish of the same age, mixed with the first 1000 in the same area. Thus, if every year 10X1000, or 1000X1000, or nX1000 fish are born, the principles of the effects of fishing remain the same.

The above calculations were greatly simplified. For example, natural or fishing mortality may vary with age of fish. This can easily be incorporated in the calculations which will show that the principles still remain valid. Another simplification is that it has been assumed that natural mortality, growth and recruitment remain constant, irrespective of the level of fishing. It has been shown in various species that the decline in stock size as a result of heavy fishing may lead to changes in *e.g.* growth or recruitment. It is clear that with a decrease in the number of larger fish in the stocks, there is less competition for food, and the egg production will also decrease. The latter does not necessarily lead, however, to a decline in recruitment as the percentage of survival of the eggs and larvae may increase at lower levels of egg production. All these so-called "density dependent factors" can again be included in the calculations. The studies carried out so far in this field have indicated that whereas these factors may alter the details of the graphs and, for instance, the position of the maximum, they do not alter the overall picture of the effects of fishing.

## Estimation of Potential Catches with different Fleet Sizes, and of State of Exploitation of Stocks

The calculations in the previous section have been made with simple arithmetic. Usually, it is found more convenient to use algebraic calculations, which simplify the work in more complicated situations. Whatever the methods of calculation, it is clear that they require good information on growth, mortality and, eventually, recruitment of the fish. If such information is available, the methods can determine at what fishing mortality rate the best total catches are obtained, etc., but they do not determine the corresponding fleet size, *e.g.* whether 100 vessels cause a fishing mortality of, say 10 or 50 per cent per year. However, if data on age composition and catches per boat is available for different periods with different fleet sizes fishing the stocks, it is possible to estimate what fleet size causes a moderate or intensive level of fishing. This requires, therefore, data over as many years as possible. It is in particular desirable to include in the analysis data from periods with very low levels of fishing, to get a picture of the situation when the only significant mortality is natural mortality. This requires that some sampling and statistical data collection is started in the very early stages of the fishery. Even though, at these stages, the work will not lead to immediate estimates of the available resources, they may prove to be of very great importance later when fishing has become more intensive and scientific advice is required on the needs for and methods of management of the fishery. The information on the virgin stock composition and density can never be obtained later when the fishery has developed and absence of this information makes the analysis later rather more difficult.

In many instances, however, the required detailed information on length and age-composition of the catches is not available, because of lack of funds or manpower to collect the information, impossibility of determining the age of a fish or other reasons. If sufficient catch statistics of the fishery are available, another way of studying the problem can be applied. In the previous section the way in which fishing affects the stocks has been discussed. If data on the fleet size, the total catches and the catches per boat are available for a series of years with different levels of fishing, the catch per boat and the total catch can be plotted against the number of boats(with certain precautions and restrictions). The form of these curves will then more or less show what is the state of the fishery, whether it can be expected that the catch will increase at higher levels of fishing, or that fishing has already reached or passed the optimum level. For this approach statistical data are needed on the number of boats (fishing effort), broken down by size and fishing method, on the total catch for all fleets fishing the same stocks and/or on the catch per boat. Again it is important to have these data from an early stage of the fishery onward, even though it has to be taken into account that in the first years of a fishery the catch data of a vessel are often not comparable with those of later when the gears have been developed, the fishermen have learned how to fish the species in the area etc.

The picture given so far is a simplified one. There are many problems in estimating the various characteristics of the stocks and of fishing, and more refined models have been developed than the simple ones describes so far to allow for greater complexity. A particular aspect which should still be mentioned is that whereas the changes in the catches discussed above are those caused by fishing, there are many other causes of variation: natural ones, such as, those due to variations in year-class strength, variations in catchability of the fish, or other effects of variations in the environment, changes in fishing due to market preferences, or to efficiency of the fleets, etc., sampling variation in the data. Often, these variations are more or less random, and in that case their major effect is that they cause irregular variations in the data which, if they are not too large, usually do not obscure the trends due to fishing. The changes may also, however, show a trend, *e.g.* a long-term fluctuation in the environment. If such a trend occurs at the same time that the intensity of fishing changes, this makes it more difficult to actually assess the effects of fishing. But whereas these difficulties complicate the work, the principles remain valid. For estimation of fish stock potentials, and of the effects of fishing on the stocks and the catches it is, therefore, essential to understand these principles.

## Exercises Characteristic of an Exploited Stock

I. In an unexploited stock, 20 per cent of the fish of each age present in the beginning of each year die during the year. Growth studies have shown that the weight of the fish at each age is:

| Age | 0 | 1 | 2 | 3 | 4 | 5 | 6 | 7 | 8 | 9 | 10 | years |
|-----|---|----|----|----|-----|-----|-----|-----|-----|-----|-----|-------|
| Weight | 0 | 13 | 37 | 81 | 147 | 233 | 325 | 420 | 512 | 595 | 650 | grams |

1. Draw the curve of the number of survivors (at the beginning of each year) of a year-class starting with 1000 fish as a function of age.
2. Draw the curve of the total weight of the survivors as a function of age.
3. At what does the year-class reach its maximum weight?
4. Calculate the average age reached by the fish of one year-class (assuming that all remaining fish die at reaching 10 years).

II. If the above stock is exploited by a fishery which starts catching the fish from 3 years old onwards with an intensity so that the numbers dying each year by fishing is equal to the numbers dying by natural mortality (total annual mortality for exploited ages is 36 per cent):

Calculate the numbers caught at each age, and draw the curve of the numbers surviving at each age.

Calculate the weight of the fish caught at each age, and draw the curve

What are the number and weight of the fish caught during the whole life of the year-class?

Calculate the average age of the fish in the total catch of the year-class.

III. Repeat exercise II for the following values :

| | Total Mortality Per year | Numbers Caught per year / Numbers Dying by Natural Causes per Year |
|-----|------------------|---------------------------|
| 1. | 22 per cent | 0.25 |
| 2. | 28 per cent | 0.5 |
| 3. | 49 per cent | 2 |
| 4. | 59 per cent | 3 |
| 5. | 67 per cent | 4 |
| 6. | 74 per cent | 5 |

The relation between the numbers caught and the numbers dying, given in the last column, is proportional to the fishing effort.

Plot, as a function of this measure of fishing effort, the following curves :

1. Total number of fish caught.
2. Total weight of fish caught.
3. Total number of fish caught, divided by fishing effort index (as a measure of catch per unit effort).
4. Total weight of fish caught, divided by fishing effort index.
5. Average age of fish in total catch.

IV. Repeat exercises I. II and III for a stock in which, when unexploited 63 per cent of the fish die each year by natural mortality, and where fishing only catches fish of one year and older, for the following values (start with 1000 fish of 0 year):

|     | Total Mortality<br>For Unexploited Ages | Numbers Caught per year<br>Numbers Dying by Natural Causes per Year |
| --- | --- | --- |
| 1.  | 78 per cent   | 0.5 |
| 2.  | 86.5 per cent | 1   |
| 3.  | 95 per cent   | 2   |
| 4.  | 98 per cent   | 3   |
| 5.  | 99 per cent   | 4   |

This species has a weight at age as follows :

| Age    | 1    | 2    | 3    | 4    | 5    | years |
| ---    | ---  | ---  | ---  | ---  | ---  | ---   |
| Weight | 11.5 | 24.3 | 36.8 | 44.5 | 49.0 | grams |

V. Repeat exercises II and III for fisheries with different selectivity catching fish from second or fifth year onwards at the indicated mortality rates.

# Chapter 7

# Species in Stress and Extinction

Fisheries have rarely been sustainable. Food and Agriculture Organization (FAO) classified more than 70 per cent of major marine fisheries as fully or over exploited. Many populations, such as the North Atlantic cod have already crashed. But despite these warning signs, FAO statistics for total global fish catches have increased since 1950. Rather, fishing has induced serial depletion, long masked by improved technology, geographic expansion and exploitation of previously spurned species lower in the food web. With global catches declining since the late 1980s, continuation of present trends will lead to supply the shortfall, for which aquaculture, can not be expected to compensate and may well exacerbate. Reducing the fishing capacity to appropriate levels will require strong reductions of subsidies. Zoning the oceans into un-fished marine reserves and areas with limited levels of fishing effort would allow sustainable fisheries based on resources embedded in functional, diverse ecosystems.

Over-fishing is not the sole cause of dramatically declining fish stocks in the North Atlantic Ocean or world wide. Environmental changes such as climate warming may be just as important and governments should consider these factors when managing fisheries. Marine ecosystems, particularly in the North Atlantic are much more vulnerable to natural fluctuations than previously realized. The natural mechanisms driving marine productivity and population dynamics must now be brought to the attention of decision makers.

Failure to reconcile ecology and commerce has been a hall mark of international fisheries policy for decades. With or without environmental trends, fishing mortality through commercial fishing pressure is still too high and must be reduced.

But the fish producer organization argued that scientists tend to hold fishermen responsible for any thing that happens, but they are certainly not to blame for environmental and climate change. Not all stocks show signs of depletion. They should fish what is there and fish it responsibly.

There are evidence for significant decadal-scale biological changes, which have major consequences for the abundance of natural resources. The impact on the marine food web of varying water temperatures and wind strengths in the North Atlantic revealed the fluctuations in the abundance, size and composition of plankton, which result in long term changes in the numbers of large commercially important fish, such as, North Sea cod.

In the past, herring populations in the Baltic Sea and cod stocks off Newfoundland have collapsed and failed to recover even after fisheries closed-indicating that factors other than fishing were in play.

To develop sustainable fisheries policy, it will be crucial to determine how much of changing mortality patterns is due to fishing operations and how much to environmental trends.

## Fisheries Productivity in the Northeastern Pacific Ocean over the Past 2200 Years

Historical catch record suggest that climatic variability has had basin-wide effects on the northern Pacific and its fish populations, such as, salmon, sardines and anchovies. However, these records are too short to define the nature and frequency of patterns. Reconstructing 2200 years record of sockeye salmon abundance from sediment cores obtained from salmon nursery lakes on Kodiak Island, Alaska, large shifts in abundance, which far exceed decadal scale variability was recorded during the past 300 years, occurred over the past two millennia. A marked multi- centennial decline in Alaskan sockeye salmon was apparent from -100 BC to AD 800, but salmon were consistently more abundant from AD 1200 to 1900. Over the past two millennia, the abundances of Pacific sardine and Northern anchovy off the California coast, and of Alaskan salmon, show several synchronous patterns of variability. But sardines and anchovies vary out of phase with Alaskan salmon over low frequency, which differs from the pattern detected in historical records. The coherent patterns observed across the large regions demonstrate the strong role of climate forcing in regulating northeastern Pacific fish stocks.

## Commercial Fishing-Reduce the Fish Age and Size at Maturity

Evolution by natural selection involves pressures that kill off individuals with unfavorable inherited traits, while those with more favorable features survive and reproduce. Fisheries would seem to provide such a pressure, most fisheries target the largest and oldest individuals, so fish that are genetically predisposed to mature at larger sizes and older ages are more likely to be caught before they can reproduce. Such selective harvesting should theoretically favor early and small-maturing genetic types- a consequence reminiscent of other circumstances, in which humans have unintentionally selected against that which they desire most.

Many fisheries scientists and managers do not acknowledge the potential for fishing to elicit genetic change despite supportive experimental and field data. However, Olsen *et al.* (2004) provided compelling evidence of genetic change in one of the most notoriously over-fished stocks, northern Atlantic cod (*Gadus morhua*) arguing that such change preceded the collapse of the stock.

In over-exploited marine fishes, world wide, few have declined, more than the Atlantic cod that range from southern Labrador to the northern half of Newfounfland's Grand Bank. By the early 1990s the numbers of northern cod had declined by 99.9 per cent relative to their abundance in the early 1960s, a rate of decline almost unmatched among living aquatic species. Concomitant with the decrease in population size were significant reduction in age and size at maturity.

As the density of a population decline, relaxed competition for food and space should lead to individuals growing at an increased rate. Fish generally respond to increased growth by maturing earlier in life. Thus fishing could lead to earlier maturity, solely as a consequence of variable phenotypic responses to growth. Alternatively, however, by selecting against individuals, whose genes predispose them to breed at older ages and large sizes, fishing might genetically alter exploited population.

Olsen *et al.*, found that before the northern cod population collapsed, there was decline in reaction norm mid-points (the ages and sizes at which the proportion of mature fish is 50 per cent). In other words, the norms shifted towards younger ages and smaller sizes. This decline was consistent with the hypothesis that heavy fishing pressure selected against genotypes, that predispose cod to maturing later and larger. These life history changes were not associated with increased growth rate, which could lead to earlier maturity. These findings suggest that genetic change provides the explanation for why age and size at maturity declined in northern cod.

In any case the potential for fishing to generate evolutionary change within harvested populations can no longer seriously discounted. If evolutionary change, in response to harvesting proves to be rule rather than exception for exploited species, it must begin to address questions concerning the magnitude of evolutionary changes, the reversibility of such change and its consequences for sustainable harvesting; population recovery and species persistence. The long term repercussions of fishing are almost certainly more complicated than previously believed.

Knowing fish's ages would enable biologists to model population dynamics, to better understand fish behavior and assess how well the creatures are recovering from the devastating harvesting of the past century.

## Threatened Sturgeon

The beluga sturgeon (*Huso huso*) was declared endangered by the World Conservation Union in 1996. Some 2 to 3 millions of the fish are thought to extinct, mostly in the Caspian and Black Seas. But they are suffering from habitat loss, pollution and over-fishing. With a single gram of the delicacy facing about 3 dollars, legal trade in the eggs is estimated to be worth 100 million dollars a year. The illegal trade is thought to be 10 times as large.

The species *Huso huso*, a fish that is prized for producing world's most expensive caviar.

The agency has declared the fish "threatened", which means the government can set strict limits or entirely ban the import of beluga caviar into the United States, the biggest market for the delicacy.

The two species of Atlantic sea sturgeon on either shore of the North Atlantic, *Acipenser sturio* in Europe and *A. oxyrinchus* in North America, probably diverged with the closure of the Tethys Sea and the onset of the North Atlantic Gyre 15 to 20 million years ago and the contact between them was then presumably precluded by geographic distance. Genetic, morphological and archaeological evidence indicate that the North American sturgeon colonized the Baltic during the Middle Ages replaced the native sturgeon there, before recently becoming extinct.itself in Europe as a result of human activities. In addition to representing a unique transatlantic colonization event by a fish that swims upriver to spawn. The findings have important implications for projects aimed at restocking Baltic waters with European sturgeon.

*A. sturio* once occurred abundantly in rivers in regions from the Black Sea right up to the Baltic, is now reduced to a relict population in southern France. *A. oxyrinchus*, however, is still found in rivers that run into Atlantic from the Gulf of Mexico to Quebec.

*A. sturio* colonized Baltic waters sometime after the Pleistocene (about 3000 years ago) followed by *A. oxyrinchus* about 1800 years later. There had been a remarkable species shift from *A. sturio* to *A. oxyrinchus* between 1200 and 800 years ago in the Baltic.

The subsequent decline of *A. sturio* and the establishment of a sustained *A. oxyrinchus* population in European waters during the Little Ice Age might have been due to selection of hypothermal conditions that characterize their likely Canadian sources. *A. oxyrinchus* spawns between 13.3 and 17.8 degree Celsius, whereas *A. sturio* does not spawn below 20 degree Celsius.

The findings have implication for restocking the Baltic Sea with sturgeon, an endeavor that has so far stagnated owing to the very limited availability of *A. sturio*. Attempts to re-introduce the North American *A. oxyrinchus* could also be hindered because this cold-water-tolerant species might no longer flourish in to day's warmer Baltic waters, which would better suit the thermal tolerance of the European sturgeon.

## Icy Death of Cod

More than 700 tonnes of Atlantic cod have frozen to death in chilly waters off eastern Newfoundland. The dead fish first began to surface the waters of Smith Sound Trinity Bay. Such mass culls are very rare, although one in north eastern United States killed an estimated 10 to 100 million warm water file fish in 1982.

At this time of the year, cod are usually found in warmer waters near the bay. Local theories on why they entered the sound include, a bid to escape from seals and a fateful pursuit of herring. Monitoring water temperature, salinity, oxygen saturation in the sound for one week and collecting and analyzing dead fish it was confirmed that they were perfectly healthy when frozen.

In early April, the temperature of water column of Smith Sound fell to -1.7 degree Celsius. Historical temperature profiles from this region indicate that such temperature are very unusual for the Sound.

Cod produce anti-freeze protein in their blood to safe guard them from very cold water, but the protein takes two months to build up to maximum levels and the dead fish had very little of them in their blood.

Some of the environmentalists are describing the mass kill, as an environmental disaster, as it destroyed one of the last remnants of the region's few cod stocks. Canada's fisheries minister banned cod fishing. Cod used to make up 70-80 per cent of the total stock in the province, but 99.9 per cent of the stock has been lost.

North Atlantic cod is classed as being of special concern by the committee on the Status of Endangered Wildlife in Canada

The North Seas dwindling cod stocks could be facing new threats. Researchers in Norway found that chemicals released by pile drilling can disrupt the ability of the fish to reproduce. In laboratory experiments male cod took on female characteristics and female spawned later when exposed to alkylated phenols, which occurs naturally in underground oil reservoirs. Field trials around drilling platforms are being conducted.

## Endangered Fishes

At one time it was presumed from the vastness of the oceans that fishing would not drive species to extinction. There have, however, been recent sharp declines in the numbers of oceanic cod, sharks, rays, tunas, marlins, sword fish and sea turtles. As the shelf fisheries in the north west Atlantic began to collapse in 1960s and 1970s, harvesting shifted to deep sea fish species, but many populations crashed within ten years because their recovery was so slow.

The common skate is on the verge of extinction in the North Sea because of overfishing. A ban on sea bed trawling in certain regions is the only way to protect bottom dwelling species, such as, skates and rays.

Deep sea fish are highly vulnerable to disturbance because of their late maturation, extreme longevity, low fecundity and slow growth. Some deep sea fish form spawning aggregations on sea mounts and the sea floor, and this increases susceptibility to over-fishing. Survey data collected over extended period are limited and that is why it has been difficult to determine the effects of deep sea fishing on both target and by-catch species.

The study on five species, live on or near the bottom of the North Atlantic Ocean continental slope (they range from the common to rare round nose grenadier, spiny eel and spiny skate) reveal that they can live 60 years of age, grow to more than one meter in length and mature in their late teens. Two out of them were commercially fished and all five are taken as by-catch in fisheries that target Greenland halibut, *Reinhardtius hippoglossoides* and red fish *Sebestes* spp. None was taken in any substantial number even in by-catch, before 1970s.

The catch data of trawl surveys in the Canadian waters of the north west Atlantic over 1978-94 revealed that all species declined in relative abundance over the 17 year period from 87-98 per cent and declines estimated for three generations, the IUCN bench mark were 99-100 per cent The overall decline in relative abundance for the two species, (*Coryphaenoides rupestris* and *Macrourus berglax*) over 26 year-year period were 99.6 per cent and 93.3 per cent respectively.

According to IUCN criteria, these five species of deep sea fish qualify as critically endangered in the north west Atlantic. The declines occurred on a time-scale equal to or slightly less than, a single generation of these species. The largest deep water skate in the north west Atlantic- the barndoor skate, *Dipturus laevis* was driven unnoticed almost to extinction.

Criteria from the World Conservation Union (IUCN) have been used to classify marine fish species as endangered since 1996, but deep sea fish have not so far been evaluated despite their vulnerability to aggressive deep water fishing as a result of certain life history traits.

A shift from shelf fisheries to deep sea is exhausting late maturing species that recover only slowly.

## Distortions of World Fisheries Catch

World fisheries catches have greatly increased since 1950, when the FAO of the United Nations began reporting global figures. The reported catch increases were greatest in the 1960s, when the traditional fishing grounds of the North Atlantic and North Pacific became fully exploited and new fisheries opened at lower latitudes and in the Southern Hemisphere. Global catches increased more slowly after the 1972 collapse of the Peruvian anchoveta fishery, the first fishery collapse that had repercussions on global supply and prices of fish meal. Even taking into account the variability of the anchoveta global catches were therefore widely expected to plateau in the 1990s at values of around 80 million tonnes, especially as this figure, combined with estimated discards of 16 to 40 million tonnes, matched the global potential estimates published since the 1960s. Yet the global catches reported by the FAO generally increased through the 1990s driven largely by catch reports from China.

These reports appear suspicious for the following three reasons; (i) The major fish populations along the Chinese coast, for which assessments were available had been classified as over exploited decades ago, and fishing efforts has since continued to climb. (ii)Estimates of catch unit effort based on official catch and effort statistics were constant in the Yellow, east China and South China Seas from 1980 to1995, that is, during a period of continually increasing fishing effort and reported catches, and in contrast to declining abundance estimated based on survey data. (iii) Re-expressing the officially reported catches from Chinese waters of a per area basis, leads to catches far higher than would be expected by comparison with similar areas (in terms of latitude, depth, primary production) in other parts of the world.

On investigation of third reason in details by generating world fisheries catch maps on the basis of FAO fisheries catch statistics for every year since 1950 to 1998 a statistical model was used to describe relationships between oceanographic and other factors and the mapped catch. Most high catch areas of the world were correctly predicted in the model. These areas typically had very high primary productivity rates driven by coastal upwellings, like those off Peru, supporting a large reduction fishery for the plankti-vorous anchoveta, *Engraulis rengens*. The exception was, the waters along the Chinese coasts. Here the high catches could not be explained by the model using oceanographic or other factors. Yet the catch statistics provided to FAO by China have continued to increase from the mid 1980s until 1998 when, under domestic and international criticism, the government proclaimed a "zero-growth policy" explicitly stating the reported catches would remain frozen at their 1998 value.

Mapping the differences between expected (that is modeled) catches and those mapped from reported statistics showed large areas along the Chinese coast that had differences greater than 5 tonnes per km per year. Overall the statistical model for 1999 predicted a catch of 5.5 million tonnes against an official report of 10.1 million tonnes. Although China was not the only FAO member country reporting relatively high catches, their large absolute value strongly affects the global total.

## Unregulated Commercial Whaling in the Name of Scientific Studies

Eighteen years after initiating scientific whaling in Antarctic waters, Japan presented a new and more ambitious program to the International Whaling Commission (IWC). Japan now wishes to more than double its annual catch of Antarctic minke whales (from about 440 to 935) and to expand lethal sampling to include an additional yearly, take of 50 humpback and 50 fin whales. Unlike catches for commercial whaling, scientific catches are unregulated. Since 1987, japan has taken some 6800 minke whales from Antarctic waters, despite on going criticism of the relevance and direction of Japan's research.

The IWC was set up to regulate commercial whaling and to conserve whale populations, under the authority of the 1946 International Convention for the Regulation in whaling. Following a well documented failure of management that led to the collapse of most global whale populations, the IWC set a zero quota for commercial whaling (the moratorium). This was made effective from 1986. Norway, the former Soviet Union and Japan initially objected to the moratorium, but Japan withdrew its objection and ceased commercial whaling in 1988.

Scientific whaling occurs under Article VIII of the Convention, whereby each member nation can grant its nationals a permit to take whales for scientific purposes. Unlike the international regulations on commercial and aboriginal subsistence whaling, the objectives of the research, and the number of whales to be killed for scientific purposes are set unilaterally by the member nation. Although the scientific committee (SC) of the IWC provides expert assessment of national research plans, the nations carrying out scientific whaling are not obliged to modify their research.

The first phase of Japan's scientific whaling commenced in the 1987-88 Antarctic season. In 1994, japan also began scientific whaling operations in the western north Pacific, originally targeting minke whales, but subsequently expanded its catches to include Bryde's whales, set whales and sperm whales. Since 1987, Japan has taken approximately 7900 minke whales, 243Bryde's whales, 140 set whales and 32 sperm whales for scientific purposes. By contrast, 840 whales were killed globally by Japan for scientific research between 1954 and, the moratorium. Together all other nations have killed about 2100 whales for scientific research since 1952. Japan's expanded program will result in annual catches that are more than half the total cumulative catches for scientific research by all nations in the past half century. Such take differ little in scale from commercial whaling and must be justified by an adequate scientific rationale.

## Conflicting Opinion

The lethal sampling for whales for scientific research is extremely controversial. Many scientific committee members have constantly complained that such catches do not have sufficient scientific basis. The strongest scientific argument in favor of lethal sampling- the collection of genetic samples for determining population structure could be conducted far more efficiently using no lethal biopsy techniques. At the meeting, a paper signed by 63 scientists representing 16 out of 30 national delegations contested the scientific claims of the Japanese proposal.

The tragedy for the scientists involved in the debate on scientific whaling is that they are labeled as either pro- or anti-whalers. This impugns objectivity and relegates any discussion to polarized politics. As long as whale catches remained small, the consequences of this gridlock were limited to political frustration. But with Japan's proposed escalation in the number of species and individual whales to be sampled, and without any regulatory process to manage these catches, the consequences for whale populations may well be more serious.

A review of Japan's scientific whaling in 1997 reported that the research conducted failed to meet its stated objectives and that the data derived were not required for management.

A further criticism by SC members is that Japan's scientific whaling occurs within the IWC's Southern Ocean, whale sanctuary where commercial whaling was specifically prohibited (so that scientists could study populations not subject to whaling). However, repeated calls by the IWC to Japan to halt its scientific whaling activities had no effect.

Japan's aims is to manipulate the ecosystem through selective culling of certain species, with explicit intention of reducing inter-specific competition and thus promoting population growth in the most economically valuable species (such as blue whales).

Japan's hypothesis that whales are competing directly for a limited resource (krill). Ignoring the fact that current whale populations and their collective consumption of prey remain at fractions of pre-whaling levels, Japan postulates that the recovery of depleted blue whales will be negatively affected by population increases of humpback, fin and minke whales (although data on abundance and population trends for all species are highly uncertain or non-existent). This hypothesis has been proposed using primarily un-reviewed and un-published data collected during the first 18-year phase of scientific whaling. Moreover, Japan proposed using a crude ecosystem approach to examine this hypothesis. This includes constructing simplistic models of competition among whale species and inadequately measuring other components of the Southern Ocean ecosystem including krill abundance and habitat features.

A better understanding of the Southern Ocean ecosystem is critical in considerations far beyond the management of whales. Oceanography and studies addressing climate change and fishery management have led to a series of successful multi-disciplinary, multi-national collaborations. The convention on the conservation of Antarctic Marine Living Resources (CCAMLR) to which Japan is a signatory, applies an ecosystem approach to the conservation and rational use of the Southern Ocean's living resources (primarily krill and fish). To this end, CCAMLR members have a strong history of ecosystem research and of developing ecosystem models. Studying the biomass and dynamics of krill predator populations (including whales the data on which come from IWC) are within the mandate of CCAMLR. In contrast Japan's proposal to unilaterally conduct its whale focused ecosystem-scale research isolate it from the benefits of multi-disciplinary scientific input and collaboration.

From a conservation perspective, Japan's planned catches of humpback and fin whales in the Southern Ocean are particularly worrying. Humpback whales are listed internationally as vulnerable and fin whales as endangered- heavy exploitation in the twentieth century saw total Southern Hemisphere catches of 723000 fin whales and 197000 humpback whales. The species have been protected from any form of legal whaling in this hemisphere since 1966 (humpbacks) and 1985 (fin whales).

Very little is known about the status of fin whales in the Southern Ocean. But some of the humpback whales feeding where Japan intends to conduct whaling come from small, highly depleted populations that breed in the tropical South Pacific. Because gunners on catcher boats can not know the population from which a particular whale is taken, catches in these regions could have disastrous effects in terms of stock recovery for these populations.

## For Review

It is time for the IWC to review the provisions of the International Convention under which scientific whaling permits are issued. Science is stipulated as the basis of management procedures within the IWC. But the lack of science based regulatory process to manage scientific whaling and the escalation of this whaling to commercial scales on the basis of poorly established and controversial scientific claims, challenge the idea that the IWC can deliver a robust frame work for whale conservation or a sustainable whaling industry.

The scientific committee (SC) must be given a real role in determining the IWC's scientific needs, the best methods to achieve these needs and what risks such research might pose to the conservation of whale population. The minimum regulations applied to any proposed lethal catches made for scientific purposes should be accepted by the SC must equal those applied in commercial whaling. Furthermore if commercial whaling resumes, any lethal catches must be part of future national quotas.

Japan's scientific whaling program yields considerable annual revenue from the commercial sale of whale meat estimated at 50 million dollars earlier this decade, this will rise considerably as catches increase. The Japanese government provides annual subsidies of some further 10 million dollars for cetacean research. These revenues are invested in the maintenance and operation of the catcher processor vessels in addition to the Japanese Institute of Cetacean Research that conducts the science associated with scientific whaling. The risk for Japan is that dependence upon these revenues could drive its quotas for scientific whaling, yet leave the real scientific questions unaddressed

Japan is having too many accidents involving critically endangered western grey whale (*Eschierchtius robustus*), the World Conservation Union IUCN) warned.

A young female grey whale found dead in a fixed net off the northeastern coast last month was the fourth since 2005. Only some 120 western grey whales are thought to be left of which 20-25 are reproductive females. The current death rate is driving the species to imminent extinction. It is essential that the causes of net entrapments are investigated thoroughly so that remedial action can be taken. Japan's Fisheries Agency will order more detailed analysis of any further deaths, but it has no plans to take action to prevent entrapment.

## Military Maneuvers and Whale Death

In recent years, naval sonar devices (mid-frequency naval sonar) have been suspected cause of an increasing number of whale strandings world wide. The whales are thought to take evasive action to avoid the noise, some times diving and surfacing until they suffer decompression sickness and die. In 2003 researchers reported that Cuvier's beaked whales (*Ziphius cavirostris*) stranded off the Canary Islands in 2002, had deadly gas-bubble lesions called emboli in their livers.

Spanish researchers investigating a mass stranding of whales (at least nine beaked whales) in the Canary Islands have found evidence that it was caused by a NATO military exercise involving dozens of ships and submarines. High intensity sonar systems used to locate submarines damaged the animal's ears and disorienting them. Injuries consistent with sonar damage in the ear cavity and lungs of the dead whales were observed.

The U.S.Navy's use of high intensity sonar system caused a rash of whale strandings and death in March, 2000. Sixteen beaked and minke whales were found stranded on beaches in the Bahamas shortly after U.S. Navy ships using high intensity sonar had passed by. Six are known to have died and the rest were pushed back into the sea. But a fall in sightings of beaked whales has led researchers working in the area to believe that many more have died. Autopsies on the animals revealed bleeding around the whales inner ears and in one instance in the brain.

But the Navy's report says that high intensity sonar may not pose a wide spread threat to marine life. Such systems are commonly used and the strandings were the result of unique local conditions. The sound waves were trapped in a layer of warm water, preventing their dissipation, and the whales could not escape because they were feeding in underwater canyons.

## Off-shore Army Base will Affect Local Sea Life

In a protest to abandon the offshore military base off the Island Okinawa, the environmentalists said that the construction (drilling sea bed at the start) will have a devastating effect on local sea life.

The site off the city of Henko plays host to coral reefs that serve as feeding grounds for a dwindling population of dugongs (*Duogong duogong*)-the large mammals, also known as sea cows, that are listed as vulnerable to extinction. Dugong population near the island might contain fewer than ten animals. The dugong is symbolic of the various kind of marine life that would be lost. A group of more than 100 conservation organizations is calling for the construction project to be abandoned.

## Harbor Threat for Coelacanths

A population of coelacanths, the rare deep water fish, once thought to have been extinct for millions of years, could be at risk if a proposed harbor project in Tanzania gees ahead, conservation experts warn.

Coelacanths (*Latimeria chalumnae*) were re-discovered in 1938 when a specimen was caught off South Africa. Off Tanzania, the first coelacanth was caught in 2003. Since then fifty or so catches of coelacanths have been reported by Tanzanian fishermen. Scientists warn that the fish are under pressure from fishing with dynamite and the use of deep sea shark nets. A population off the Comoros Islands in the Indian Ocean is now stable due to conservation measures initiated almost 20 years ago.

The international community should take very seriously anything that threatens such an important species. Conservation experts discussed options for a Marine Protected Area for coelacanths, which the Tanzanian Government promised to create,

## Massive Fish Kills

Massive fish kills in mid-Atlantic USA estuaries involving several millions Atlantic menhaden, *Brevoorita tyrannus* have been attributed to dinoflagellates of the toxic *Pfiesteria* complex (TPC). Potent ichthyo-toxins secreted during Pfiesteria blooms are thought to be responsible for mortality as well as for deeply penetrating so-called *Pfiesteria*- specific skin ulcers in these fishes. *Pfiesteria shumwayae* kills fish by micropredation. Myzocytosis resulting in wide spread skin damage and rapid mortality.

*Pfiesteria*, belonging to a group of planktonic organisms, called dinoflagellates kills fish by direct method. Along the eastern seaboard, with a range from Delaware to Alabama, it has been associated with massive fish kills, especially off North Carolina. *Pfiesteria* is lethal when cells are in direct contact with the fish. It has been known for many years that *Pfiesteria* cells extend a suction cup-like appendage called a peduncle to digest fish tissue. Fish die because *Pfiesteria* literally sucks the life out of them. It attaches to fish skin using the peduncle extending finger-like protrusions, called, filopodia, then ingests cell matter from the fish. They multiplies to high numbers to cause harmful "blooms".

Many of other plankton blooms produce potent nerve toxins, sasitoxin, that are dangerous when ingested by higher organisms.

# Chapter 8
# Conservation in World Oceans

## Towards Sustainable Fisheries

Fishing is the catching of aquatic wild life equivalent to hunting on land. Thus industrial fishing should generally not be sustainable as industrial scale of hunting on land. Examining the history of fishing and fisheries makes it abundantly clear that human have had for thousands of years, a major impact on target species and their supporting ecosystems. Indeed the archaeological literature contain many examples of ancient human fishing, associated with gradual shifts through time to smaller sizes and the serial depletion of species that we now recognize as the symptoms of over-fishing.

This literature supports the claim that historically, fisheries have tended to be non-sustainable, although not unexpectedly, there is a debate about the cause for this, and the exceptions. The few uncontested historical examples of sustainable fisheries seem to occur, where a super-abundance of fish supported small human populations in challenging climates. Sustainability occurred where fish populations were naturally protected by having a large part of their distribution outside of the range of fishing operations. Hence many large old fecund females, which contribute overwhelmingly to the egg production that renews fish populations, remain untouched. How important such females can be illustrated by the example of a single ripe female red snapper, *Lutjanus campechanus* of 61 cm and 12.5 kg which contains the same number of eggs (9300000) as 212 females of 42 cm and 1.1 kg each. Where such natural protection is absent, that is, where the entire population was accessible to fishing gears, depletion ensued, even if the gear used seems inefficient in retrospect. This was usually masked, however, by the availability of other species to target, leading to early instances of depletions observable in the changing size and species composition of fish remains, for example, in middens.

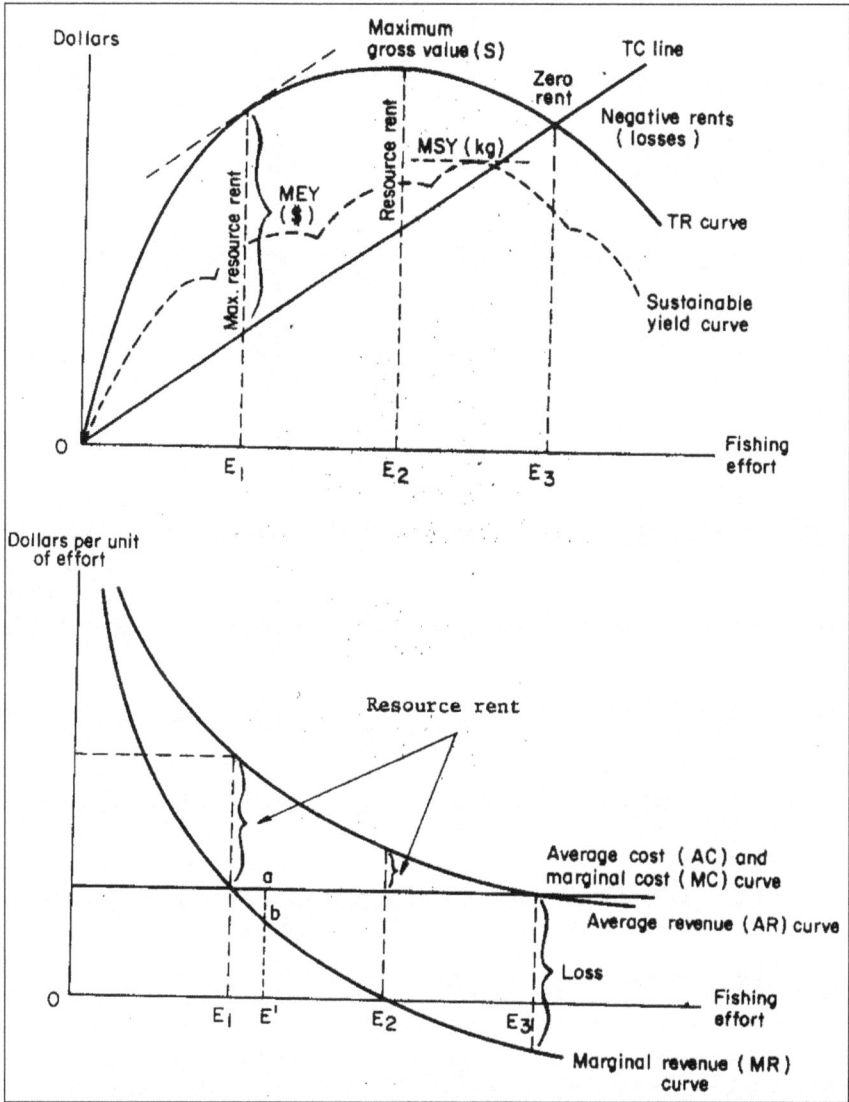

**Figure 38: A Bio-economic Model for Fisheries Management.**

Maximum sustainable yield (MSY) and maximum gross value of catch (maximum total revenues) are not the most appropriate objectives of fishery management, as they-do not make the best possible use of the fishery resource even if the objective is maximum protein (from all sources). The maximum resource rent or maximum (net) economic yield (MEY) is obtained at $E_1$ level of effort where the marginal revenue of effort equals the marginal costs of effort. This level of effort, however, is not tenable in an unregulated open-access fishery which gravitates towards a much higher level of effort ($E_3$) where all resource rents are dissipated. (Note that the average cost and average revenue curves show, respectively, the cost and revenue per unit of effort at each level of effort, while the marginal cost and marginal revenue curves show, respectively, the change in total cost and total revenue, resulting from a change in the level of effort.)

The fishing process became industrialized in the early nineteenth century when English fishers started operating steam trawlers, soon rendered more effective by power winches and after the First World War, diesel engines. The aftermath of the Second World War added another piece of dividend to the industrialization of fishing, freezer trawlers, radar and acoustic fish finders. The fleets of the Northern Hemisphere were ready to take on the world.

Fisheries science advanced over this time as well; the two world wars have shown that strongly exploited fish populations, such as those of North Sea, would recover most, if not all their previous abundance when released from fishing. This allowed the construction of models of single species fish populations, whose size is affected only by fishing pressure, expressed either as fishing mortality rate (F or catch/biomass ratio), or by a measure of fishing effort (f for example trawling hours per year) related to F through a catchability coefficient (q),

$$F = qf;$$

Here q represents the fraction of a population caught by one unit of effort, directly expressing the effectiveness of a gear. This q should be monitored as closely as fishing effort itself, if the impact of fishing on a given stock, as expressed by F, is to be evaluated. Technology changes tend to increase q, leading to increases referred to as "technology coefficient" which quickly renders meaningless any attempts to limit fishing mortality by limiting only fishing effort.

The conclusion of these models, still in use even now in greatly modified forms, is that adjusting fishing effort to some optimum level should generate "maximum sustainable yield MSY), a notion that the fishing industry and the regulatory agencies eagerly adopted, if only on theory. In practice, optimum effort levels were very rarely implemented (the Pacific halibut fishery is one exception). Rather the fisheries expanded their reach, both offshore, by fishing deeper waters and remote sea mounts, and by moving outs the then untapped resources of West Africa, and south east Asia and other low-latitude and Southern Hemisphere regions.

## Single Species Stock Assessments

Single species assessments have been performed since the early 1950s, when the founders of modern fishing science attempted to equate the concept of sustainability with the notion of optimum fishing mortality, leading to some form of maximum sustainable yield. Most of these models, now much evolved from their original versions (some to baroque complexity involving hundreds of free parameters) require catch-at-age data. Hence government laboratories, at least in developed countries, spend a large part of their budget on the routine acquisition and interpretation of catch and age-composition data.

Yet single species assessment models and the related policies have not served particularly well, due to at least four broad problems. First, assessment results, although implying limitation on levels of fishing mortality, which would have helped maintain stocks, if implemented, have often been ignored, on the excuse that they were not "precise enough" to use as evidence for economically painful restriction of fishing (the "burden of proof" problem).

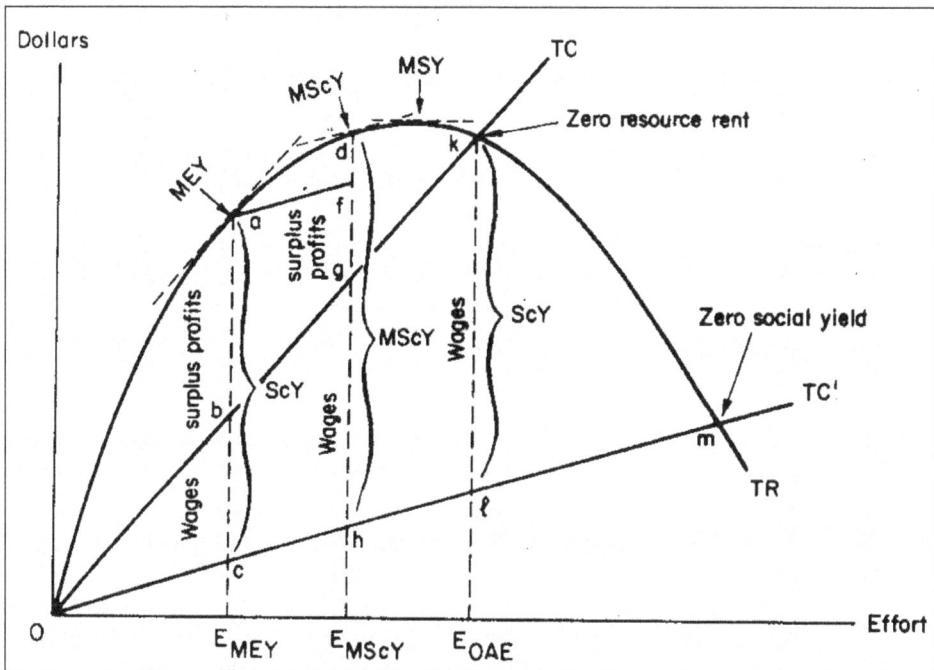

**Figure 39: Maximum Social Yield (MScY) in the Absence of Alternative Employment Oppor-tunities. (Note: social yield (ScY) = wages + profits).**

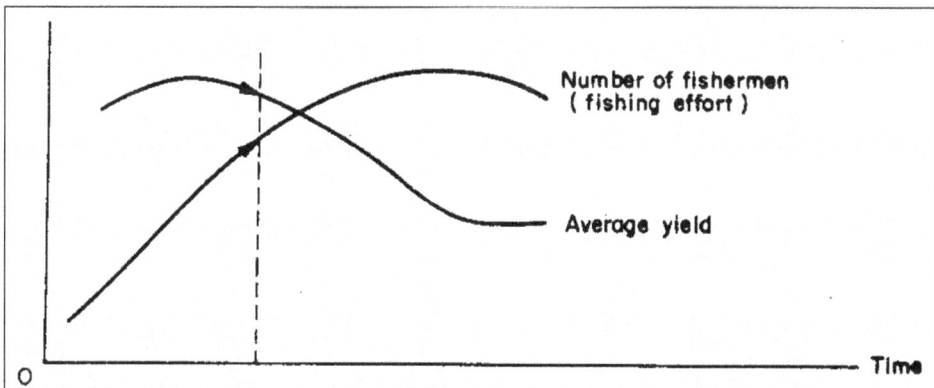

**Figure 40: Time Lag between the Decision to Invest in Fishing Assets (Based on over-optimistic forecast of yield) and Actual Entry into the Fishery. The number of fishermen (or fishing effort) keeps increasing even at a time when the average yield is falling and profitability is declining.**

Second, the assessment methodology failed badly in a few important cases involving rapid stock declines and in particular led to grossly under-estimate the severity of the decline and the increasing (depensatory) impacts of fishing during the decline.

Third, there has been insufficient attention in some cases to regulatory tactics, the assessments and models have provided reasonable overall targets for management (estimates of long-term sustainable harvest), but management failed to implement and even to develop effective short term regulatory systems for achieving those targets. Fourth, it is seen apparently severe violation of the assumptions usually made about "compensatory responses" in recruitment to reduction in spawning population size. It is usually assumed that decreasing egg production will result in improving juvenile survival (compensation) so that recruitment (eggs x survival) will not fall off rapidly during a stock decline and will hence tend to stop the decline. Some stocks have shown recruitment failure after severe decline, possibly associated with changes in feeding interactions that are becoming known as cultivation/depensation effects. According to this phenomenon, adult predatory fish (such as cod) can control the abundance of potential predators and competitors of their juvenile offspring. But this control lost where these predatory fish become scarce. This may well lead to alternate stable states of ecosystems, which has severe implications for fisheries management.

Jointly, these four broad problems imply a need to complement the single-species assessments by elements drawn from ecology, that is, to move towards ecosystem based management. What this will consist of is not clearly established, although, it is likely that, while retaining single-species models at its core, it will have to explicitly include trophic interaction between species habitat, impacts of various gears, and a theory for dealing with the optimum placement and size of marine reserves. Ecosystem-based management will have to rely on the principles of, and lessons learnt from single-species stock assessments, especially regarding the need to limit fishing mortality. It will certainly not be applicable in areas where effort or catch limits derived from single-species approaches can not be implemented in the first place.

Throughout the 1950s and 1960s, this huge increase of global fishing effort led to an increase in catches so rapid that their trend exceeded human population growth, encouraging an entire generation of managers and politicians to believe that launching more boats would automatically lead to higher catches.

The first collapse with global repercussions was that of the Peruvian anchoveta in 1871-1972, which was often perceived as having been caused by an El Nino event. However, much of the available evidence, including actual catches (about 18 million tonnes) exceeding officially reported catches (12 million tonnes) suggest that over-fishing was implicated as well. But attributing the collapse of the Peruvian anchoveta to "environmental effects" allowed business as usual to continue and in the mid 1970s this led to the beginning of a decline on total catch from the North Atlantic. The declining trend accelerated in the late 1980s and early 1990s when most of the cod stocks off New England and eastern Canada collapsed, ending fishing traditions reaching back for centuries.

Despite these collapses, the global expansion of effort continued and trade in fish products intensified to the extent that they now become some of the most globalized commodities, whose price increased much faster than the cost of living index. In 1996, FAO published a chronicle of global fisheries showing that a rapidly increasing fraction of world catches originate from stocks that are depleted or collapsed, that is,

" senescent" in FAO's parlance. Yet global catches seemed to continue, increasing through the 1990s according to official catch statistics. This surprising result was explained recently, when massive over-reporting of marine fisheries catches by one single country, the Peoples Republic of China was uncovered. Correcting for this, showed that the reported world fisheries landings have in fact been declining slowly since the late 1980s, by about 0.7 million tonnes per year.

## Impact on Ecosystem and Bio-diversity

The position within ecosystems of the fishes and invertebrates landed by fisheries can be expressed by their trophic levels, expressing the number of steps they are removed from the algae (occupying trophic level I) that fuel marine food webs. Most food fishes have trophic levels ranging from 3.0 to 4.5, that is, from sardines feeding on zooplankton to large cod or tuna fish feeding on miscellaneous fishes. Thus the observed global decline of 0.05-0.10 trophic levels per decade in global fisheries landings is extremely worrisome, as it implies the gradual removal of large long-lived fishes from the ecosystem of the world oceans. This is clearly illustrated by a recent study in the North Atlantic showing that the biomass of predatory fishes (with a trophic level of 3.75 or more) declined by two-thirds through the second half of the twentieth century, even though this area was already severely depleted before the start of this time period.

It may be argued that so-called fishing down marine food web's is both a good and unavoidable thing, given a growing demand for fish. Indeed the initial ecosystem reaction to the process may be a release from predation, where cascading effects may lead to increased catches. Such effects are, however, seldom observed in marine

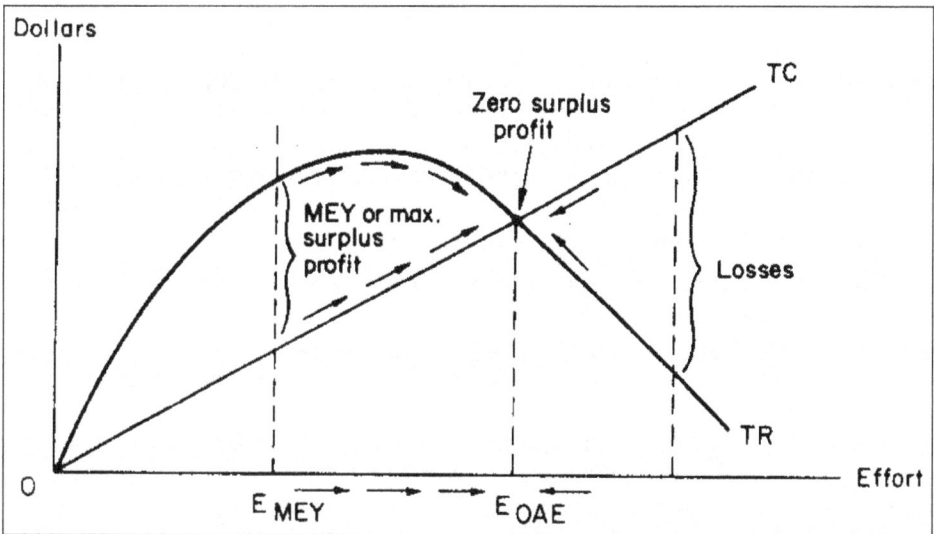

**Figure 41: The Maximum Economic Yield (MEY) cannot Prevail as a Long-term Equilibrium in an Open Access Fishery. As long as there are (excess) profits to be made, new entrants would be attracted and effort would expand until a zero-profit or open-access equilibrium (OAE) is reached at $E_{OAE}$ level of effort.**

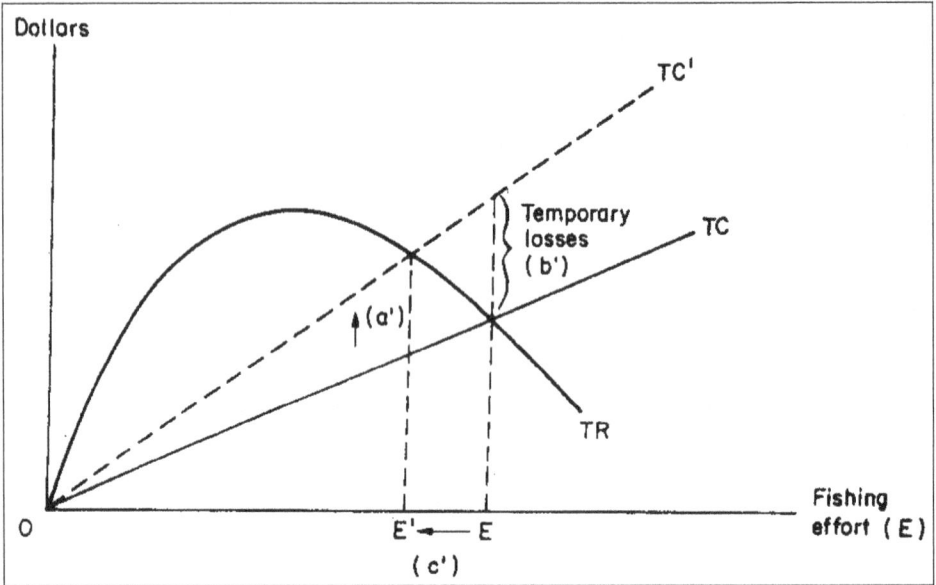

**Figure 42: The Effects of a Rise in Fishing Costs in a Biologically Overexploited Fishery: A rise in cost (a') - - temporary losses (b') - - exit (c') until a new open-access equilibrium (TR = TC) is established; no long-term effects on fishermen's incomes or on economic profits, but a rise in catch.**

ecosystems mainly because they do not function simply as a number of unconnected food chains. Rather predators operate within finely meshed food webs, whose structure (which they help to maintain) tends to support the production of their prey. Hence the concept of "beneficial predation" where a predator may have a direct negative impact on its prey, but also an indirect positive effect, by consuming other predators and competitors of the prey. Thus removing predators does not necessarily lead to more of their prey becoming available for humans. Instead it leads to increase or outbursts of previously suppressed species, often invertebrates, some of which may be exploited (for example squid or jelly fish and latter a relatively new resource exported to east Asia) and some outright noxious.

The principal direct impact of fishing is that it reduces the abundance of target species. It has often been assumed that, this does not impose any direct threat of species extinction as marine fish generally are very fecund and the ocean expanse is wide. But the past few decades have witnessed a growing awareness that fishes can not only be severely depleted, but also be threatened with extinction through over-exploitation. Among commercially important species, those particularly at risk are species that are highly valued, large and slow to mature, have limited geographical range and/or have sporadic recruitment. There is actually little support, though for the general assumption that the most highly fecund marine fish species are less susceptible to over-exploitation, rather it seems that this, perception is flawed. Fisheries may also change the evolutionary characteristics of populations by selectively removing larger fast growing individuals, and one important research question is whether it induces irreversible changes in the gene pool. Overall, this has implications for research, monitoring and management and it points to the need for incorporating ecological consideration in fisheries management, as exemplified by the development of quantitative guide line to avoid local extinctions.

Another worrisome aspect of fishing down marine food webs is that it involves a reduction of the number and length of pathways linking food fishes to the primary producers, and hence a simplification of the food webs. Diversified food webs allow predators to switch between prey as their abundance fluctuates and hence to compensate for prey fluctuations induced by environmental fluctuations. Fisheries induced food web simplification, combined with the drastic fisheries induced reduction in the number of year-classes in predator populations, makes their reduced biomass strongly dependent of annual recruitment. This leads to increasing variability, and to a lack of predictability in population sizes, and hence in predicted catches. The net effect is that it will increasingly look like environmental fluctuations impact strongly on fisheries resources, even where they originally did not. This resolves, if in a perverse way, the question of relative importance of fisheries and environmental variability as the major driver for changes in the abundance of fisheries resources.

It seems unbelievable in retrospect but there was a time when it was believed that bottom trawling had little detrimental impact or even a beneficial impact, on the sea bottom that is ploughed. Recent research shows that the ploughing analogy is inappropriate. Indeed, the productivity of the benthic organisms at the base of the food webs leading to food fishes is seriously impacted by bottom trawling, as is the survival of their juveniles when deprived of the biogenic bottom structure destroyed by that form of fishing. Hence given the extensive coverage of the world's shelf ecosystems by bottom trawling, it is not surprising that generally longer-lived demersal (bottom) fishes have tended to decline faster than shorter lived pelagic (open water) fishes, a trend also indicated by changes in the ratio of piscivorous (mainly demersal) to zooplanktivorous (mainly pelagic) fishes.

It is difficult to fully appreciate the extent of the changes to ecosystems that fishing has brought, given shifting base lines as to what is considered a pristine ecosystem and continued reliance on single-species models. These changes, often involving reductions of commercial fish biomass to a few percent of their pre-exploitation levels, prevent taking much guidance form the concept of sustainability, understood as aiming to maintain what we have. Rather challenge is rebuilding the stock in question.

## Trophic Levels as Indicators of Fisheries Impact

There are many ways ecosystems can be described, for example in terms of the formation, that is exchange as their components interact or in terms of size spectra. But the most straight forward way to describe ecosystems is in terms of the feeding interactions among their component species, which can be done by studying their stomach contents. A vast historical data base of such published studies exists, which has enabled a number of useful generalizations to be made for the ecosystem-based management of fisheries. One of these is that marine systems have herbivorous (zooplankton) that are usually much smaller than the first order of carnivores (small fishes), which are themselves consumed by much larger piscivorous fishes and so on. This is a significant difference from terrestrial systems, where, for example, wolves are smaller than the moose they prey on. Another generalization is that the organisms so far have been extracted from marine food webs have tended to play therein roles very different from those played by the terrestrial animals we consume. This can be shown in terms of their trophic level (TL) defined as 1 + the mean TL of their prey.

Thus in marine systems, algae is at the bottom of the food web (TL = 1, by definition), herbivorous zooplankton feeding on the algae (TL = 2), large zooplankton or small fishes feeding on herbivorous zooplankton (TL = 3), large fishes (for example, cod, tuna and groupers) whose food tends to be a mixture of low-and high TL organisms (TL = 3.5-4.5).

The mean TL of fisheries landings can be used as an index of sustainability in exploited marine ecosystems. Fisheries tend at first to remove large, slower growing fishes and thus reduce the mean TL of the fish remaining in an ecosystem. This eventually leads to declining trends of mean TL in the catches extracted from that ecosystem, a process now known as, "fishing down marine food webs". Declining TL is an effect that occurs within species as well as between species. Most fishes are hatched as tiny larvae that feed on herbivorous zooplankton. At this stage they have a TL of about 3, but this value increases with size, especially in piscivorous species. Because fisheries tend to reduce the size of the fish in an exploited stock, they also reduce their TL.

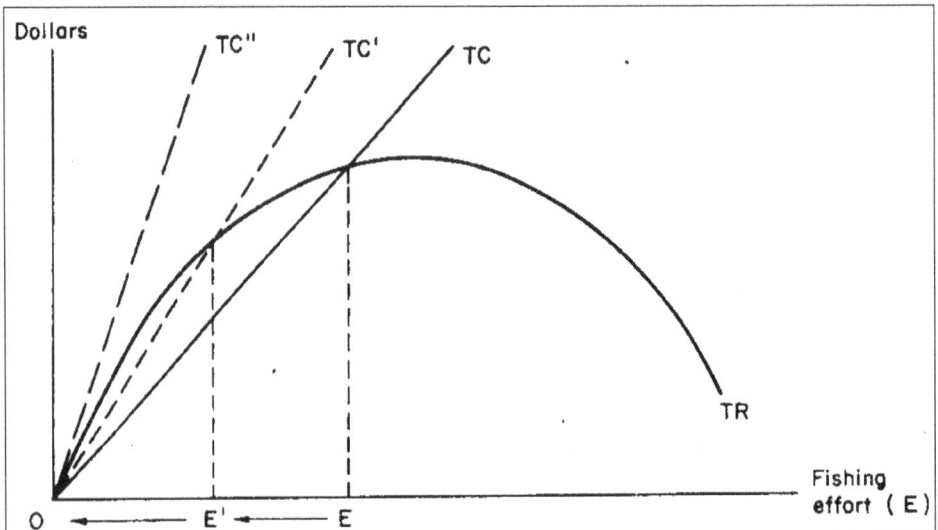

**Figure 43: The Effects of a Rise in Fishing Costs in a Biologically Underexploited Fishery: same as Figure 42 Except that Catch Falls. Fishing costs may rise to the point where the fishery becomes unprofitable and effort and catch are reduced to zero. This may even happen in a biologically overexploited fishery if the costs rise sufficiently.**

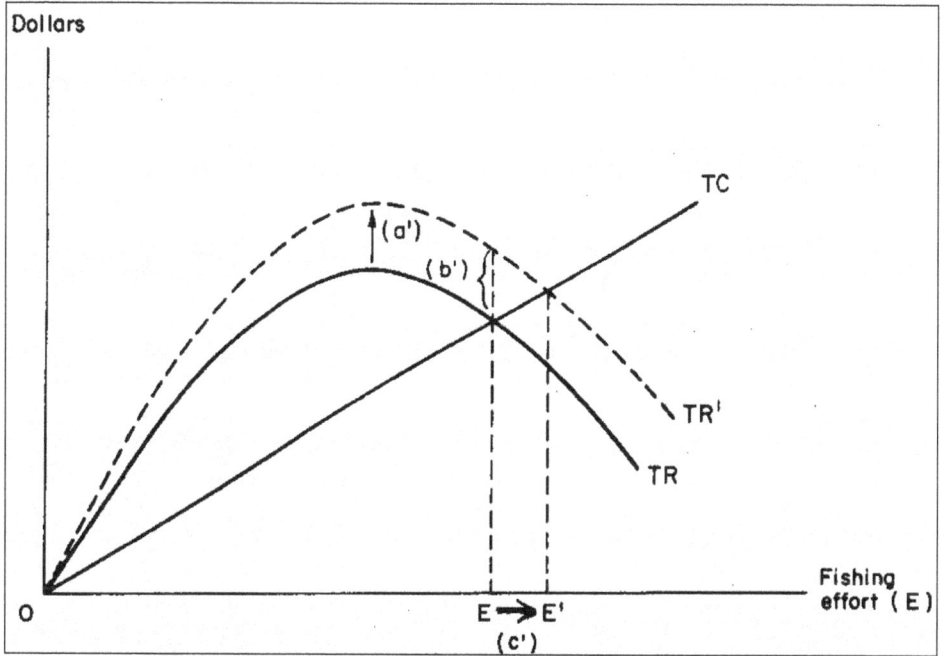

**Figure 44: Effects of Rise in the Price of Fish.** Rise in price (a') - - temporary profit (b') - - entry (c') until a new open-access equilibrium (TR' = TC) is established. No long-term effects on fishermen's income. Economic surplus continues to be zero. If too many new fishermen are attracted into the fishery by the temporary profit, existing fishermen may incur losses if they happen to be less efficient and more immobile than the new entrants.

## Reducing Fishing Capacity

There is a widespread awareness that increase in fishing-fleet capacity represent one of the main threat to the long time survival of marine capture fishery resources and to the fisheries themselves. Reasons advanced for the over-capitalization of the world's fisheries include the open-access nature of many fisheries; common pool fisheries, that are managed non-cooperatively; sole-ownership fisheries with high discount rates and/or high price-to-cost ratios; the increasing replacement of small-scale fishing vessels with longer ones; and the payment of subsidies by governments to fishers, which generate profits even when resources are over-fished.

The fishing over-capacity is likely to built up, not only under open access, but also under all forms of property regimes. Subsidies, which amount to 2.5 billion dollars for the North Atlantic alone, exacerbate the problems arising from the open access and/or "common pool" aspects of capture fisheries, including fisheries with full-fledged property rights.

Even subsidies used for vessel decommissioning schemes can vave negative effects. In fact, decommissioning schemes can lead to the intended reduction in fleet size only if vessel owners are consistently caught by surprise by those offering this form of subsidy. As this is an unlikely proposition, decommissioning schemes often end up providing the collaterals that banks require to underwrite fleet modernizations. Additionally, in most cases, it is not the actual vessel that is retired, but its license. This means "retired" vessels can still be used to catch species without quota (so-called under utilized resources, which are often the prey of species for which there is a quota) or deployed along the coast of some developing country, the access to which may also be subsidized. Clearly, the decommissioning schemes that will have to be implemented if we are ever to reduce over-capacity will have to address these deficiencies if they are not to end up, as most have so far, in fleet modernization and increased fishing mortality.

It is clear that a real drastic reduction of over-capacity will have to occur if fisheries are to acquire some semblance of sustainability. The required reduction will have to be strong enough to reduce F by a factor of two or three in some areas, and even more in others. This must involve even greater decreases in f, because catches can be maintained in the face of dwindling biomasses by increasing q (and hence F), even when nominal effort is constant. Indeed, this is the very reason behind the incessant technological innovation in fisheries, which now relies on global positioning systems and detailed maps of sea bottom to seek out residual fish concentrations, previously protected by rough terrain. This technological race, and the resulting increase in q, is also the reson why fishers often remain unaware of their own impacts on the resource they exploit and object so strongly to scientists claims of reduction in biomass.

In fact, reduction if done properly, it should result in an increase in net benefits (rent) from the resources, as predicted by the basic theory of bio-economics. This can be used via taxation of the rent gained by the remaining fishers, to ease the transition of those who had to stop fishing. This would contrast with the present situation, where taxes from outside the fisheries sector are used, in form of subsidies, to maintain fishing at levels that are biologically unsustainable, and which ultimately lead to depletion and collapse of the underlying resources.

## Biological Constraints to Fisheries and Aquaculture

The strongest factor behind the politicians use of tax money to subsidize non-sustainable, even destructive fisheries, and its tacit support by the public at large, is the notion that, some how, the oceans will yield what is needed, Indeed, demand projections generated by national and international agencies largely reflect present consumption patterns which by some means the oceans ought to help to maintain, even if the global human population were to double again. Although much of the deep ocean is indeed unexplored and "mysterious" enough is known about ocean processes to realize that its productive capacity can not keep up with an ever-increasing demand for fish.

The assumption that the expanse and depths of the world's oceans will provide in the ways that its more familiar coastal fringes have is very wrong. Of the 363 million square kilometers of ocean on this planet, less than 7 per cent - the continental shelves are shallower than 200 meter and some of this shelf area is covered by ice. Shelves generate biological production supporting over 90 per cent of global fish catches, the rest consisting of tuna and other oceanic organisms that gather their food from the vast desert-like expanse of the open oceans.

The overwhelming majority of shelves are now sheltered within the Exclusive Economic Zone (EEZ) of maritime countries, which also include all coral reefs and their fisheries. According to the 1982 United Nations Convention on the Law of Seas, any country that can not fully utilize the fisheries resources of its EEZ must make this surplus available to the fleet of other countries. This along with the eagerness for foreign exchange, political pressure and illegal fishing has led to all of the world's shelves being trawled for bottom fish, purse seined for pelagic fishes and illuminated to attract and catch squid (to the extent that satellites can map the night time location of fishing fleet as well as that of cities). Overall about 35 per cent of the primary production on the world's shelves is required to sustain the fisheries

The constraints to fisheries expansion that this implies, combined with declining catches alluded to above, have led to suggestions that aquaculture should be able to bridge the gap between supply and demand. Indeed, the impressive recent growth of reported aquaculture is often cited as evidence of the potential of that sector to meet the growing demand for fish, or even to feed the world.

Three lines of argument suggest that this is unlikely. The first is that the rapidly growing global production figures underlying this documented growth are driven to a large extent by the People's Republic of China, which reported 63 per cent of the world aquaculture production in 1998. But it is now known China not only over-reports its marine fisheries catches, but also the production of many other sectors of its economy. Thus there is no reason to believe that global aquaculture production in the past decades has risen as much as officially reported.

Second, modern aquaculture practices are largely unsustainable, they consume natural resources at a high rate, and because of their intensity, they are extremely vulnerable to the pollution and disease outbreaks they induce. Thus shrimp aquaculture ventures are in many cases operated as slash-and-burn operations, leaving devastated coastal habitats and human communities in their wake.

Third, much of what is described as aquaculture, at least in Europe, North America and other parts of the developed world, consists of feed lot operations, in which carnivorous fish (mainly salmon, but also various sea bass and other species) are fattened on a diet rich in fish meal and oil. The idea makes commercial sense as the farmed fish fetch a much higher market price than the fish ground up for fish meal (even though they may consist of species that are consumed by people, such as, herring, sardine or mackerels forming the bulk of pelagic fishes). The point is that operations of this type, which are directed to wealthy consumers, use up much more fish flesh than they produce, and hence can not replace capture fisheries, especially in developing countries, where very few can afford imported smoked salmon. Indeed, this form of aquaculture represents another source of pressure on wild fish population.

## Sustainable Coral Reef Fisheries

Globally 75 per cent of coral reefs occur in developing countries where human populations are still increasing rapidly. Although coral reefs account for only 0.1 per cent of the world's ocean, their fisheries resources provide tens of millions of people with food and livelihood. Yet their food security, as well as other ecosystem functions they provide is threatened by various human activities, many of which including forest and land management, are unrelated to fishing.

It has often been assumed that the high levels of primary productivity, reported for coral reefs, imply high fisheries yield. However, the long held notion that coral reef fishes are first turn over species, capable of high productivity, is being increasingly challenged. Yield estimates for coral reefs vary widely, ranging from 0.2 to over 40 tonnes per square kilometer per year, depending on what is defined as coral reef area and as coral reef fishes. Taking yields from the central part of this range (5-15 tonnes per square kilometer per year) and the most comprehensive reef area estimate available, it can be derived an estimate for total global annual yield of 1.4 to 4.2 million tonnes. Although these estimates represent only 2-5 per cent of global fisheries catches, they provide an important, almost irreplaceable source of animal protein to the populations of many developing countries

Clearly, maintaining the bio-diversity that is a characteristic of healthy reefs is the key to maintaining sustainable reef fisheries. Yet coral reefs throughout the world are being degraded rapidly, especially in developing countries. Concerns regarding over-exploitation of reef fisheries are wide spread. The entry of new, non-traditional fishers into reef fisheries has led to intense competition and the use of destructive fishing implements, such as, explosives and poisons, a process known as "Malthusian over-fishing.

Another major problem is the growing international trade for live reef fish, often associated with mobile fleets using cyanide fishing and targeting species that often have limited ranges of movements. This lead to serial depletion of large coral reef fishes, notably humphead wrasse (*Cheilinus undulates*, Laliridae), groupers (serranidae) and snappers (Lutjanidae) and to reefs devasted by cyanide applications.

These fisheries, which destroy the habitat of the species upon which they rely, are inherently unsustainable. It can be expected that they will have to cease operating within a few decades, that is, before warm surface waters and sea-level rise over come what may be leftof the world's coral reefs

## Perspectives

It is believed that the concept of sustainability upon which most quantitive fisheries management is based have been flawed, because there is little point in substantial stocks whose biomass is but a small fraction of its value at the onset of industrial scale fishing. Rebuilding of marine systems is needed and it is foreseen a practical restoration ecology for the oceans that can take place alongside the extraction of marine resources for human food. Reconciling there apparently dissonant goals provided a major challenge for fisheries ecologists, for the public, for management agencies and for the fishing industry. It is important here to realize that there is no reason to expect marine resources to keep pace with the demand that will result from the growing population, and hopefully, growing incomes in now impoverished parts of the world, although it is noted that fisheries designed to be sustainable in a world of scarcity may be profitable.

It was argued in the beginning that, whatever semblance of sustainable fisheries in the past might have had was due to their inability to cover the entire range inhabited by the wildlife species that were exploited, which thus had natural reserves. It is further argued that the models used traditionally to assess fisheries, and to set catch limits tend to require explicit knowledge on stock status and total withdrawl from the stocks, that is knowledge that will inherently remain imprecise and error prone. It was also showed that generally over-capitalized fisheries, are heading, globally to the gradual elimination of large, long lived fishes from marine ecosystems and their replacement by shorter-lived fishes and invertebrates, operating within food webs that are much simplified and lack their former buffering capacity.

If these trends are to be reversed, a huge reduction of fishing effort involving effective decommissioning of a large fraction of the world's fishing fleet will have to be implemented along with fisheries regulations incorporating a strong form of the precautionary principle. The conceptual elements required for this, are in place, for example, in form of the FAO code of conduct for Responsible Fisheries; but the required political will has been lacking so far, an absence that is becoming more glaring as increasing numbers of fisheries collapse throughout the world and catches continue to decline.

Given the high level of uncertainty facing the management of fisheries which induced several collapses, it has been suggested by numerous authors that closing a part of the fishing grounds would prevent over-exploitation by setting up an upper limit of fishing mortality. Marine protected areas (MPAs), with no no take reserves at their core, combine with a strongly limited effort in the remaining fishable areas, have been shown to have positive effects in helping to rebuild depleted stocks. In most cases, the successful MPAs were used to protect rather sedentary species, rebuild their biomass and eventually sustain the fishery outside the reserves by exporting juveniles or adults. Although migrating species would not benefit from the local reduction in fishing mortality caused by an MPA, the MPA would still help some of these species by rebuilding the complexity of their habitat destroyed by trawling and thus decrease mortality of their juveniles. Enforcement of the "no take" zones within MPAs would benefit from the application of high technology (for example, satellite monitoring of fishing vessels) presently used mainly to increase fishing pressure. There is still much fear among fisheries scientists, especially in extra-tropical areas, that the export of fish from such reserves would not be sufficient to compensate for the loss of fishing ground. Although it is agreed that marine reserves are no panacea the present trends in fisheries, combined with low degree of protection, presently afforded (only 0.01 per cent of the world's ocean is effectively protected) virtually guarantee that more fish stocks will collapse, and that these collapses will be attributed to environmental fluctuations or climate change. Moreover many exploited fish populations and eventually fish species will become extinct. MPAs that cover a representative set of marine habitats should help prevent this.

Focused studies on the appropriate size and location of marine reserves and their combination into networks, given locale-specific oceanographic conditions should therefore be supported. This will lead to the identification of reserve design of that would optimize export to adjacent fishing areas, and which could thus be offered to the affected coastal fisher communities, whose consent and support will be required to establish marine reserves and restructure the fisheries. The general public could also be involved through eco-labelling and other market driven schemes and through support for conservation oriented non-government organizations, which can complement the activities of governmental regulatory agencies.

In conclusion it is thought, that the restoration of marine ecosystems to some state that existed in the past is a logical policy goal. There is still time to achieve this and for fisheries to be put on a path towards sustainability.

## Conservation of Fish Stocks

George Sugihara, who had built a formidable reputation among ecologists by analyzing the population dynamics of fish and plankton was a prize catch.

Applying his experience in finance to marine conservation, he wants to harness market forces to prevent over-fishing, which governments and the scientists, who advise them have mostly so far failed to achieve.

The analysis of environmental fluctuations and ecological catastrophes in the North Pacific suggests that fishing quotas may need to be set more conservatively and adjusted more frequently to compensate for environmental conditions than is typically the case. The way fishing quotas are set is wrong, it does not fit nature and reality.

Sugihara hopes that the Ocean Resource Exchange will provide an incentive to preserve fish stocks, that does not rely on a detailed understanding of complex biological systems and instead taps into people's basic instincts. They should be shown how to make more money. The first derivative is likely to be a future contract for a certain percentage of a fishermen's catch at an agreed price at a specified time. Another planned derivative is an instrument for trading fish quota allotments, called "individual transfer quota".

Essentially, these are tradable options for fishing rights. Fishermen and investors could hedge their bets, which should be the tendency for catches to swing between boom and bust and give all stake holders a tangible financial incentive not to cheat and plunder the ecosystem for the maximum short return.

As a test of the idea, Sugihara has modeled the concept using data from Californian squid fishery, where about 200 vessels bring in a haul worth up to 36 million dollars per year. But both catches and prices can fluctuate widely, making it a prime candidate for a market in derivatives. The market forces here can be used for conservation.

## Fishing's Secretive Controllers

As the international agency controlling fishing for 30 migratory species in the Atlantic Ocean, the International Commission for the Conservation of Atlantic Tunas (ICCAT) has a vital ecological role. From the spawning waters of the Gulf of Mexico, up across the feeding grounds of the North Atlantic and into stock-rich regions of the Mediterranean, ICCAT decisions on allowable commercial catches can have a huge environmental impact. They affect target species, such as, bluefin tuna or sword fish, creatures ensured as by-catch, notably sharks or dolphins, and their food webs.

Timely, proper assessments of the stocks of specific species, analysis of the age and size of captured fish, and understanding of the effect of years of over-fishing should be integral components of ICCAT deliberations. These should lead to science-based management decisions on the economically important and culturally rich resources under the stewardship of Madrid-based agency. They don't.

Disturbingly, the media and public are blocked from observing ICCAT discussions. Transparency is essential to understand what is happening to ocean resources. The Convention on Biological Diversity operates in such a manner.

## Population Structure of Bluefin Tuna

Giant bluefin tuna are the largest members of the family Scombridae, attaining abody sizes of more than 650 kg. They are unique among teleosts for their endothermic capacity and cardiovascular physiology. These traits undertake their capacity to exploit environments ranging from sub-arctic feeding grounds to sub-tropical spawning areas. Top pelagic predators, such as bluefin tuna are in precioitous decline globally because of over-exploitation. The International Commission for the Conservation of Atlantic Tunas (ICCAT) manages Atlantic bluefin tuna as distinct western and eastern stocks, separated by a management boundary at the 45 degree west meridian. The spawning stock biomass of western Atlantic bluefin tuna has decreased by 80 per cent or more since 1970. A 20-year re-building plan was enacted in the early 1980s in the western Atlantic. The most recent assessment indicates that the western stock continues to decline, yet mortality throughout the North Atlantic remains high. Key questions remain on thebiology of the species, Establishing the location and timing of reproduction, the mean age of maturity, spawning site fidelity, the ontogeny of movement patterns and the influence of climate variability on movements will improve stock assessment and subsequent management.

The spatio-temporal distribution of Atlantic bluefin tuna was determined with electronic tags, which discriminate two potential spawning populations and recorded spawning site fidelity to the Mediterranean Sea.

The electronic tagging data reveal two populations of Atlantic bluefin tuna that overlap on North Atlantic Ocean foraging grounds and sort to independent spawning areas located primarily in the Gulf of Mexico (GOM) and Mediterranean Sea. A bluefin tuna was assigned to the Western Atlantic spawning unit if it visited a known western Atlantic ICCAT spawning area (Gulf of Mexico, Bahamas or Florida Straits) for more than 7 days in winter or spring and occupied surface, water temperatures of at least 24 degree Celsius, the SST reported for western spawning activity Bluefin tuna that displayed transatlantic movements into the Mediterranean Sea and were re-captured in the spawning season (June to August) in the Straits of Gibralter (May to August) were classified as potential eastern spawners. Bluefin tuna that remained in the North Atlantic throughout the track duration without visiting the known ICCAT spawning areas were classified as neutral. Comparing the distributions of the 62 bluefin tunas, identified as potential western or eastern spawners, calculated a spatial overlap of the positional data sets of 47 per cent in North Atlantic waters. These mixing zones were primarily in the western and central Atlantic. Importantly no mixing occurred in the Gulf of Mexico and Mediterranean spawning areas.

The results of tagging indicates that one component of the transatlantic migration is associated with of potential eastern origin moving back into the east Atlantic and Mediterranean Sea. A second component is associated with western breeding fish moving into eastern foraging grounds where encounters occur with eastern fishers.

The transatlantic movements observed in electronic tag data sets are corroborated by conventional tagging data, which demonstrate that 10 per cent of tag recaptures from fish tagged and released in the South Atlantic Bight (1994-2000) occur in the eastern Atlantic and Mediterranean Sea. Conventional tagging in the eastern Atlantic (1911-1990) indicated that 4.5 per cent of recaptured juvenile bluefin tuna, released in the eastern Atlantic were recaptured in the western Atlantic. However, in these studies, no giant bluefin tuna conventionally tagged in the eastern Atlantic was recaptured in the western Atlantic. Consistent with this result is the observation that no electronically tagged fish that moved into the Mediterranean Sea during spawning season has so far returned to the western Atlantic management unit. The conventional and electronic tagging data indicate that some juvenile fish tagged in the eastern Atlantic swim to the western Atlantic, where they remain for several years before returning to Mediterranean spawning areas. It can thus be hypothesized that once an eastern spawned bluefin tuna returns from the North Atlantic to the Mediterranean it is less likely to forage along the North American coast. Fish identified as western spawners can move to the eastern Atlantic and back, crossing to 45 degree west meridian several times over the course of one or more years. The over lap areas identified in the central and eastern Atlantic seem to be foraging areas for these western spawners.

Five conclusions with management implications are apparent. First, the results support the existence of two North Atlantic bluefin tuna stocks with discrete spawning areas, primarily in the Gulf of Mexico and the Mediterranean Sea. Second, the two stocks over lap on North Atlantic foraging grounds as adolescents and adults, but there is no evidence for movement between the two major spawning areas in the Gulf of Mexico and the Mediterranean Sea. Third, fish identified as western or eastern spawners are subjected to fishing pressures within their designated management unit during the spawning season. Fourth, the northern slope waters of Gulf of Mexico are a critical habitat for bluefin tuna during the spawning season, and these fish could be protected with time-area closures to reduce the incidental catch of giant bluefin tuna by pelagic long line fisheries operating in the Gulf of Mexico. Fifth, transatlantic movements of western tagged fish have two components, one associated with tuna of eastern origin moving back to the Mediterranean spawning grounds, and another with western origin fish moving into eastern Atlantic foraging grounds.

Collaborative studies that combine electronic tagging data, otolith micro-chemistry and genetics should provide a method for validating and quantifying the extent of mixing between the putative stocks. Significant question remaining including the relationship of the two North Atlantic bluefin tuna stocks tagged in the western

Atlantic to the recently identified genetically distinct stock in the eastern Mediterranean Sea. Quantifying the extent of spawning in one location relative to another, establishing whether individual adult bluefin tuna spawn every year and determining the influence of physical and biological oceanographic conditions on movements are essential to improved management strategies.

## Recruitment of Cod

The Atlantic cod (*Gadus morhua*) has been over-exploited in the North Sea since the late 1960s and great concern has been espressed about the decline in cod biomass and recruitment. In addition to the effects of over-fishing, fluctuations of plankton have resulted in long term changes in cod recruitment in the North Sea (bottom up control). Survival of larval cod is shown to depend on three key biological parameters of their prey; the mean size of the prey, seasonal timing and abundance. It is suggested that a mechanism, match/mismatch hypothesis, by which variability in temperature affects larval cod survival and concluded that rising temperature, since the mid-1980s has modified the plankton ecosystem in a way that reduces the survival of young cod.

## Whale Population at Risk

As the whale's biggest of whale meat, Japan has a special interest in whale conservation. While fighting tenaciously to protect its whaling industry, it publicly supports the need for conservation In a statement 2006, june it called on the International Whaling Commission (IWC) to protect endangered and depleted species, while allowing the sustainable utilization of abundant species under a controlled, transparent and science based management regime.

Japan has placed considerable emphasis on research into whaling, spends about 7 million dollars each year to establish whether there enough whales to support whaling (and in the case of minke, at least it finds that there are). And it works hard to get support in the IWC, sometimes from member nations that have no obvious interest in whaling.

When it comes to the events on high seas, however, Japan's action leave much to be desired. Lately there have been repeated cases of western grey whales (*Eschrichtius robustus*) being caught in the Japanese fishing nets. Only about 120 of these whales, which migrate along the Pacific coasts of Asia are thought to survive, although a much larger, sustainable population of eastern grey whales lives off in the west coast of North America. The World Conservation Union (IUCN) estimates that the population of the reproductive female western grey whales totals only about 30 animals. But four females have been trapped in Japanese fishing nets and accidently killed in two years, 2005 and 2006.

Japan has expressed concern over this issue. Its fisheries agencies says it has been asking fishermen to report sightings of the whales, and to release them, when trapped, instead of keeping them and selling their meat, as permitted under the law. The agency claims that its effort has worked so far, with no meat from grey whales being sold in the market

However, the agency's efforts have not actually prevented the deaths, even though such could be done to that end, including supporting better research into the whale's migration and breeding habits and the development and use of fishing nets that can release trapped animals. One might expect the Institute of Cetacean Research (ICR) which heads Japan's research whaling program to take charge of this effort. But it says that responsibility rests with other research institutes and with the fisheries agency. The overall result has been in action.

The ICR is often characterized by its critics as little more than a cover for Japan's whaling industry. If it is to claim a real role in whale conservation, it could start by responding more energetically to the clear and present danger to the grey whale.

## Tracking Whales

Satellite-based tracking system, developed by a Japanese research team set to fuel the international debate on whale conservation. Tokyo based Institute for Cetacean Research (ICR) says that whale stocks are sufficient to warrant hunting. But the International Whaling Commission disagrees. To prove its point Japan has been carrying out controversial "research whaling", killing about 400 whales per year.

Both sides know too little about the whale's ecology to reach a conclusion. Researchers will tag the whales by using an air gun to shoot a titanium pin into the brudder and a probe attached to the pin by a two meter rope will send signals to the satellite. Apart from allowing monitoring of migratory patterns and whale acoustics, the probes will record pressure and temperature and take geo-magnetic readings during whale dives, which can last for 10 to 30 minutes. Sperm whales are thought to dive 2000 to 3000 meters during this time. A propeller-like machine that will derive energy from the whale's motion through the water will recharge the probe's batteries.

This "epoch-making" research will help to work on rational stock management.

## Detection of Endangered Species

Mass spectrometers relies on the fact that elements, such as, carbon, hydrogen and nitrogen have more than one isotope. The isotopes differ in their mass, so a mass spectrometer can reveal how much of each isotope a sample contains. Because different foods have different isotopic make ups, the ratios of carbon and nitrogen isotopes in the tissue of animals can reveal what they have been eating and suggest the type of area they have inhabited. And some elements, such as, hydrogen have isotope ratio, that vary over the blobe; researchers can also see where an animal has been, by tracing its path across isotope landscape or isoscape.

Such studies are allowing researchers to reconstruct the behavior of many endangered species, yielding information that could prove invaluable to efforts to conserve them

## Threat to Olive Ridley Turtle

The increasing numbers of Olive Ridley turtles inadvertently caught by fishing trawlers and found dead on Odisha's beaches during the 1990s had led some scientists to suggest a sharp decline in the populations of Olive Ridley turtles was imminent.

But observations over the past decade indicate and increase in the number of sites for mass nesting on Odisha coasts and fishing related mortality has not increased. Their population seems to be more stable today than what it seemed to be 10 years ago, the turtles are still dying, but this appears for now to be not threatening the population.

Conservation scientists estimate that between 100000 to 200000 Olive Ridley turtles come up for mass synchronized nesting at various sites along India's east coast each year. Among the largest mass nesting sites are Gahirmatha and Rushikulya in Odisha. Through the 1990s, teams of marine biologists had documented the deaths of up to 10000 turtles each year at sites along the beaches of Odisha, causing concern among section of scientists and conservation groups and turning marine turtles into "flagships or icons of marine conservation".

The conservation campaign has had some impact, the company that built the Dhamra Port, north of the Gahirmatha nesting sites, had consulted conservation groups and scientists, seeking suggestions to reduce the risk to turtles. But the port pose the risk to the turtles and their mass nesting grounds. The loss of habitat through the construction of new ports or activities such as oil exploration continue to threaten the Olive Ridley turtles. Even bright lights on a beach can disorient hatchlings and make them stray away from water.

Studies by the Bombay Natural History Society suggest that plantations of Causarina species along sections of the beach on Sriharikota island in Andhra Pradesh may also interfere with mass nesting. Such plantations may also provide shelter mammalian predators of turtles.

## Conservation in Indian Seas

India has a long coastline, of about 8000 km, stretching along ten States and two archipelagos. The coast is indented by a number of rivers, which form estuaries, lagoons, mangroves, backwaters, salt marshes, mud flats, rocky shores and sandy stretches. Besides, there are three gulfs, one on the east coast, The Gulf of Mannar and the two on the west coast, Gulf of Kachchh and Gulf of Lambath. The two island ecosystems Lakshadweep and Andaman and Nicobar Islands add to the ecosystem diversity in India. The Gulf of Mannar, Gulf of Kachchh and the two island ecosystems have rich coral reefs harboring valuable marine biodiversity.

The continental shelf of India occupies 414686 square kilometer (including islands) which represents about 0.55 per cent of the surface area of the Indian Ocean. The Indian EEZ has 1.8 million sq.km area and represents about 2.7 per cent of the Indian Ocean. In India the EEZ on the west coast (including Lakshadweep) constitutes 42.5 per cent, Andaman and Nicobar Islands 29.7 per cent and the east coast 27.8 per cent of area.

## Indian Marine Protected Areas

Marine Protected Areas in India covers entire areas in intertidal/subtidal or sea-water mangroves, coral reefs, lagoons, estuaries and beaches (Singh, 2002)

1. Mahathama Ganghi Marine National Park, located at Wandoor (South Andaman, covering an area of 281.50 square kilometer was declared as protected in 1983. The ecosystem characterized by tropical evergreen forest, mangroves, coral reefs, creeks and sea water.

2. Rani Jhansi Marine National Park (Ritchies Archipelago) Andaman covering an area of 256.14 square kilometer was declared as protected in 1996. The ecosystem represents evergreen forest, mangroves and coral reefs.

3. Lahabarrack (Salt water crocodile) Sanctuary in South Andaman with dense mangroves (tidal forest), littoral forest, creeks, marine water and tropical evergreen forest, covering an area of 100 square kilometer was declared as sanctuary in 1987.

4. In 1982, Gulf of kachchh (Jamnagar), Gujrat covering an area of 295.03 square kilometer having mangroves, coral reefs, mudflats, creeks, beaches and scrub forest was declared marine national park and protected.

5. Gulf of Kachchh, covering an area of 295.03 square kilometer having mangroves, intertidal mudflats, beaches and coral reefs was declared as marine sanctuary in 1980.

6. In 1987, an inter tidal area, marine water, coral patches and sandy beach of Sindhudurg, Maharashtra was declared as Malvan Marine Sanctuary and protected.

7. In 1988, Bhitar Kanika of Cuttack, Odisha the estuary, delta and mangroves covering an area of 145 square kilometer was declared as protected National Park.

8. The estuary, mangroves, terrestrial forest and ecotone with marine of Bhitar Kanika, Kendrapara, Odisha covering an area of 672 square kilometer was declared as sanctuary in 1975.

9. Sea water, sandy beach, estuary, mangroves and ecotone with marine environment, covering an area of 1435 square kilometer of Gahirmatha of Kendrapara, Odisha was declared as Marine Sanctuary in 1997.

10. 15.5 square kilometer of Nalban area of Chilka, in Khurda, Puri and Ganjam, Odisha covering island, lagoon and brackish water was declared protected in 1987.

11. Twenty one islands, coral reefs, mangroves, sea gress beds and beaches of Gulf of Mannar in Ramanathapuram, Tuticorin, Tamil Nadu covering an area of 6.23 square kilometer was declared as National Park in 1980.

12. Brackish water, mangrove and estuarine environment of Pulicat Lake, Tiruvellore, Tamil Nadu covering an area of 153.67 square kilometer was declared as Bird Sanctuary in 1980.

13. Tidal swamp, mangroves, creek and ever green forests of Point Calimere, Nagapattinam, Tamil Nadu covering an area of 17.26 square kilometer was declared Sanctuary in 1967.

14. Mangroves, estuary, back water, creek and mud flats of Coringa, East Godavary, Andhra Pradesh covering an area of 235.7 square kilometer was declared as Wildlife Sanctuary in 1978.

15. Mangroves, back water, creeks and mud flats of Krishna, Guntur, Andhra Pradesh covering an area of 194.81 square kilometer was declared as Wildlife Sanctuary in 1999.

16. Brackish water, mangroves, estuarine and algal beds of Pulicat Lake, Nellore, Andhra Pradesh covering an area of 500 square kilometer was declared as Bird Sanctuary in 1976.

17. Mangroves, estuaries, creeks, swampy islands and mud flats of Sundarbans covering an area of 1330.1 square kilometer was declared as national Park-Tiger Reserve (North and South 24-Pargana, West Bengal) in 1973 and 1984.

18. 5.95 square kilometers of mangroves, estuaries, swampy islands and mud flats of Halliday, South 24-Pargana, West Bengal was declared as Sanctuary in 1976.

19. 38 square kilometer of mangroves, estuaries, creeks, swampy islands and mud flats of Lothian Island, South 24-Pargana, West Bengal was declared as Sanctuary in 1998.

20. Mangroves, estuaries, creeks, swampy islands and mud flats covering an area of 362.4 square kilometer in Sajnakhali, South 24-Pargana, West Bengal was declared as Sanctuary in 1976.

In the category II Andaman and Nicobar Islands and Lakshadweep Islands, which have major parts in marine ecosystem and some part in terrestrial ecosystem have been decalared as Marine Protected Areas as detailed below.

1. North Buttan, Middle Andaman – Evergreen and littoralforest, mangroves, beach and coral reefs – 0.44 square kilometer in 1987.

2. South Buttan, Middle Andaman – Evergreen and littoral forest, mangroves and beach – 0.03 square kilometer in 1987.

3. North Reef Island, North Andaman – Evergreen and littoral forest, mangroves and beach – 3.48 square kilometer in 1987.

4. South Reef Island, Middle Andaman – Beach and coral reefs – 1,17 square kilometer in 1987.

5. Cuthbert Bay, Middle Andaman – Splendid beach and creek – 5.82 square kilometer in 1987.

6. Cingue Sanctuary, South Andaman – Evergreen forest, coral reef and beach – 9.51 square kilometer in 1987.

7. Galathea Bay sanctuary – evergreen forest and mangroves in Great Nicobar – 11.44 square kilometer in 1997.

8. Parkinson Island Sanctuary, Middle Andaman – Evergreen and littoral forest and mangroves – 0.34 square kilometer in 1987.

9. Mangrove Island Sanctuary, Middle Andaman – Mangroves and marine life – 0.39 square kilometer in 1987.

10. Blister Island Sanctuary, North Andaman – Mangroves and beach – 0.26 square kilometer in 1987.

11. Sandy Island Sanctuary, South Andaman – Sandy islands – 1.58 square kilometer in 1987.

12. Pitti Wildlife Sanctuary – A small sandy island surrounded by sea – 0.01 square kilometer in 2000.

## Biosphere Reserves in Marine Areas

☆ Sundarbans – West Bengal – 9630 square kilometer – notified in 1989.

☆ Gulf of Mannar – Tamil Nadu – 10500 square kilometer – notified in 1989.

☆ Great Nicobar – Andaman and Nicobar – 885 square kilometer – notified in 1989.

# Chapter 9

# Management and Policies

## Basic Concepts of Fishery Management

Fishery management is the pursuit of certain objectives through the direct or indirect control of effective fishing effort or some of its components (the indirect control of effort includes the case in which a management authority does not get involved in the control of effort, but simply creates the appropriate environment for its control by the fishermen themselves, *e.g.*, community property rights). For example, a minimum mesh size may be instituted and enforced for the purpose of regulating the size of fish at capture and increasing the productivity of the resource; or a system of licences may be introduced in order to control entry into the fishery for the purpose of maximizing the economic returns from the fishery. Fishery development on the other hand, is the expansion of effective effort through a set of assistance programs again for the purpose of attaining certain objectives. For example, the fishing range of crafts may be expanded through subsidized motorization for the purpose of exploiting underutilized resources and increasing fish supplies and fishermen's incomes. Fishery development may be defined more broadly to include, in addition to the expansion of fishing effort, improvement in post-harvest technology, marketing and transportation of fishery products as well as the provision of infrastructure and other related facilities.

Because of its "control" feature, fishery management is thought to be required once a fishery becomes "overexploited", while fishery development is thought to apply while a fishery is still "under-exploited". One need not wait for overfishing to occur before management measures are taken. Overfishing is better avoided by judicious management measures taken along with development. Similarly, the need for development is not confined to under-exploited fisheries.

As management of overexploited fisheries sooner or later involves the regulating of fishing effort, development, fishery-related or otherwise, is needed to absorb the surplus labor and capital. In many developing countries, enforcement of management regulations is virtually impossible without development of sufficiently attractive employment alternatives elsewhere. Moreover, further "development" of an already "overexploited" fishery (the catch is less than the maximum possible due to excess fishing effort) may not be as unwarranted as it sounds if the purpose is a temporary solution of otherwise intractable social problems.

These interrelations notwithstanding, the priority in overexploited fisheries for management and in underexploited fisheries for development. Thus, the general objective of both management and development is the attainment of the "optimum" rate of exploitation of the fishery. How this optimum is defined depends, of course, on the specific objectives of the policy-makers. If the policy objective is maximum fish production then the optimum rate of exploitation is defined by the maximum sustainable yield (MSY), that is, the maximum catch that can be obtained on a sustained basis. If the actual catch is less than the MSY because of insufficient fishing effort the fishery is said to be "biologically" underexploited and further development is possible, while if the catch is less than MSY because of excess effort the fishery is "biologically" overexploited and management is called for (this is not to say that MSY is a biological concept). There is nothing "biological" about it except that it corresponds to maximum natural growth of the stock and it has been suggested by early fishery biologists as a possible objective of fishery management. MSY is, in some sense, an economic concept without, however, full cognizance of all economic factors as it ignores the cost of fishing and the value of the catch. Thus it is not sufficient to know the MSY and to compare it with the actual catch; the fishing effort required to obtain MSY is also needed to compare it with actual effort.

If on the other hand, the policy objective is to maximize the economic benefit to the national economy from the fishery, the optimum rate of exploitation is defined by the maximum economic yield (MEY), that is, the maximum sustainable surplus of revenues over fishing costs. Alternatively, MEY may be thought of as a modification of MSY to take into account the value of fish caught and the cost of catching it. The fishery is said to be underexploited in the economic sense and to require further development if the actual catch falls short of MEY due to insufficient effort. Analogously, the fishery is said to be overexploited in the economic sense and to call for management if the actual catch falls short of MEY due to excess fishing effort.

In cases where social considerations, such as the improvement of socio-economic conditions of small-scale fishermen, generation of employment opportunities and improvement of income distribution matter, the optimum rate of exploitation is defined by a third concept, the maximum social yield (MScY) (MScY as the objective of fisheries management takes full cognizance of the likely conflict between income and employment objectives, more employment may lead to overfishing and a reduction of aggregate fishing income. Employment objectives may be weighted more heavily than income objectives only when there are no other effective means of redistributing income to lower-income groups.). This is the level of catch and corresponding effort which provides the best possible solution to social problems given the policy objectives and all possible alternatives. Alternatively, the MScY may be thought of as modification of the MEY to account for non-purely-efficiency aspects, such as poverty and distribution. Introduction of social considerations may limit the speed with which management measures are introduced, or it may justify a more intensive rate of fishing than is justified on purely economic grounds. Thus, levels of effort below the one corresponding to MScY may be termed socio-economic underexploitation, while levels of effort above it, socio-economic overexploitation. This latter concept, MScY, is the one most applicable to the case of small-scale fisheries in which socio-economic considerations often override both biological and strictly economic concerns.

However, estimation of MScY cannot be made independently of MSY and MEY. As biological aspects enter the economic model, which more appropriately may be termed "bio-economic", so do both biological and economic parameters enter the determination of MScY, which may be more appropriately termed a "bio-socio-economic" model. Thus before attempting to construct such a model for determining MScY, it is necessary to review the basic biological and economic aspects of fishery management and corresponding models.

## Biological Aspects

### The Single Species, Single Gear, Single Community Model

While fisheries biology is a science in itself, the fishery administrator needs only to be familiar with some basic biological concepts and relationships of direct relevance to fisheries development and management. In the simplest case of a single species, single gear fishery, the relevant relationship is the one between "sustainable catch" and "fishing effort". Sustainable catch is the quantity of fish in terms of weight of biomass which can theoretically be caught year after year without a change in the intensity of fishing. Fishery managers are interested in the sustainable catch rather than any temporary changes in the catch because fish, being a renewable resource, is capable of being harvested on a sustainable yield basis. Fishing effort, on the other hand, is a composite index of all inputs employed for the purpose of realizing this catch. Fishing effort is understood in effective rather than nominal terms, that is, in terms of its effect on the fish stock (Often fisheries biologists use the term fishing mortality to denote effective fishing effort). One is interested in effort because it is the main parameter under the control of man.

The relationship between sustainable catch and effort is a basic production relationship relating output (catch) to inputs (effort) but, unlike other production relationships, there is no direct relationship between output and fishing effort. This is due to the fact that fishing effort, while the only input supplied by men, is in fact combined with a natural resource, the fish stock.to "produce" catch. Were the fish stock a fixed factor, just like land, we would expect output to continue increasing (though at a decreasing rate) in response to increases in effort except at the extreme point of overcrowding when output might actually decline. However, the fish stock being a living resource, rather than a fixed factor, reacts to changes in fishing effort in a manner which complicates the catch-effort relationship. Hence to understand this relationship, some basic biological features of the resource need to be considered.

A basic biological concept is the "net natural growth" of fish stock which is the net increase in the biomass of the fish population between two points in time. Net natural growth (henceforth "growth" for brevity) is equal to recruitment (new young fish entering the stock) plus individual growth of fish already in the stock minus natural mortality. The growth of the stock is an important concept because it is the amount of fish which can be caught on a sustainable basis without affecting the size of the stock. Hence, it is important to know what determines the growth rate of a given fish stock.

One theory, known as the Schaefer Growth Model, postulates that the growth of a stock of fish depends on the size of the stock (more complicated models such as Beverton and Holt (1957) and Ricker (1958) consider the age structure of the stock and the effect of fishing on recruitment. These models require detailed biological data on individual growth rates, recruitment, natural mortality, size at first capture, etc., which in many cases are not readily available. Here the simple Schaefer (1954) model will be reviewed with extensions, where possible, to account for factors such as the effect of fishing on recruitment, the age structure and the species composition of the stock). At a small stock size, the growth is small but it increases as the stock becomes larger until a point of maximum growth is reached beyond which growth declines with further increases in the stock due limits placed by environmental factors (food, space etc.). This implies an inverted U-shape curve, with the same growth obtainable at two different stock sizes; at a small stock size growing relatively fast and a large stock size growing relatively slowly.

Fishing effort enters the model as a form of fishing mortality in addition to natural mortality. The larger the fishing effort, the higher the fishing mortality and lower the (equilibrium) size of the stock. That is, there is an inverse or negative relationship between fishing effort and the size of the standing stocks: as effort expands the fish stock shrinks.

By combining this negative relationship between equilibrium stock and fishing effort on the one hand, and the inverted U-shape relationship between net natural growth and stock on the other, a U-shape relationship between groth and fishing effort can be obtained. Too little effort means too large stock and hence too little growth (because of overcrowding); more effort means smaller stock (less crowding) an hence higher growth; but,too much effort results in too little stock and hence, again, in too little growth. Since the sustainable catch exactly equals growth at the corresponding level of effort, the sustainable catch-effort relationship is identical to the growth-effort relationship. Thus, the same sustainable catch can be caught with little effort operating on a large stock or with a lot of effort operating on a smaller stock.

The fishery administrator needs to keep the inverted U-shape of this curve in mind because it describes the long-term response of catch to changes in fishing effort which is the main variable under his control: in the early stages of exploitation of a fishery, expansion of effort brings about more or less proportional increases in catch; but the more effort expands the smaller the growth in catches until a point, known as maximum sustainable yield (MSY), is reached beyond which additional effort reduces, rather than raises, the sustainable catch. This is not to imply that it is not possible to catch temporarily more fish by increasing effort beyond the level corresponding to MSY; however, such increases in catch cannot be sustained over the long run, at least not by the fishery as a whole.

Temporary increases in catch following an expansion in fishing effort should not mislead the fisheries administrator into believing that there is still potential for further intensification of fishing. Only when the increase in catch is shown to be sustainable over time is there scope for expansion and, yet, it should be noted that even in an underexploited fishery, as fishing is intensified, additional effort brings forth smaller and smaller increases in catch as MSY is approached.

The diminishing efficiency of effort as exploitation increases can be seen more clearly by expressing catch per unit effort (cpue) as a function of effort. This is done by dividing the vertical coordinate (catch) of the sustainable yield curve by its horizontal coordinate (effort) to obtain cpue which is then plotted against effort. The resulting curve, known as the catch rate curve, steadily drops as fishing effort increases, reflecting the reduction in the biomass of the stock as fishing is intensified. As indicated earlier, at moderate levels of effort this reduction in the biomass might enhance rather than damage the stock's capacity to reproduce, because of the resource's intrinsic compensatory mechanisms. However, when fishing is intensified beyond the MSY the compensatory mechanisms fail to maintain the productivity of the resource. The progressive decline in sustainable yield beyond MSY has two causes: firstly, if the size at first capture and more generally the age structure of catches is not modified, the yield per recruit tends to decline beyond a certain level of fishing effort; in addition, average recruitment into the stock, and so the sustainable yield produced by that recruitment, tend also to decline when the parental stock is reduced by heavy fishing to very low levels.

Both the sustainable yield curve and the catch rate curve were drawn on the assumption of a given age at first capture or a given age structure of the catch. They can be shifted up or down by manipulating the average age at first capture through a variety of means such as changes in mesh size or in the type of gear, or apartial and seasonal distribution of effort. For example, reductions of trawl mesh size up to a point may increase catch above certain levels of effort and raise the sustainable yield curve, but too fine nets have the opposite result. In open-access fisheries, where the race for the limited resource often leads to very fine mesh sizes as well as fishing in spawning and nursery areas and seasons, there is an appreciable scope for raising the yield curves through raising the age at first capture. The higher the fishing effort is, the higher is the gain in sustainable yield to be accrued from an increase in mesh size; in other words, the justification for mesh size regulation increases as fishing effort goes up. Thus, a second parameter which the fishery administrator can control and use to increase the yield from a fishery is the average age of fish at first capture. This may make a dual contribution to the improvement of the total value of the catch: higher volume of catch and higher unit value for fish of larger size.

To sum up, a fishery administrator may achieve the maximum possible catch from a fishery on a sustainable basis by simultaneously adjusting the level of fishing effort which corresponds to the highest point on the chosen sustainable yield curve and the age at first capture which puts the fishery on the highest possible sustainable yield curve. It must also be kept in mind that, after a change in either the level of fishing effort or in the age at first capture, sufficient time (depending on the lifespan of the species concerned) must be allowed for the age structure of the stock to stabilize at the new conditions of exploitation.

The sustainable yield and catch rate curves can become operational, that is, useable in a real world fishery, by plotting catch and cpue figures from the fishery against the corresponding effort figures. It is often easier and more accurate to do this by specifying a mathematical form for these curves and estimating its parameters through statistical techniques such as linear regression. As an example, catch and effort data from the demersal fishery of the Gulf of Thailand have been plotted. It was found that the maximum sustainable yield of demersal fish in the gulf of Thailand is 550000 tonnes and the corresponding effort about 6 million standard fishing hours. More importantly, it was obtained the intercept and the slope of the yield curve which give, respectively, an index of the virgin biomass and the rate at which this biomass index and the corresponding catch rate have declined with the expansion of effort to the present level. The fisheries administrator can use these values to assess the level of exploitation of the fishery (whether under- or overexploited) and to predict the change in the cpue and in the sustainable yield in response to a change in effort, keeping in mind that such extrapolations will cease to be valued, as soon as the exploitation pattern, as reflected by the age structure of catches, is appreciably modified.

The accuracy of any long-term forecasts would also depend on the stability of the environment and on the length a nd accuracy of the time-series on catch and effort used in estimating the catch-effort relationship. In the theoretical model, it has been implicitly assumed that environmental conditions remain unchanged or, at most, they are subject to random fluctuations which average out unto the average yield curves. However, when non-random or evolutionary changes in the environmental conditions, whether favorable or otherwise to the stocks under consideration, are taking place, it is important that predictions consider also the present state of the environment, its likely effects on the strength of the year classes making up the stock to be exploited in the forthcoming years and, as far as possible, its possible evolution. Moreover, some of the year-to-year variability in the size of the stocks and the corresponding sustainable yields may be neither random nor evolutionary but may arise from the intensification of fishing and the consequent reduction in the number of age classes on the stock which, in turn, reduces the in-built stability of the stock (Troadec, 1982). Finally, the natural variability of the stocks depends on their nature and location as well as on their interaction with the biotic and abiotic environment. The stocks of coastal pelagic species show generally more inter-annual variability than do demersal stocks. Tropical stocks consist of generally short-life species but their spawning seasons generally extend over longer periods, thus counterbalancing the stock variability resulting from the fewer number of broods of which they are made; they interact more with their biotic environment (other stocks) than with their abiotic environment (temperature etc) which is normally less variable than in the temperate waters (Pauly, 1979). This means that a stock or a species may show considerable annual variability because of (changes in) the intensity of fishing on other stocks or species as well as in its own rate of fishing rather than because of changes in its (abiotic) environment.

The natural variability of the stocks as well as the possible decline in recruitment and the increase in variability associated with intensive fishing suggest that, on purely biological considerations, even MSY may be "too risky" an objective for development or management.

For simplicity of exposition it has been assumed, thus far, a homogeneous fishery in the sense of a single-species stock fished by a single group of fishermen using one type of gear. However, the tropical fisheries which account for the bulk of small-scale fisheries around the world are distinctly characterized by multi-species stocks exploited by distinct groups of fishermen using a variety of fishing gear. These factors certainly complicate the picture and make more difficult the control of fishing effort and the selection of the "optimum" age at first capture, but the basic inverted U-shape sustainable yield curve still provides a good approximation of the response of the multi-species resource accessible to a community of artisanal fishermen to the expansion of the effort it can deploy.

## The Multi-Species Fisheries

Another complication raised by tropical fisheries is the multi-species composition of the stocks and the consequent technological and biological interactions within the fishery. A technological interaction is said to exist when non-discriminatory gear is applied to a stock comprised of several species in which case it is impossible to allocate the overall fishing effort between the constituent species of the stock. A biological interaction, on the other hand, involves either competition between two or more species for the same food or a predator/prey relationship. In certain fisheries, such as those for tunas, the number of species may be small and they may have similar characteristics of productivity, commercial value, and likelihood of capture. However, this is rarely the case in tropical demersal fisheries where it is not uncommon to find more than one or two hundred species in the same haul ranging from almost worthless trashfish to high-value crustaceans. Perhaps more importantly, there is a complex network of competition and predation relationships and differential likelihood of capture and risk of extinction among constituent species subjected to the same overall fishing effort. When a given overall level and distribution of effort over the constituent species are maintained for a sufficiently long time, a certain species composition, age structure, and aggregate biomass are established and reflected in the catch. Changes in fishing intensity alter this ecological configuration of ages, species and overall biomass. It is quite possible that the relative abundance of some species increases while others altogether fall to low levels in the catch. However, total biological extinction is quite unlikely for most species, notably owing to the existence of natural reserves (*e.g.* untrawlable grounds).

Under these circumstances, trying to maximize sustainable catch becomes a complicated if not a totally elusive task. In fact, it is quite possible that, as the fishery expands, there will be a sequential collapse of certain species and "emergence" of new species, *e.g.*, cephalopods, which had failed to achieve a dominant status in the presence of more efficient and better adapted species. An example is found in Pouly

(1979) who reports that flat fishes *(Heterosomata)* in the Gulf of Thailand had been kept in check by small prey fishes *(Leiognathidea)* despite the former's superior reproductive capacity. It was only when the small prey fishes were reduced by heavy fishing and by their predators that the flat fishes found an opportunity to proliferate. This hypothesis, if correct, may help explain why the catches from the Gulf of Thailand keep increasing despite the expansion of effort levels that would imply heavy overfishing in the light of earlier estimates of MSY.

Selection of a single optimum size at first capture is operationally difficult since what is optimum size for one species is likely to be too small or too large for some other species. In a multi-species fishery, a compromise mesh size will be required; certain species will be overexploited and others under-explioted depending on the fishing technology and the biological relationships between species. The latter could be particularly complex because competition and predation affect differently the various age groups of different species *(e.g.,* large predators can prey on small pelagic species which prey on the eggs of the former). These complexities obscure the effect of intensive fishing of one species on the abundance of another species.

The task of the administrator in a multi-species fishery is further complicated by the fact that the species composition, the age structure, and the total biomass of the stock do not vary only in response to man-made stresses (changes in fishing intensity), but also as result of natural stresses. Ecosystems are subject to both short-time fluctuations and evolutionary changes in their composition and geographical distribution, as the experience with several coastal pelagic fisheries has shown. Given our limited knowledge of the structure and behavior of ecosystems and of their reactions to man-made and natural stresses as well as the need for simple, easily understood and implementable management schemes, fishery administrators should start with a pragmatic and practical approach to management;

1. Observe the average species and age composition of the catch and monitor its response to changes in the intensity and pattern of fishing (overall increase in fishing effort, modification of mesh size, introduction of new gear types, change in seasonal and spatial distribution of effort etc.).

2. Develop a multi-species production model and translate it into socio-economic terms in a manner analogous with the single species fishery, *i.e.*use theprices of each species as weights to aggregate the multi-species catch obtained at different levels of effort; then, express this aggregate value of catch as a function of total fishing effort to obtain what might be called a total revenue or gross economic yield curve.

3. Examine whether this gross economic yield curve could be raised through manipulation of the controllable factors, that is, by changing the total level of fishing effort and the distribution of available fishing capacities on the component species through changes in mesh size, type of gear and the distribution of fishing operations over space and time.

4. Keep in mind that natural variability of the resource base is an inherent characteristic of fisheries that is hardly possible to predict, and that it is extremely difficult to adjust the volume of fishing and processing capacities and the size of fishermen communities to its year-to-year fluctuations.

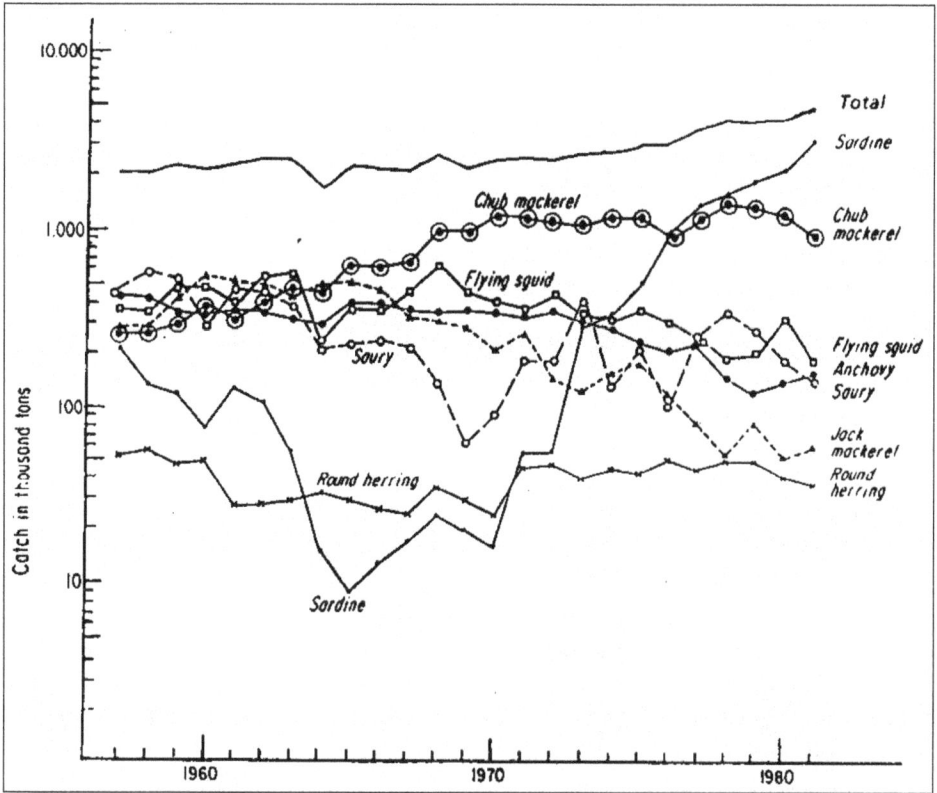

**Figure 45: Annual Change in the Catch of Major Coastal Small Pelagic Fish taken from the Waters around Japan from 1957 to 1981 (Nagasaki, 1983).**

A multi-species production model may be constructed by summing up the individual curves of the component species. The resulting aggregate sustainable yield curve has more or less the same overall shape as the yield curve of the single-species fishery; basically, catches increase with effort up to some maximum and then decline. It is of crucial importance, however, to keep in mind the aggregate nature of the curve; movements along the curve by increasing total effort do not only change total catch and age structure but also its species composition. The kinks on the overall sustainable yield curve may imply the practical disappearance of certain species from the catch for certain levels of effort. As the variability in the species composition and size of the stock, as well as the risk of irreversible changes, tend to increase with the intensity of fishing, the fisheries administrator needs to be particularly cautious to select fishing rates and catch levels below the aggregate MSY. Similarly, when the pattern of fishing (mesh size, spatial and seasonal distribution) has been manipulated to raise the sustainable yield curve through changes in the age structure and species composition of the catch, possible irreversibilities as well as the economic value of the so modified catch should also be considered.

This essentially experimental (or trial and error) approach to multi-species fisheries management is probably the only option available at the current state of knowledge and management capabilities. It has the added advantage that it involves considerable learning by doing and it is amenable to modifications as new knowledge is accumulated and management capabilities improve.

While it is possible to obtain an aggregate sustainable yield curve for a multi-species fisheries, it does not provide with a meaningful management tool. A more appropriate device would be the gross economic yield or total revenue (TR) curve obtained by multiplying the catch of each species (at different levels of fishing effort) by its unit price, summing up over all species, and expressing the resulting aggregate value or total revenue as a function of total fishing effort.

## Management of Multi-Species and Multi-Gear Fisheries

The problems involved in the management of multi-species fisheries in Japan can be categorized into four major groups, namely (1) the incidental by-catch problems generated by the structure of fishing gear, (2) the "successional fishing operations" directing fishing effort to a variety of fish species, (3) the irregular and large changes in stock abundance and/or species composition of an exploitable fish community brought about by natural causes, and (4) the efficient utilization of the ecosystem as a whole in a limited area/water.

Incidental catch problems are generated by fishing gear that catches more than one species by a haul or a shot, regardless of whether this is intentional or not. In a highly efficient gear such as bottom trawl or purse seine, the amount of by-catch taken is sometimes so large that it causes serious problems in the management of fisheries and resources.

There are two possible ways to deal with the by-catch problem. One is to manage the fishing to minimize the by-catch by adjusting gear and grounds as far as possible, and the other is to introduce suitable management measures specifically designed to reduce by-catch component of the fishery or fisheries in question. In Japan a combination of these two approaches has been employed, which has worked fairly well. However it may be noted that the Japanese type management scheme is unique in that the catch quota system has rarely been employed for management purposes, especially for catching finfish.

By-catch also hampers the effective application of the regulations on mesh size for certain species. Since the theoretically derived optimum mesh size differs largely by species, it is technically impossible to apply a single mesh size regulation to a number of different species.

## Successional Fishing

A structural feature inherent in small scale fisheries also needs to be taken into account when examining multi-species problems. Local small-scale fisheries usually tend to employ simple and easy-to-operate gear aimed at catching high value fish species. Success in fishing operation is determined by various factors, *e.g.* fishing methods, accessibility of fishing grounds and the density of the target fish schools. Therefore, at the early stages of the development of these fisheries, the fishing gear employed is quite simple and the fishing grounds are confined mostly to near shore waters. However, competition or conflicts between fishermen are not serious at that time since the fishing populations is small.

As the fisheries developed, the fishing for a few specific fish species of high commercial value began and became more and more widespread. Competition among these fishermen thus arose in coastal waters, and was strengthened being coupled by a steady increase in the fishing population. Near shore fisheries became less profitable for individual fishermen owing to a decrease first in the individual catch rate and second in the total catch, which boosted further competition among coastal fishermen. This general pattern can be seen during the development of many coastal fisheries before suitable management measures have been introduced. It should be noted, however, that a similar situation still exists in many coastal fisheries in the world today owing to a lack of adequate management actions.

In order to minimize the uncertainty involved in fishing, it is better or safer for a fisherman to rely on multiple fish species rather than depending on only a single or a few target species. Such fishing operations can be performed with less risk and profitably by changing fishing gear in different seasons and grounds. Such operations also enable fishermen to increase the length of fishing season or operation. The fishing strategy employed under such a multi-disciplinary philosophy can be called successional fishing.

## Irregular Change in Stocks

Apart from the over-fishing, a shift in target species is sometimes required by the change in abundance caused by natural factors beyond human control. The large fluctuations frequently observed in the abundance of coastal pelagic fish stocks are typical examples. To cope with such natural fluctuations, the fisheries have to change target species in accordance with the substantial change first in the abundance of a specific fish species and second in the species composition of the exploitable community in the waters concerned. A fisheries forecasting service would be an effective way to reduce the uncertainty involved in fishing for these stocks.

## Utilization of an Ecosystem as a Whole

When fisheries operate both extensively and intensively, harvesting various fauna and flora in the waters in question, the fishing strategy must be based on a different approach, namely the harmonious and systematic utilization of the ecosystem in the waters as a whole. In such cases, isolated management schemes aimed at a specific (or a few) living resources may not effectively protect that resources and the entire community in the waters. To achive this end, full account must be taken of the followings; (1) the structure of the ecosystem in the waters in question, (2) the inter-species or inter species-group relationships among all components of the fish community and (3) the socio-economic conditions of the fishing community.

Generally speaking, each fishery (all the fisheries include, all the fishing activities harvesting some living resources in the sea, *e.g.* seaweeds, sea urchins, jellyfish, crustaceans, shellfish, cephalopods, other invertebrates, finfish and marine mammals etc) selectively utilizes only a segment of various living resources which compose an entire ecosystem in the waters. In the sea, the fish of commercial value are mostly at higher trophic levels, which implies that the total biomass of those fish is strictly limited by the biomass of prey at lower trophic levels, resulting in a relatively small quantity of commercially valuable fish. The biomass of planktivorous fish is, in contrast, generally huge but the catches are of lower commercial value.

In waters where a variety of resources are available at various trophic levels of the ecosystem, a careful choice must be made regarding the priority species to be utilized. For instance, a decision must be taken on whether to catch (a) only highly valuable fish in relatively small quantities but with higher profit, (b) less valuable fish in large quantities, or (c) a combination of these. Furthermore, the strategy decided on should be flexible.

## Experience of Fisheries around Japan

The multi-species fisheries around Japan are multi-gear fisheries. They can however, be roughly grouped into two categories according to their size and which fishing grounds they are permitted to use; (1) large to medium-type fisheries in offshore waters and (2) small-scale fisheries in near-shore waters.

The structure of the first group is rather simple, being composed of a few types of highly efficient gear. These include offshore trawls (larger than 15 gross tons), larger one-and two-boat purse seines (over 40 gross tons), medium-type purse seines (5-40 gross tons), saury stick-held dip net and squid-jigging fisheries. They are not allowed to operate in nearshore waters. The second group is a complex of smallscale fishing gear forming a highly complicated multi-gear fishery in each of the nearshore waters where fishing is permitted. The fishing vessels employed in the second group are mostly less than 5 gross tons except the small-scale mechanized trawls in defined sea areas and the boat seines in the Seto Inland Sea (5-15 gross tons for each fishery).

It can therefore, be said that fisheries have a two-layered structure. However, if the situation is looked at in detail, especially that in nearshore waters, the structure can be further divided and becomes multi-layered, with fisheries being defined and characterized by various fishing rights and licences.

The structure of the fisheries and the deployment of their fishing operations in each of the defined sea areas are, of course, the results of the management decision currently taken by central and local governments. However, they are, at the same time, the results of fishermen adapting to the natural conditions in each area throughout the long history of the development of the fisheries. In other words, they currently reflect the tradition and customs kept to throughout the history of each fishing community on the coast. These customs have been shared not only by fishermen but also by almost all social and economic sectors of the fishing communities. They are particularly strong in nearshore waters.

As is well known, Japan is one of the traditional fishing nations in the world, where fishing has been one of the most important industries, providing not only subsistence for fishermen and a supply of animal protein for the nation but also a global improvement in the social and economic status of fishing communities and the entire nation (Nagasaki, 1983, Chikuni, 1985, Yamanaka *et al.*, 1988). In this

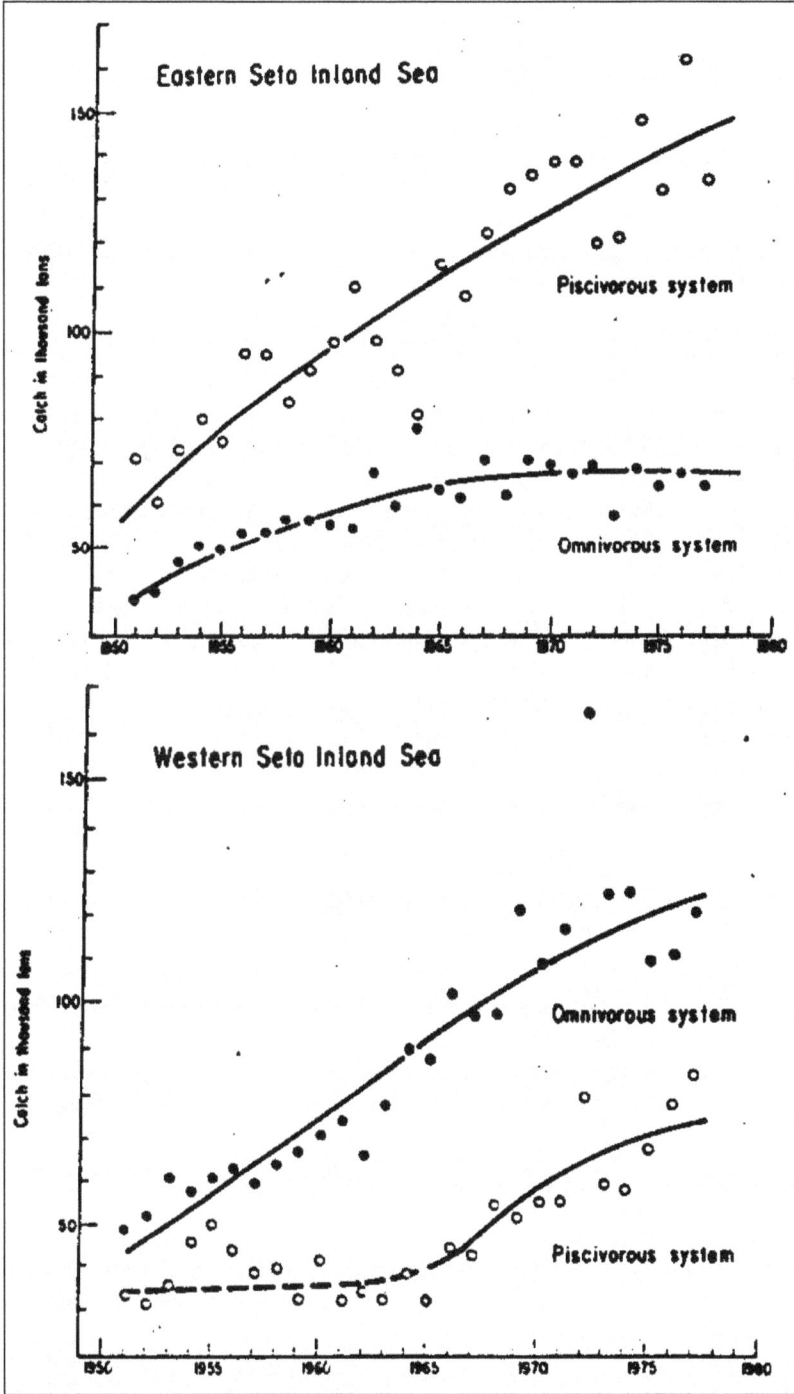

**Figure 46: Annual Change in the Total Catch by Sub-ecosystem and Sub-region of the Seto Inland Sea (Tatara, 1981a, modified by the authors).**

regard, tradition and customs have functioned fairly positively in maintaining social tranquility in each fishing community, and have been extremely effective in resolving conflicts among fishermen.

This deep-rooted philosophy is shared not only by the people in fishing communities but also by the nation as a whole. This is one of the reasons why, in establishing modern, democratic legal arrangements (laws and acts), those traditions and customs have had to be taken into account. This is also one of the main reasons for the success in organizing various fisheries co-operatives as autonomous co-ordinating bodies at a grass roots level.

## Management

The main components of the management scheme in Japan (these are (1) the establishment of the exclusive-use right in nearshore zones, (2) the control of total fishing intensity of particular fisheries in defined waters during the prescribed season, (3) the establishment and enforcement of various conservation measures and (4) promotion of co-ordination and co-operation among fishermen) completely cover the management of multi-species resources and multi-gear fisheries as well as the other fisheries in Japan. There are four distinctions to be made between this system and those in other countries. They are (1) measures highly complicated, detailed and comprehensive, (2) flexibility in engaging in different fishing operations is allowed within a defined fishery in a defined sea area, (3) a combination of the limitation of total fishing intensity and various conservation measures is the standard and universal regulatory system, and (4) the active participation of fishermen in the management of resources and fisheries is mandatory and the self-regulatory scheme has been widely established by fisheries co-operatives.

## Complexity, Comprehensiveness and Attention to Detail

These arrangements have been made aiming to cope with target resources that vary greatly over space (regionally and locally) and over time (annually and seasonally) and complex of fisheries with double- and multi-layered structures.

So far as the coastal resources are concerned, almost no measure has been employed in Japan aimed at managing only a single stock. A regulation or directives has usually been designed to cross-refer to other measures or directives. The entire system can thus cover all resources and fisheries with measures whose functions overlap. This is another reason why a catch-quota system is impractical in Japan. .

## Allowance of Flexible Fishing

Permission to engage in different kinds of fishing is granted only when detailed and comprehensive measures are strictly enforced covering all resources, fisheries and fishing grounds. In the Japanese system, such permission and the strict measures are not contradictory but complimentary to one another.

For instance, the economic loss to fishermen caused by various seasonal closures (grounds or fishing) for conservation purposes can be offset by allowing the fishermen to engage in other fishing. However, arbitrary shifts in fishing by fishermen beyond

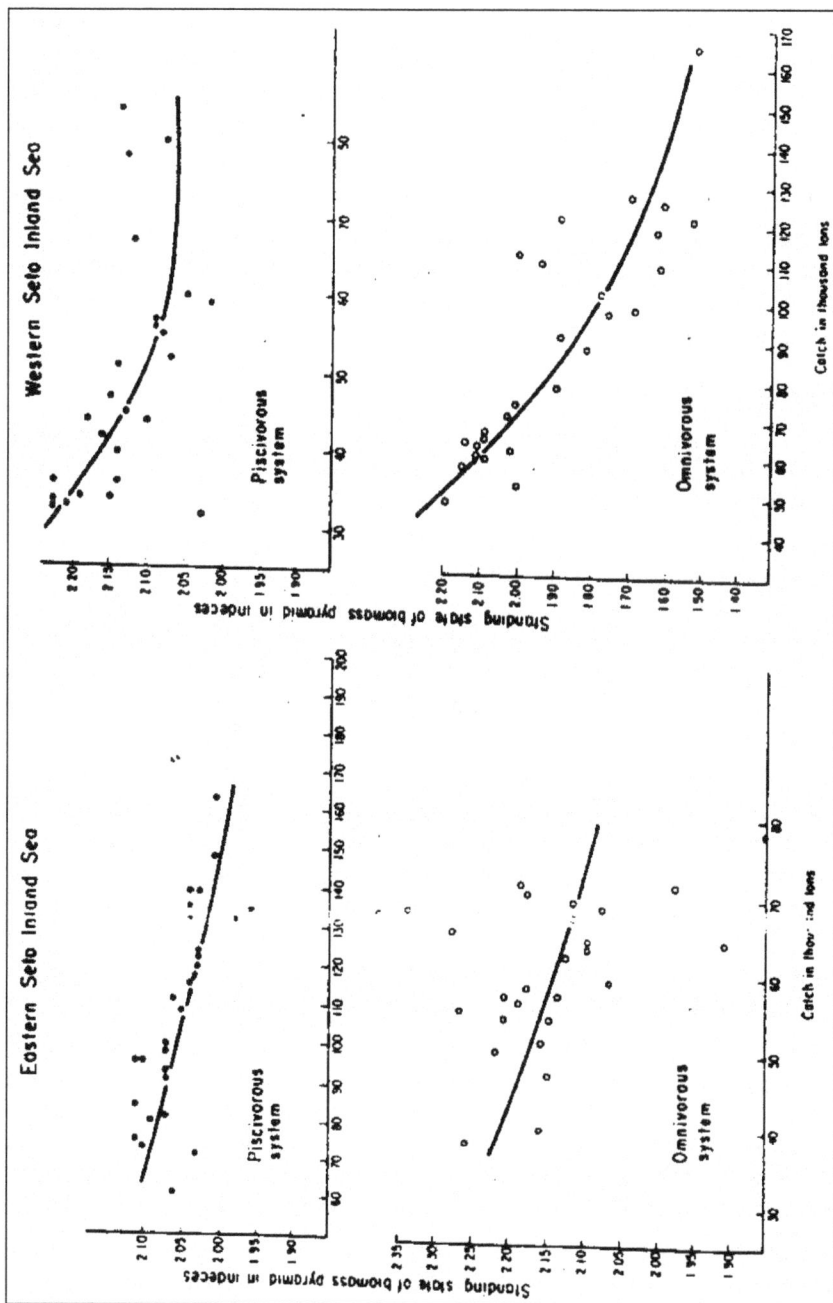

Figure 47: Relationship between the Annual Total Catch and the Index of the "Standing State" of the Biomass Pyramid of the Catch by Sub-ecosystem and Sub-region of the Seto Inland Sea (Tatara, 1981a, modified by the authors). The index shows the "centre of gravity" of the biomass pyramid of the catch, which shows also a relative position of trophic level.

the regime established by the authorities or fishing communities are strictly prohibited. In other words, the management measures in a specific sea area have to be based on comprehensive knowledge of both the resources to be utilized and the fishing communities that will exploit in the area. The latter includes the structure of fisheries and types of gear, profitability of each fishery and type of gear, tradition and customs in the area.

The acquisition of information like examples of both failure (overfishing, pollution and contamination) and success (recovery of depleted stocks and rehabilitation of the environment) is important for comprehensive management scheme employed in a limited sea area.

The allowance of flexible fishing has also worked out well for coastal pelagic fisheries when a drastic change in the abundance of a specific fish stock has taken place for natural reasons.

## Limitation of Total Fishing Intensity

This is quite unique, and a controversial issue when discussed on a worldwide basis. As already noted, the catch-quota system has rarely been applied in Japan but the control of total fishing intensity has been applied to all fisheries.

The Japanese system has been derived from both (1) the complicated structure and biological features of the target multi-species resources and (2) the complex and varied structure of the fisheries, and socio-economic conditions of the fishing communities. The system is therefore, highly theoretical in terms of its biological and socio-legal concepts, but it tends indirectly to control fishing mortality by making use of analytical methods to calculate population dynamics which have been commonly applied to fisheries in the other advanced fishing countries.

The strong and frequent argument employed against the Japanese system is the "untimeliness" of measures or the "time lag" before they take effect. That is, control of total fishing intensity sometimes tends to be too late to cope with a rapid decline in stock abundance, especially that caused by overfishing. This is true, first because the formalities necessary for a reduction of fishing intensity (a reduction in the number of vessels or the number of days they can fish) take some time to be completed and agreed upon, and second because a reduction in the expected catch of the target species is a somewhat vague idea since fishing would be continued in some way.

However, it is also true that catch limitation is generally impractical and is sometimes inapplicable to the coastal fisheries around Japan. There is no doubt about the effectiveness of a catch quota or catch-limitation system as a direct measure if applied when monitoring and surveillance can be properly carried out. Even in Japan, such measures have been taken when these conditions were satisfied, although these have mostly been on a local basis and limited to a few species.

Apart from the question of practicability, measures to control total fishing intensity involve a few critical disadvantages from a biological point of view. First, expectations of a reduction of a specific catch may not always be fulfilled, owing to fishermen's preferences; second, the process involved in the reduction of a catch is generally a vague one, lacking a clear visual evidence; third, recovery of depleted

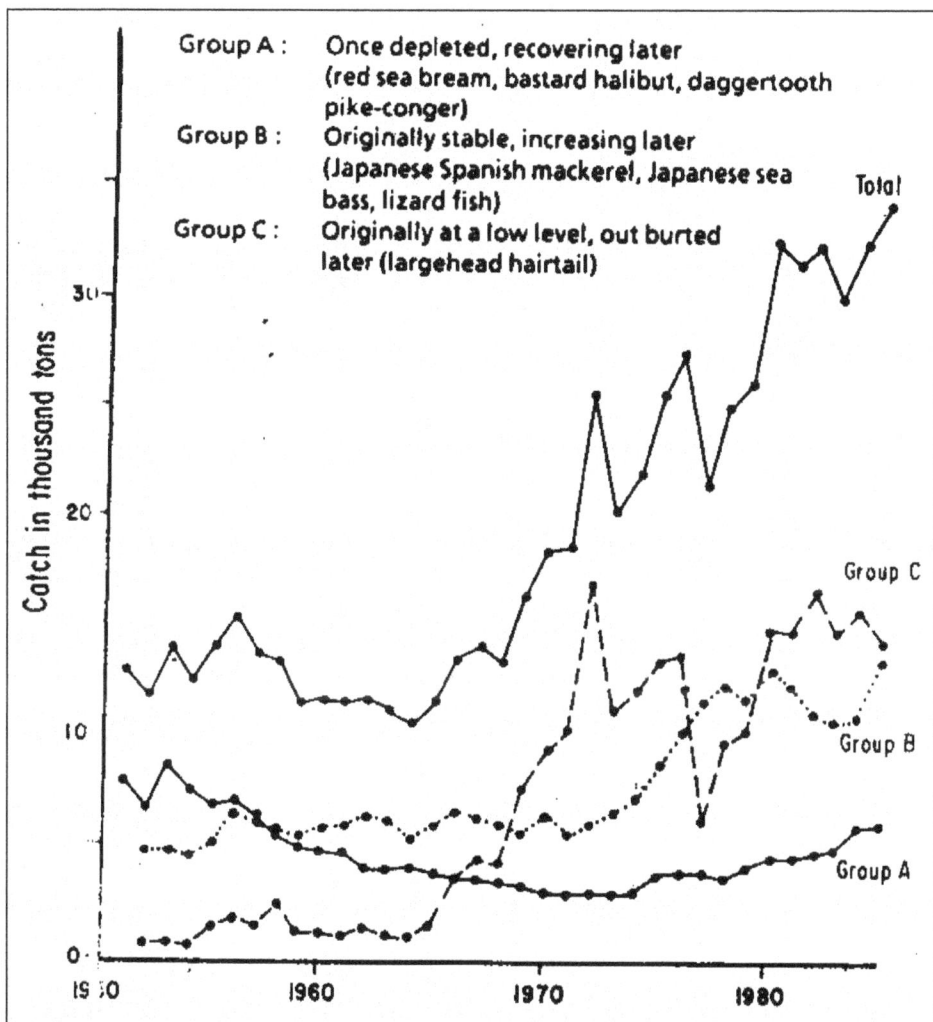

**Figure 48: Long-term Changes in Annual Catch of Major Carnivorous Fish Species of High Commercial Value by Fish Group Caught in the Seto Inland Sea, 1951-85.**

resources requires a long time enough to allow the process to continue over a few generations. The time required will depend on the life cycle and reproductive potential of the stocks in question.

However, the system has worked out quite well for a few depleted stocks of commercial value in a highly complicated multi-species fish community harvested by various multi-gear fisheries. The recovery of three stocks of commercial value in the Seto Inland Sea provide a firm evidence for the above. This recovery has taken a long time (10-20 years). However, the fisheries have survived by changing to other types of fishing, employing the successional fishing that is another distinctive feature of Japanese multi-species fisheries.

The time required for stocks to recover can be shortened if stronger regulations are employed and strictly enforced, but such action is not always practical in Japan from a socio-economic point of view. This is because multi-species resources in coastal waters around Japan, which support a huge fishing population along the coast, are continuously harvested by various fisheries allowed to perform successional fishing. Fisheries administrations must have up-to-date information all the time on the status of stocks in question, and they must examine carefully all the likely effect of measures, particularly severe ones, that may be adopted; but the decisions on the kind and magnitude of regulations to be employed are only technical. They are the responsibility of the political sector, and are decided according to the priotity areas regarding local and national policies.

## Participation of Fishermen in Management and Co-ordination

The fishermen's (including their families) active participation in fishery management and co-ordination has been achieved depending completely upon the socio-economic conditions of the fishing communities and the general philosophy conceived by the entire nation. The tradition and customs upheld by the fishermen have been fully taken into account in political arrangements and they are all understandable and generally acceptable to most of Japanese society.

It can be said that tradition and customs providing harmony, fairness and equity always preceded the legal arrangements or political action taken by governments during the initial stages of fisheries development. Then modernization and democratization were incorporated into the system in accordance with the development of the fisheries (in terms of technologies, economic returns and living standards), acquisition of knowledge on resources and overall improvement in industry and national economy. That is, various political arrangements were made to maintain the position of the fisheries sector among other national industries (subsidies and incentives, both direct and indirect, which include various programs on the rehabilitation of fishing and nursery grounds, deployment of artificial reefs, the fisheries forecasting services, fish farming and artificial seeding, etc).

Second, enough information on the details of (a) the resources and environment (biological, ecological, oceanographic and topographic) and (b) fisheries (technological, functional, traditional, and socio-economic) in question is indispensable for both the establishment and the enforcement of the self-regulatory measures. In other words, the governments (national and local) have to provide adequate advice on a continuing basis on both the biological and practical aspects of the management to be employed. In Japan, a service able to provide this has given top priority in the resources research and assessment being carried out by both national and local institutes.

## Applicability of Management in General Resources and Environment

Generally speaking, the complexity and instability of multi-species fish resources may be universal to the world's oceans, although the magnitude of the diversity and variability differs greatly from one region to another. The fishermen and fisheries, in any part of the world, who intend to harvest a multi-species resource, therefore have to adapt to the manifold local conditions. Intensive research and studies on the resources and the environment must first of all be carried out to meet requirements for the management of multi-species resources.

## Fisheries

In contrast to the biological and environmental features, there may be few universal elements involved in the fisheries, especially those in coastal waters. This is chiefly because of the highly tradition oriented nature of local fisheries. This nature tends to be strongest in countries where fishing has historically contributed to both the local and national economy and welfare (a so-called "fishing nation"). This important fact must be taken into account when a management scheme is established or adjusted in such a country. The factors that must be taken account of in setting up such a scheme naturally differ greatly from one nation to another.

In a country where fishing has been performed without such tradition or social involvement (a so-called non-fishing nation), the fisheries are more simply structured being governed mostly by the economic principles (industrial profitability) or by political concepts (*e.g.* the need to provide a supply of animal protein or employment opportunities). The management issues and strategy are therefore quite simple, and are probably limited to considering how to maximize profits and/or ensure a sustainable yield. However, the management measures to be employed are not simple even in these cases, from a technical point of view, if the fisheries are composed of various types of gear with different selective functions.

In any case, enough information on fisheries is indispensable to decide the kind and magnitude of management measures required. The coverage and quality of the information is specifically crucial for management purpose in the first case.

## Fishermen and Organization

In a "fishing nation" the socio-economic condition of fishermen (including their families), and the fishing community, and the relationship between that community and local society are critically important to establish an adequate strategy and tactics. Organizations or associations of fishermen (and fisherwomen, wives), if soundly established, are extremely useful for all kinds of activities important to the community but not falling under the heading of management of resources and fisheries (e.g extension, education, training, making arrangements for security, mutual and social welfare etc). However, the organizing of such bodies needs to be based on a thorough knowledge of the socio-economical conditions of the fishing communities.

Making provision for harmony, fairness and equity among fishermen and fisheries is the most important consideration. Studies on conflicts and their history could make a most useful examinations to help in sorting out practical approaches.

The kind of organizations to be established will vary according to the conditions (*e.g.* socio-economic, structural, legal etc) in the country and the fishing communities in question. These should be considered case by case.

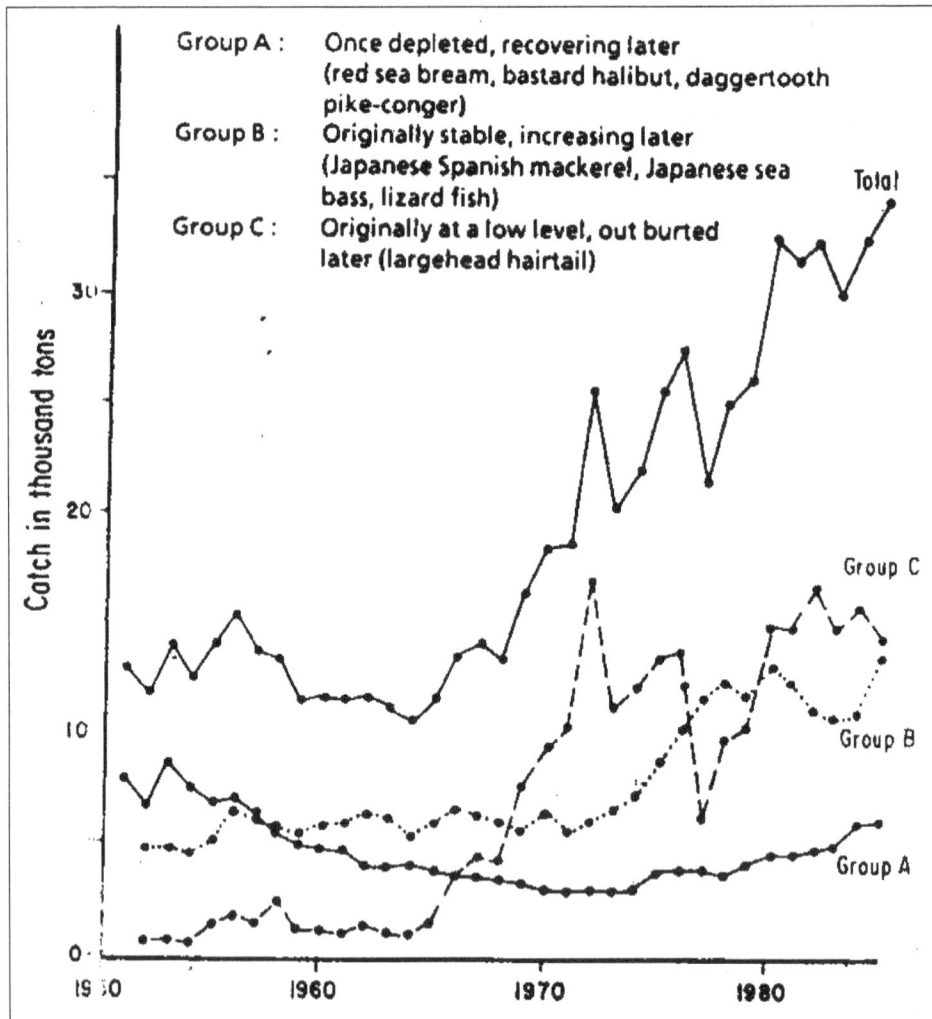

Figure 49: Long-term Changes in Annual Catch of Major Carnivorous Fish Species of High Commercial Value by Fish Group Caught in the Seto Inland Sea, 1951-85.

## Strategy

The establishment of an adequate strategy is the responsibility of the fisheries administrations at both national and local levels. The issues discussed earlier must be taken fully into account in establishing a strategy. The tactics discussed below are also indispensable elements in establishing the strategy. In short, a global and thorough examination needs to be made.

For instance, overfishing of specific fish stocks may not always be crucial to the fishing community, society or country. On some occasions, a political decision needs to be made on whether to aim for (i) a larger catch of less commercial value, (ii) a smaller catch of high commercial value, or (iii) a combination of these. Furthermore, such a choice needs to be flexible in accordance with the changes in resources and fisheries. This is not easy, especially when the guiding principles of harmony, fairness and equity must be borne in mind.

## Tactics, Infrastructure and Incentives

### Measures

Management and conservation measures applicable to resources and fisheries vary greatly from one case to another. The applicability of all the conceivable measures should be examined in connection with the issues concerning the resources and fisheries. Thus a comprehensive list of all appropriate and applicable measures could be made. For instance, if the situation allows, a system based wholly or partially on catch-quotas could be introduced. If not, alternatives like the Japanese system or a combination of these two could be introduced.

There may be no simple or easy-to-apply measure in managing multi-species resources and multi-gear fisheries, with the probable exception of a drastic regulation like "total ban" of a particular fishing gear. The situation is more complicated when the strategy is chosen to combine the large low-value catch and the small high-value catch. In such a case, a comprehensive scheme with various complicated and detailed measures is required, as it is in Japan.

In short, a combination of all measures that can be applied to the local conditions in each of the communities in question should be employed. Besides the technical aspects of the measures, their acceptability to fishermen and the costs and benefits to governments need to be taken into account.

## Infrastructure, Incentives and Encouragements

Apart from the general arrangements that have to be made by governments, the self-regulatory system run by fishermen themselves and the resources research and communication with fishermen are also essential.

## Organization of Fishermen

It is believed that the Japanese-type fisheries cooperative system is one of the best ways to organize the self-regulatory system. Such a system, if it can be applied, must contribute toward management and conservation in other countries too. However, the Japanese system is closely related to the Japanese socio-economic conditions and is partly a result of Japanese policy including various incentives arranged by both central and local governments. Careful studies of the socio-economic conditions and legal framework in the country are strongly recommended in this regard too.

## Resources Research and Communication with Fishermen

The communication between the research institutes and fishermen is another element to be highlighted in the effective enforcement of resources and fisheries management. In Japan, the national institutes (8) are rather academic, but the local institutes (150) are highly fisheries oriented, communicating regularly with the local fishermen. Daily communication with fisheries cooperatives and their members is routine. Under such circumstances, the information from the stations is regarded by fishermen as their own. This has been very important to success of the self-regulatory system. If such information and encouragement had not been provided by public institutes, none of the cooperatives could themselves established biologically sound self-regulation or achieved proper enforcement of it.

In conclusion, when planning the establishment or adjustment of multi-species fisheries management, careful examination of all relevant factors has to be undertaken by the government, specifically (1) the environmental conditions and resources available, (2) the structure of the fisheries, (3) the socio-economic conditions of the fisheries and fishing communities, (4) the governmental infrastructure, (5) the costs and benefits of the enforcement of management.

## Precautionary Management Approach

One of the most difficult issues in the management of fisheries is to evaluate the effects of fishing on the context of a changing environment. Statistics from the FAO of the United Nations and recent studies indicate that many commercially important fish populations have been declining in the past several decades. However, the extent to which such declines are due to fishing, to environmental change or to some combination of these effects remains a matter of debate.

Understanding how fishing and environmental variability interact to produce an effect on exploited populations (commercially targeted species) is an unsolved problem of fishery science. For example, it is not known, how fishing and environmental variability can either magnify or diminish management risk by affecting the variability (resilience) of exploited populations. Lack of understanding of the sources of temporal variability in fish abundance affects biological reference points, decision making and risk assessment in precautionary fisheries management and determination of extinction risk for populations, it is largely responsible for the uncertainty and indecision that have led to past failures in managing fisheries. In many historical cases, fisheries management has failed to recognize the possible fishing effects until population collapse.

It was shown that fishing effects may appear even in the absence of significant declining trends in populations. It was found that fishing increases population variability (fluctuations of populations through time) and that this is an indication that fishing is having a negative impact on populations that is not yet reflected in declining abundance. Fishing effects was evaluated by comparing temporal variability in the larval abundance of exploited species to that of unexploited species living in the same ecosystem. Larval abundance is an established proxy for adult biomass. Although no environmental variables were directly examined, environmental effects were implicit in the measurements of the temporal variability of fish population.

Fishing is a selective process. Thus the exploited and unexploited groups may not be random with respect to other potential explanatory variables that could relate to the coefficient of variation. In addition to fishing, there could be systemic differences with respect to other factors, such as, life history traits that could influence the coefficient of variation. Therefore, to isolate the effect of fishing as an explanatory variable multiple regression analysis is used to factor out variables that could produce biases associated with fishing. These variables include life-history effects, abundance, ecological traits and phylogeny. It was considered that life-history traits are known to influence population responses to fishing and the environment. In theory, the coefficient of variation of annual larval abundance is negatively related to maximum length, length of maturation, age of maturation, spawning duration and trophic levels and positively related to fecundity. Abundance is included in the regression model, because higher variability could be statistically associated with higher abundance. Finally, ecological traits (geographic regions, habitat and spawning mode) and phylogenetic constraints were examined.

The separations of the effect of environmental variability from the impact of fishing has been elusive, but is essential for sound fisheries management. The environmental effects can be distinguished from fishing efforts by comparing the temporal variability of exploited versus unexploited fish stocks living in the same environment. Using the unique suite of 50 year long larval surveys from the California Cooperative Oceanic Fisheries Investigations, fishing was analyzed as a treatment effect in a long term ecological experiment. Here the present evidence from the marine environment that exploited species exhibited higher temporal variability in abundance than unexploited species. This remains true after accounting for life-history effects, abundance, ecological traits and phylogeny. The increased variability of exploited populations is caused by fishery induced truncation of the age structure, which reduces the capacity of populations to buffer environmental events. Therefore, to avoid collapse, fisheries must be managed not only to sustain the total viable biomass, but also to prevent the significant truncation of age structure. The double jeopardy of fishing to potentially depleted stock sizes and more immediately, the amplify the peaks and valleys of population variability calls for a precautionary management approach.

## Reorganization of Fisheries Policy

A heavy weight, the Pew Oceans Commission, funded by the Pew Charitable Trusts containing 18 prominent environmentalists, scientists and officials from government and the fisheries industry wants fisheries policy to be based explicitly on ecosystem management. They are calling for a drastic overhaul of US fisheries policy and the creation of an independent government agency to manage the oceans surrounding the United States.

To prevent further harm from over-fishing, ocean pollution and invasive species, the commission recommends the creation of an independent national ocean agency, the adoption of a national ocean policy act, doubling of ocean research spending over five years and the establishment of a network of national marine reserves or protected areas.

Marine experts say that the Pew Commission's recommendations would help to streamline the convoluted array of agencies and budgetary committees that currently manage US oceans.

The problem with the ocean is that it is nobody's backyard, it is a national resource .The Pew Commission calls for most of the ocean responsibilities of the

National Oceanic and Atmospheric Administration (NOAA) as well as ocean related functions of other government agencies to be transferred to a new ocean agency, outside the Department of Commerce of which NOAA is a part.

But such reorganization is notoriously hard to execute in Washington. The Pew Commission's recommendation of ecosystem based fisheries management may also prove contentious, remarked the Deputy Director of NOAA. It has not been resolved what ecosystem based management really means. Some people think it is just setting up of marine protected areas.

Indeed many marine biologists support such reserves. If no such network of marine protected areas is implemented, there is no way that stocks are not going to continue crashing.

## Tracking Tuna

A research program to investigate populations of Atlantic bluefin tuna has been shelved by that international commission charged with conserving the fish. The first phase of the project failed to win approval at the meeting of the International Commission for the conservation of Atlantic Tunas (ICCAT) with the ground that the annual budget of the commission can not accommodate the (E 250000) initial cost of research program. But scientists and the environmental group, who back the program claim it was scuppered because some ICCAT parties do not want to hear the likely results of the research.

European government officials are charged as they are worried that if stronger links are established between the bulefin populations on the two sides of the Atlantic Ocean, there would be greater pressure on them to cut European tuna fishing. The ICCAT's failure to persue the research will hasten the collapse of the bluefin population.

ICCAT currently allows an annual quota for eastern Atlantic of 32000 tonnes of bluefin, but even its officials acknowledge that the actual catch is probably more than 40000 tonnes. Fishermen in the Mediterranean say that they would probably benefit from more research and tighter quotas on their catches.

The research proposal was developed in 2003 by an international panel appointed by ICCAT. It would aim to develop a better understanding of the bluefin's life cycle, and to determine if there really are two separate stocks-one in the east spawning in Mediterranean and the other in the west Atlantic spawning in the Gulf of Mexico.

The fish is currently managed as two separate stocks, and fishing in the west Atlantic is far more tightly restricted, with an annual quota of just 2700 tonnes. But studies of electronically tagged bluefin indicate that some fish cross the ocean, and many marine biologists think that the population in American waters is being depleted by European fishing.

## Claims for Increased Catch Quotas

European fishermen are claiming that the new catch quotas agreed by the European union (EU) will destroy some fishing communities. Yet scientists advising the EU say the measures may not be enough to avoid complete collapse of some fish stocks.

The annual catch quotas is replaced by science-based management plans, which also mean the end of state subsidies for building and modernizing fishing vessels by 2004. Catch quotas for North Sea cod will be reduced by 45 per cent from February, 2003.

But although the cut in cod allowances will mean job losses in the fishing industry, it falls short of the moratorium recommended by the International Council for the exploration of the sea, which gives scientific advice to fisheries authorities.

## Fishing Ban in North Atlantic

Unprecedented restrictions on commercial fishing in European Union (EU) waters have been proposed by leading fisheries scientists. The International Council for the Exploration of the Sea (ICES), which provides scientific advice to fisheries management authorities says that all cod and haddock fisheries in the North Sea, the Sqagerrak, the Irish Sea and off the Western Coast of Scotland should be closed for an undetermined period to allow stocks to recover.

According to the ICES assessment carried out using data from fisheries laboratories in the Council's 19 member states, the spawning stock biomass (SSB) of cod and haddock in the northeast Atlantic are at new historic lows. The number of young fish surviving to adulthood is also the lowest on record.

Closure of parts of the most heavily fished oceans has long been recommended by conservation biologists as one way to rebuild stocks. EU member states often relax the stringent catch quotas recommended by ICES in order to appease their fishing industries, but the scale of the problem means that politicians must now accept large short term losses.

Fisheries scientists also warn that the relatively stable cod and haddock catches in the northeast Atlantic in recent years are not reliable indicators of the abundance of fish in EU waters. They pointed to the Canadian Grand Bank fisheries off Newfoundland, which were closed in 1992 after the cod population collapsed, Canadian authorities failed to realize that intensified effort by fishing vessels was masking decline in stocks. Only independent data gathered by research vessels can give an unbiased picture of the state of stocks.

It is an incapable conclusion that the cod stocks around the United Kingdom are seriously depleted. Given that all management practices tried before have failed, closures are about all it can be done in this rather extreme situation.

## Management Practices of Indian Marine Ecosystems

The extent, diversity and regional variation in the environmental, economic and social features associated with the India's marine regions are vast. Accordingly management responses to the issue need to be designed carefully to ensure that they are addressed at the right geographical scale and within the right time frame, recognizing the importance of ecosystems and the effect that direct and indirect human activities may have on these ecosystems.

Our knowledge and understanding that govern the behavior of the majority of Indian marine ecosystems are poor. This is especially true for ecosystems in the open ocean and coastal regions. To have confidence that use of resources is sustainable and that ecosystems maintain their health, productivity and functionality, it is necessary to develop national environmental indicators that distinguish "natural" variability and trends in ecosystems form change caused by human activity. Knowledge of India's marine environment is currently insufficient to meet these challenges, and must be supplemented.

India's marine zones encompass most climatic types, different depth ranges, and include many different types of ecosystems. Human uses and subsequent direct and indirect impact on these ecosystems range in scale from minimal to significant. However, these is limited understanding of how human activities affect marine ecosystems and how managing human activities in Marine Protected Areas (an important provision of "Agenda 21") may be used as an instrument to manage for sustainability.

Improved understanding of why marine ecosystems behave as they do, how human activity affects ecosystems and organism behavior, and the utility of marine protected areas as management instruments, is needed to underpin informed and robust management of the many uses we make of our maritime zones.

Proper mapping and monitoring is necessary to develop national resources for facilitating coastal planning decisions, reducing uncertain for industry, and increasing certainly for conservation objectives. It is also important to improve our understanding of land-sea interactions and the role these play in ecosystem dynamics. In this regard, there is a strong need to develop an integrated approach to land, freshwater and marine research, monitoring and management. A truly comprehensive monitoring and information system should integrate economic and social data to maximize its usefulness as a management tool.

In the Antarctic marine environment, the Schirmacher Oasis at the Princess Asterid Coast, is an area that India manages within an agreed international framework. The primary agreements are the Antarctic Treaty and associated international conventions, such as the Convention on the conservation of Antarctic Marine Living Resource (CCAMLR) and the Madrid Protocol Environment.

## Marine Fisheries Management in India

Marine fisheries management in India followed the global trends, despite the fact that there were no instances of a collapsed fishery here unlike the temperate waters where operational fisheries collapsed several times due to various factors. Similar concerns and situations simulated for Indian marine fisheries created a school of thought redeeming marine capture fisheries research *per se* to a conservationist mode relying more on sustainability neglecting many a time the possible production process.

## Limitations of Marine Fisheries Management in India

Generally fishery managers opt to say that Indian fishery is managed as an open access fishery. On the contrast, Indian marin fishery is regulated but with different management options suiting to the area of fishery with some limitations. The following reasons are attributed to limitations in marine fisheries management research and operations in the coastal waters of India.

### 1. Stock Assessment Models Devised for Marine Fisheries Management Fail at Operational Level

In an open access natural resource, a fishery is rarely optimally allocated leading to economic inefficiency and over fishing. Dynamic bio-economic models provide a suitable platform for solving these issues. But theoretical models often fail to become operational. With multi-species and multi-gear operations being carried out, there is no mechanism to implement the management of results obtained using stock assessment models. Further the models devised for temperate waters fail to establish the ground realities in tropical countries. These models utilize the growth parameters estimated by length-frequency method. Total mortality is estimated by length converted catch curve method and natural mortality by the empirical relationship derived by Pauly (1980). Natural growth rates often are better than the predicted rates where life of fish is short spanned as in most tropical fishes. Incorporation of laboratory tested growth rates based on individual species into assessment models can produce better results.

### 2. Ecosystem Based Management of Marine Fisheries with more Complexities and Input Data Requirement

Intricacies of ecosystems always remained a passion for researchers to unveil the probable outcomes of biotic and abiotic factors affecting its progression. Anthropogenic and related activities disturbed a smooth flow of ecological progression and resulted in repercussions from nature. Despite the ingenious curiosity, ecological and ecosystem models started producing new trend in the decision making mechanism of management of natural resources. Simulated pictures showing the possible outcome of prevailing activities and enormous amount of data generated during the modeling process evoked a sense of eco-friendly approach in the management of natural resources. Marine ecology, being a conglomeration of still more elements in its own emerged as a focused area of research in the last two decades. Mathematical tools aided with software assistance paved the way for a breakthrough in the assessment and evaluation of marine ecology. But most of these numerical models have high dependence on input data, as enormous and complicated as the ecosystem being studied. The output of these models are highly subjective and not implementable on an operational scale. The end results often restricts on a qualitative inference confirming the existing results. With the advent of satellite oceanography and information communication technologies ecosystem based management of marine fisheries remains a possibility but not an operational concept for the entire Indian fishery resources.

### 3. Fisheries Management as a State Subject Lacking Coherence in Uniform Regulations

Developmental departments in all States and Union territories of India manage the fisheries for the territorial waters under their jurisdiction which often tend to become an ineffective and inefficient mechanism of implementation due to their own jurisdictional limitations. One of the major management measures adopted in India is the seasonal ban on mechanized fisheries for 45 days or more both on east coast and west coast with different timings. However, the fishing by non-mechanized fisheries is allowed. The regulations followed vary from State to State and not implemented coherently. Thus this has limited impact on conservation.

## 4. Limitation on a Scientific Estimation of Harvestable Catch from Seas

Assessment of marine resource potential off Indian EEZ has been a vital task to be carried out before crucial planning interventions of the government. Apart from fin and shell fishes, the marine domain is peppered with many biota which have direct and indirect role in deciding the potential of the EEZ. As the resource domain and its actual extent of spread in an unknown entity, predictions based on indices obtained on shore have played a major role in reassessing the marine resource potential. Based on theoretical considerations, marine fisheries potential were estimated at the aegis of union government based on the National Fisheries Data Center data of CMFRI. Although this data base is based on multistage stratified random sampling method (which is an internationally accepted estimation procedure for marine capture fisheries of India) this necessitates the need for a pragmatic estimation procedure for establishing the harvestable marine fisheries potential of Indian EEZ.

## 5. Lack of Integration of Data Base on Individual Species into a Multi-species Management Scenario

Indian marine fisheries being a multi-species and multi-gear effort, it will be ideal to have a decision support tool which can integrate the database on individual species into a holistic one for operationalising the fisheries management. But most of the models working on Indian marine fisheries sector tend to limit it to information till species level. The data support for most of these models are from a post-mortem analysis of fish landed from the coastal waters. They fail to examine the real *in situ* production process supporting the fishery.

## 6. Mesh Size of Gear-Recommendations vs Implementation

Various recommendations for the mesh size to be followed for different fish species are in vogue. According to these the fine meshes of gears like trawls and bag nets cause large-scale destruction of juveniles of many fishes.

Recently in the month of September the regions of Samiyarpettai (11 degree 50 minute N and 79 degree 74 minute E), Parangipettai (11 degree 3 minute N and 79 degree 48 minute E) and Cuddalore port (11 degree43 minute N and 79 degree 49 minute E) showed a shocking trend of heavy catch of juvenile oil sardines at 10 to 20 meters from the open sea using purse seines. The average length and weight of the fish was 102 mm and 29.6 gram respectively.

The oil sardine is a highly migratory, schooling pelagic fish, living in photic zone at depths of 20-200 m, along the continental shelf. Feeding on phytoplankton and small crustaceans, it breeds once a year off the west coast of India, when temperatures and salinity are low during the southwest monsoon months. Spawning

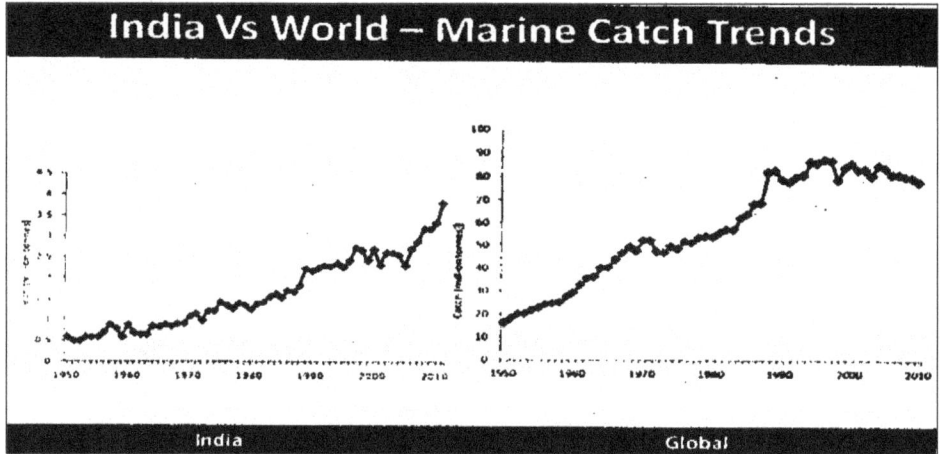

Figure 50: Fish Production Trends during the Last Seven Decades in India (CMFRI) as well as Global Marine Capture Fisheries (FAO).

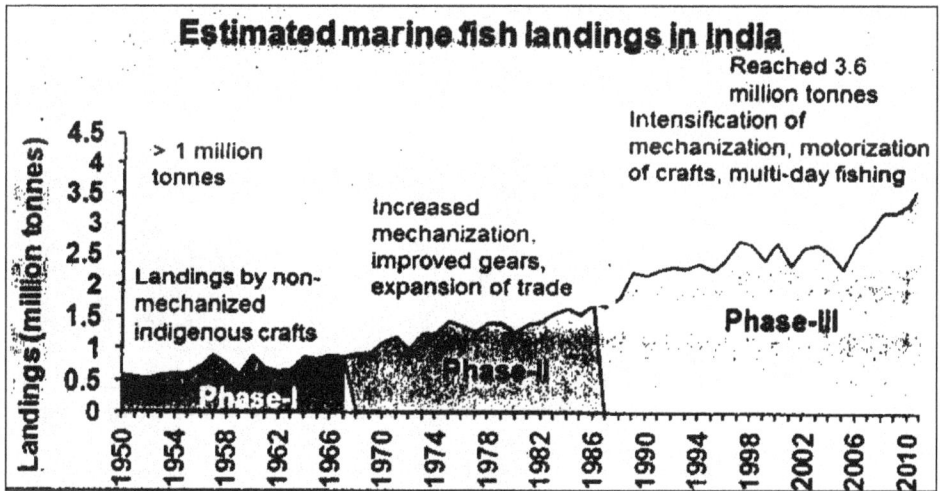

Figure 51: Fish Production Trends during the Last Seven Decades in India (CMFRI) with the Three different Phases of Sectorial Expansion.

happens to be is at its peak from August to September. The population size is highly erratic and fluctuates annually.

This recent trend could be an indicator of a far bigger collapse in the sustainable stock across the east coast capture fishery resource. As the number of mechanized boats have been increasing the total annual landing has been also increasing but with no proper regulation and this prevents maintenance and sustainability. According to some estimates, illegal fishing by trawlers in the artisanal zone along Tamil Nadu coast results in losses ranging 460 to 1220 tonnes seasonally, with peak levels in Nagapattinam and Rameshwaram. The number of economically important

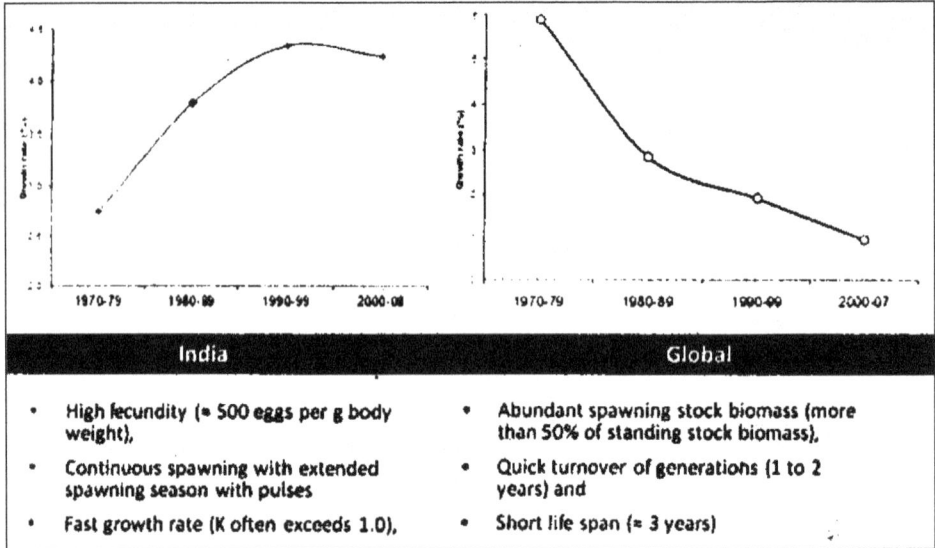

| India | Global |
|-------|--------|
| • High fecundity (≈ 500 eggs per g body weight), | • Abundant spawning stock biomass (more than 50% of standing stock biomass), |
| • Continuous spawning with extended spawning season with pulses | • Quick turnover of generations (1 to 2 years) and |
| • Fast growth rate (K often exceeds 1.0), | • Short life span (≈ 3 years) |

**Figure 52: Decadal Averages Depicting the Trends in Marine Fish Production during the Last Seven Decades in India (CMFRI Data) and World (FAO Data).**

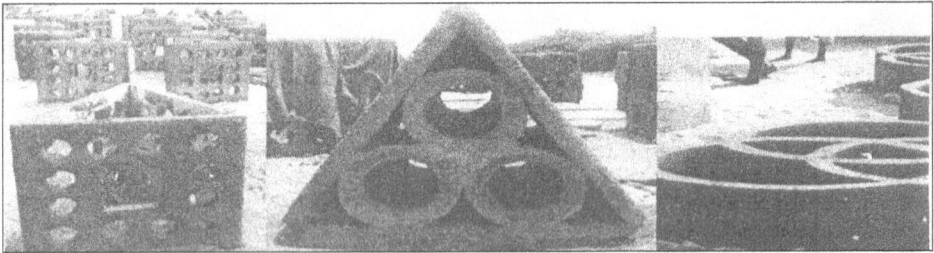

**Figure 53: Three Types of Modules 70 each from a Cluster, Occupying 1000 m³ Area, with about 500 m³ Volume and Offering about 3000 m² Surface Area for Attachment.**

fish species are decreasing day by day due to selective fishing, as indicated by the present increase in oil sardine catches.

Most of the economically important fishes like shark, tuna and mackerel are predators. These are over-exploited due to selective fishing resulting in increase in forage fish like oil sardines, which are economically less important. Hence annual landings are dominated by oil sardines, resulting in a steady increase in the quantity of landing but not in quality or variety of economically important fish that would support the fishing and export industry.

Selective fishing of economically important fish along with by-catch (containing ecologically important organisms) that is discarded into open sea led to destruction of sea bed habitats and spawning ground due to the anoxic environment created by dead by-catch decaying on the ocean floor. The last decade has seen a rise of 912.75 thousand tonnes increase in fish landings of Tamil Nadu from 2295.49 thousand metric tonnes to 3207.21 metric tonnes between the years 2005-2009. But fishermen report that the catches of economically important fish like mackerel, tuna, elasmobranches, pomfret and flying fish decreased in number and catch per unit effort (CPUE) values came down due to over-exploitation.

There were recommendations on Minimum Legal Size (MLS) for different categories. But these recommendations fail to become operational due to the multi-species, multi-gear fishery existing in the coastal waters of India. For a biological management system to be effective, monitoring and surveillance are necessary, which turn out to be very expensive.

## 7. Fleet Strength

The Indian marine fisheries are characterized by about 2000 varieties and caught mostly by mechanized trawlers, purse seiners, gillnetters and long-liners apart from several mechanized and non-mechanized small boats. However, in western temperate countries the marine fishery is mainly constituted by a few large varieties of fish, managed under quota system unlike Indian fisheries. In spite of several management measures western fisheries often face crisis and crash periodically. In India the marine fishery are characterized by 0 to 3 year class fishery with more generation turn over are caught by multi-species gears making it very difficult to post-manage in spite of processing huge scientific data over the years.

When compared to the world fisheries scenario the Indian marine fisheries are still showing upward trend in total catches and catch rates. The common fisheries management method of imposing an upper limit on the Total Allowable Catch (TAC) by restricting the number of vessels also has short comings. Fishing capacity of crafts can be enhanced using new designs that satisfy the restrictive rules, and by including new fishing devices and efficient gears. Hence, license restriction or TAC also fails to impress upon as an effective management measures.

## 8. Ban on Fishing and Protected Areas

Indian marine fisheries are managed similar to wildlife with closed areas. Thirty one marine protected areas and thirty three marine national parks and sanctuaries (Singh, 2003) and closed seasons (trawl/fishing ban) being practiced widely for regulating the fishing pressures. But with respect to the gear and craft, there are few recommendations for regulating their usage in coastal waters. Fishing reserves will not work for migratory species. Location of fishing reserves are often dubious and the spawning aggregations, nursery and spawning grounds of all major species should be studied befor enacting regulations on marine protected areas. All the fish in the sea lay eggs which will be drifted close to the coast where the depth of water is less than 20 m. Coastal areas are the best nursery ground for the larvae that come out of the eggs as these areas are highly productive and rich with planktonic food essential for their survival and sustained growth. After attaining the juvenile stage, fishes migrate to their habitats. Hence any fisheries management must address the protection of the nursery areas during spawning time and habitats during maturation phase for sustaining the fisheries.

There are limitations on the existing marine fisheries management measures and these limitations invoke the need for novel methods to reduce fishing pressure but enhance the production using sustainable measures of management.

## 9. Management for Sustainable Production in Marine Fisheries of India

For augmenting the production from marine fisheries sector, interventions are required in the following areas of research on a contingent basis.

### Artificial Reefs

Sustaining and rebuilding the marine ecosystems- tidal mudflats, wet-lands, mangroves, marshes, estuaries, beaches, lagoons and coral reefs; have also become a prime responsibility in marine fisheries management. Along with the fishing pressure, there is a concern on habitat degradation also. Artificial reefs will automatically reduce unwanted fishing as trawlers cannot operate in areas of artificial reefs as trawl operations in such areas will result in severe gear damage.

Under Indian circumstances the best measure is to deploy the artificial reefs along inshore areas around 10 to 20 meters depth contours. Artificial reefs are triangular concrete structures/modules deployed to the bottom of the sea bed. They provide shelter to brooder fish and juveniles. They also offer surface areas for attachment of eggs after spawning. The major seed resources like seer fish, mackerel, tuna etc are available only at shallow depth of less than 10 meters. Thus, the nursery grounds of these fishes can be protected by installation of artificial reefs and thereby enhancing the recruitment for the entire Indian EEZ. Deployed artificial reef areas become unfit for trawling and purse seine operations rendering the area as a natural "Marine Protected Area (MPA), thus protecting the biodiversity, habitat and brood-stocks. Healthy broodstock of fishes will be a spawning stock biomass for supplying young fish to the fishing areas in a sustainable manner (recruitment). It is emphasized that the major aim of marine fisheries management is mainly to sustain the fisheries with limited scope to increase production by at least 1 per cent cumulatively in the next 35 years (by 2050).

CMFRI in association with the Government of Tamil Nadu has deployed the artificial reefs in coastal waters near 50 villages resulting in the enhancement of traditional fisheries by 2 to 5 times over the last ten years. Consequently, there is an increased demand from the traditional fishermen to install more of artificial reefs in Tamil Nadu. This example can be taken as a national model for creating more of awareness among the fishermen in other states and for conducting awareness training programs. Each module cluster may cost about 30 lakh rupees and is sufficient for about one km. If the entire coastline is provided with the same impetus over a period of at least next 10 years costing 10000 crores of rupees, the marine fish catch is likely to reach at least 6 million tonnes by 2050.

## 10. Indian Fisheries Forecasting System

Heavy investment in harvest and harvest sectors in Indian fisheries during 1980s rendered good exploitation of many marine resources. Landing to the tune of 3.06 million tonnes, a record reckoning achievement could be ensured by the end of this phase, but with an alarm on the sustainability of the fishery. Researchers are wavering from values ranging from a few lakhs to 11 million tonnes for the estimated marine fish resource potential of India (Raghuprasad, 1970), and hence there is a need for a comprehensive revalidation of the earlier exercises. Present production values recording new heights close to 3.94 million tonnes indicate that the Indian marine fishery has still more potential as indicated by Raghuprasad (1970).

In the changed regime where climate driven forces are prevalent influencing the resource stability along with the on-going intensified fishing efforts, a multi-disciplinary approach for re-assessment of resources has come into vogue. There are alarming gaps for a policy planner to look upon. Prime focus on future fisheries resource research will be oriented towards building up of a spatio-temporal database in GIS platform as a decision support tool. Numerical and time-series models have taken a priority over real time observations, such as, surrogate databases from RS-GIS sources and have revolutionized the research. But the evident gaps in observation and assessment of fishery resources have to be nullified through regular survey, sampling and analysis. Automation of landing data estimation, Geo-referencing of fish catches, local spawning and fishing ground delineation, resolving physical process supporting the fishery resources for better understanding of the resource vulnerability to climatic change, resource economic evaluation and international trade policies impacting the resources are few focused research areas to be given due attention in the next few years to augment the fisheries resources and sustain their present level of exploitation.

Towards establishing a scientifically deduced relationship between the marine environment and the resource availability on a realistic basis, there is a need for a focused application of established easy surveillance of oceanic, geophysical and physico-chemical parameters and their direct or latent influence upon the plankton which happens to be the self-replenishing source of food and nutrition for the fishery resources spread in our EEZ. The spatio-temporal fluctuations of the plankton richness which can be remotely sensed have long been established as a major factor in predicting fisheries resource richness. Taking cue from these established models, patterns can be designed to predict the resource availability from easy-to-observe parameters after a thorough validation of the prediction scenarios put together with the estimated catch from various fishing grounds. The change in the pattern of fishing, period of absence and the composition of fish caught per haul, when analysed for a range of geo-spatial expanses would helf refining and augmenting a comprehensive prediction algorithm. Further such models would come in handy in the assessment of marine resource potentials and their periodic revalidation on a homogenous platform with a proper measure of confidence interval. Such exercises are of immense importance to the government and policy makers. The history of co-integrating plankton availability and resource landings were initiated at CMFRI since the early 1960s. Collaborative efforts between marine fisheries research and space applications resulted towards the identification of potential fishing zones (PFZ) in the 1980s and 1990s.

With the climate change impacts making Indian fisheries sector vulnerable to forces other than over-exploitation, the ChloRIFFS (Chlorophyll based remote-sensing assisted Indian Fisheries Forecasting System) program calls upon a systematic revalidation and interdisciplinary efforts in marine fisheries research to point out the lacunae and set-right the staggering contradictions between predicted and harvested resources.

## 11. GIS Based Marine Fisheries Management

Most of the fisheries management options are temporal in nature without giving much thrust on the spatial component. Ever since fishing has emerged as an industry, operating far and wide from the operating center, the spatial information on the fishing ground became an essential component to come out with precise regional implementable policies in fisheries management. Even though the importance of spatial analysis of fishery data for better management of the fishery was known for long, the spatial data collection was not affordable during the past days and equipments like GPS were rare in use. Now GPS is available with all commercial fishing fleets and getting spatial data is as easy as getting the fish samples for analysis and more over GIS technology has developed in all sorts of terrestrial applications, and in marine applications also the technology is in ready use form. Geographical Information Systems (GIS) combined with other analytical tools and models permit improved spatial management which can provide various dimensions to the data analysis.

One of the major reasons for stagnation of marine fisheries production has been attributed to the high degree of juvenile exploitation, especially in trawl fisheries. Mostly the juvenile catches are incidental, which is mainly happening due to the lack of information on the seasonal spatial distribution of juveniles and adult fishes. It was found that reduction of juvenile exploitation had been enhancing the fish production in subsequent years. In recent years 20 to 30 percent of the trawl landings in India is constituted by juveniles of commercial species and it is estimated that a reduction of 10 per cent of juvenile landing from the present level can increase the fish production in subsequent years at least 2.05 per cent. For understanding the distribution of juvenile and adult population in the fishing ground, GIS will be a reliable tool, which will help researchers to suggest operational restrictions to reduce juvenile fishery and can thus contribute to the increase in marine fisheries production. GIS can be an efficient tool for decision making in the declaration of marine protected areas (MPA) and essential fish habitats (EFH) on the basis of qualitative and quantitative assemblage of juveniles or spawners in particular geographical area and GIS also will be a reliable tool for finalizing the sites for artificial reef installation for biodiversity conservation. From fishery biology point of view, time bound studies in selected fishing grounds can reveal the biological characteristics of resident taxa like, *in situ* growth, *in situ* mortality, measure the effect of fishing pressure, spawning area, spawning period, larval, juvenile and spawning and feeding migrations.

In the era of green fishery and in terms of reduction of carbon dioxide emission in marine fisheries sector, time series GIS based information collected on the fishery distribution is of paramount importance. In the present marine fishing scenario, 10 to 25 percent of fuel is being spent on searching of target species. This is leading to considerable amount of carbon dioxide emission in fishing sector and also increasing the expenditure per kg of fish production. Analysis of GIS-based time series data will enable to predict the fishing ground for various fishes and seasons of their abundance with high degree of precision. Such attempts will be of great help for the fishermen in reducing the searching time for the resources seasonally, thus improving their economy and also helping in protecting the environment by reducing carbon dioxide emission considerably. Application of GIS can provide illustrative proof, which in turn will enable the policy makers to convince stakeholders regarding the scientific basis of policy interventions. The data base when created on GIS platform with illustrations in the form of maps will work as a tool for the policy makers to find mutually agreeable solution to tackle problems in conserving and managing the fishery with the active participation of all stakeholders.

## 12. Cage Culture in Reducing Fishing Pressure visa-vis Increasing Fish Production

The cage culture technology is purely indigenous and highly economical and sustainable. It is very easy for adoption. Capital investment for a 6 meter diameter circular cage in the sea is about 3 lakh rupees initially, including the cost of cage frame, nets, mooring seed and feed. By adopting culture of high valued fish species, the production of 3-5 tonnes/cage can be attained with an economic return of 6 to 10 lakhs per harvest, spread over a period of 6-8 months depending on the species. The life of cage frame is above 5 years. Since the Ministry of Agriculture/National Fisheries Development Board have recognized this as government scheme eligible for 40 per cent subsidy, the technology is gaining lot of popularity. The inputs are abundantly available along the coast and fishermen are skilled in garnering them. Feasibility of several species emerging as candidate species for cage culture due to the ongoing breeding programs, the possible collection from the sea may be deemed to be sustainable in the long run. Similarly there are about five large feed mills in Andhra Pradesh with high production potential for manufacturing suitable feed for marine fish.

Recent research findings from CMFRI's grow-out experimental feed for Pompano based on feed formulation by the company, produced commendable results. Hence feed is also not a limiting factor. Similarly there are millions of hectares of flow-oriented saline areas which are not utilized and can be brought under mariculture with suitable incentives from the government/NFDB.

Sustainable fisheries management options, if implemented without fallacies indicate possible enhancement of a harvestable potential in Indian EEZ to a possible extent of 6 million tonnes or more, than reducing it.

# Chapter 10
# Marine Protected Areas

San Andres archipelago and an assortment of other islands and reefs became the center piece of Colombia's Power Biosphere Reserve. The reserve covers 300000 square km, occupying 10 per cent of the Caribbean Sea. In 2005, a core region of 1000 square km was designated a Marine Procted Area (MPA), with associated restrictions on fishing, tourism and the like.

Marine ecologists widely agree that a global system of such MPAs is the last hope for many reef systems and their associated fisheries, but the step between designating MPAs and making them truly effective, both ecologically and bureaucratically, has been notoriously challenging.

Two key factors in the MPAs apparent success are a historical lack of strong marine regulations in the area and a significant amount of local autonomy. Following the adoption of its new constitution in 1991, in 1993, Colombia's legislature transferred most of the control of and responsibility for environmental resources to 33 so-called regional autonomous corporations. The corporation for the Sustainable Development of the Archipelago of San Andres Old Province and Santa Catalina, known as CORALINA is responsible for environmental planning, management and research with a hand everything from training scuba divers in best practices for protecting the region's reefs to teaching school children the value of the region's resources.

Like many remote areas of Colombia, the archipelago suffers from endemic unemployment, so CORALINA is working to develop vocational programs. Some, but not all these are tailored to fishermen affected by conservation efforts. One focus is to promote the islands reefs and under water cliffs as attraction for scuba divers and other eco-tourists. Because development is restricted, the islands have no five star resorts and nor will they, the visitors CORALINA has in mind are interested in a purer remote island experience, especially on providence.

## Local Involvement

Unlike most environmental agencies, CORALINA can single handedly develop and implement management plans that cover both the land and surrounding seas, and the law gives it the muscle it needs to enforce its regulations. Between 1995 and 1997, the agency issued multiple warnings to two hotels on San Andres for failing to comply the new sewage treatment regulations CORALINA had imposed. When its warnings were ignored, CORALINA shut down the hotels.

The most essential elements of the CORALINA model is the mandated involvement of local people This provides the sort of accountabilities that avoids regulations and restraints being easily dismissed as the impositions of outsiders. The agency is overseen not by Government, but by a board of 14 directors, elected from local businesses as well as representatives of national and local Governments. At least 3 out of 14 board members have to be from islands native people. Each board member's vote has the same weight.

As well as playing a specific role in governing CORALINA, locals have been heavily involved in the process of tailoring regulations to specific places. Whereas some environmental measures, such as ban on fishing with nets, apply to the whole of the biosphere reserve, others, such as, measures needed to protect an important conch habitat, need to be more specific. These more restricted areas are parts of the MPA set up in 2005, which includes extensive no-fishing zones and even a no-access zones, accessible only for research and monitoring. They have managed to designate a fairly significant portion of that large archipelago a no-take status which is very important.

To delineate the reserves' various restricted zones, CORALINA sponsored hundreds of workshops, with various stake holders mapping out what they knew about the best and most critical resources, and saying which areas they wanted to see protected. Later work included scientific surveys. Using geographical information system to manage the various inputs, CORALINA proposed a variety of potential zoning schemes, which were further in consultation with locals. Hundreds of stake holders were consulted on to the scheme before official enactment by CAROLINA and many locals embraced the results. According to a survey commissioned by CAROLINA, 96 per cent fishermen say they believe that the MPA will benefit them.

But the support is not universal. The people still have some resistance, but not the majority. The fishermen are not concerned so much about the closed areas, but rather with enforcement. CORALINA recognizes that the ultimate long term success of the reserve and the MPA will require a number of changes, especially stepping up of enforcement and monitoring work, set up buoy lines around protected zones and establish dedicated MPA offices instead of handling management out of CORALINA's limited existing facilities.

## Clustering Large Marine Ecosystems (LMEs)

The Johannesburg Plan of Implementation of the World Summit on Sustainable Development, noting the Reykjavik Declaration on Responsible Fisheries in the Marine Ecosystem, set the goal of encouraging the application by 2010 of the ecosystem approach to responsible fisheries. This is an internationally agreed starting point for a new approach to fisheries management and fishery related studies utilizing a multinational, interdisciplinary approach, which integrates information concerning productivity, ecology, fisheries, socio-economic aspects and governance. Since mid-1980s, it has been developed the definition of Large Marine Ecosystems (LMEs) that represented a proposal to give an ecology-based partion of global oceans. The LMEs project called for a more ecologically sensible monitoring of fishery resources, to go beyond the purely biological and socio-economic view of marine resources and improve the awareness of shared resources among countries.

Initially, 49 LMEs were identified and the 50th was proposed. LMEs were defined on the basis of, consideration og distinct bathymetry, hydrographic productivity and tophically dependent populations. This definition is rather broad. For some of the 50 LMEs, not only the ecological aspects but also geopolitical aspects have been considered. In other LMEs, distinct habitats and ecosystems have been put together. For these reasons, and following the publication of numerous papers, books and research results, the list has been expanded and some LMEs subdivided in order to increase their ecological significance, and to expand the coverage of all main shelf areas. The latest list, available at the LME web site managed by NOAA includes 64 LMEs.

The definition of the LME has been further refined as, " Large Marine Ecosystems are regions of ocean space encompassing coastal areas from river basins and estuaries to the seaward boundaries of continental shelves and the outer margins of the major current systems" For these reasons, only capture statistics of species spending most of their life cycles in the shelf areas have been considered in the analysis, thus excluding all species items classified as oceanic for the other study.

As the short period of data availability did not allow a thorough analysis of trends by LMEs, this study mainly focuses on the fishery characteristics of LMEs with reference to the major species groups caught in each LME and tries to identify similar patterns among the various LMEs. The ten years series (1990-1999) of capture data available for each LME have been grouped on the basis of the " International Standard Statistical Classification for Aquatic Animals and Plants" (ISSCAAP) which has been recently revised and a LME cluster analysis of the similarity of the average total catches of each group for the studied period. This has produced 11 clusters of LMEs which have similar characteristics in their capture profiles.

## Rearrangement of FAO Capture Statistics by LME and Grouping of Species Items

A data sub-set from the FAO capture database was created including the 1990-99 catches for all non-oceanic species items. Only capture production of fishes, crustaceans and mollusks were considered, excluding catches of marine mammals, miscellaneous aquatic animals and products, and aquatic plants. Catches of freshwater and diadromous fishes reported as caught in marine waters (in the Baltic Sea) have also been included. A dataset comprising 867 species items was obtained. The total catches of these species items represent about 90 per cent of the global marine catches as the oceanic species constitute the remaining 10 per cent . This figure is close to a previous estimate of LMEs producing approximately 95 per cent of the world total marine capture production (Sherman, 1994).

**List of the 50 Large Marine Ecosystems (as from Sherman and Duda, 1999)**

| LME No. | LME Name | LME No. | LME Name |
|---------|----------|---------|----------|
| LME 1 | Eastern Bering Sea | LME 2 | Gulf of Alaska |
| LME 3 | California Current | LME 4 | Gulf of California |
| LME 5 | Gulf of Mexico | LME 6 | Southeast US continental Shelf |
| LME 7 | Northeast US continental Shelf | LME 8 | Scotian Shelf |
| LME 9 | Newfoundland Shelf | LME 10 | West Greenland Shelf |
| LME 11 | Insular Pacific-Hawaiian | LME 12 | Caribbean Sea |
| LME 13 | Humboldt Current | LME 14 | Patagonian Shelf |
| LME 15 | Brazil Current | LME 16 | Northeast Brazil Shelf |
| LME 17 | East Greenland Shelf | LME 18 | Iceland Shelf |
| LME 19 | Barents Sea | LME 20 | Norwegian Shelf |
| LME 21 | North Sea | LME 22 | Baltic Sea |
| LME 23 | Celtic-Biscay Shelf | LME 24 | Iberian Coastal |
| LME 25 | Mediterranean Sea | LME 26 | Black Sea |
| LME 27 | Canary Current | LME 28 | Guinea Current |
| LME 29 | Benguela Current | LME 30 | Agulhas Current |
| LME 31 | Somali Coastal Current | LME 32 | Arabian Sea |
| LME 33 | Red Sea | LME 34 | Bay of Bengal |
| LME 35 | South China Sea | LME 36 | Sulu-Celebes Sea |
| LME 37 | Indonesian Seas | LME 38 | Northern Australian Shelf |
| LME 39 | Great Barrier Reef | LME 40 | New Zealand Shelf |
| LME 41 | East China Sea | LME 42 | Yellow Sea |
| LME 43 | Kuroshio Current | LME 44 | Sea of Japan |
| LME 45 | Oyashio Current | LME 46 | Sea of Okhotsk |
| LME 47 | West Bering Sea | LME 48 | Faroe Plateau |
| LME 49 | Antartic | LME 50 | Pacific Central American Coastal |

Although in one of the LME definitions (Sherman *et al.*, 1993) it is mention that " the seaward limit of the LMEs extends beyond the physical outer limit of the shelves to include all or a portion of the continental slopes as well", the principal characteristics described in studies on single LMEs. Sherman and Tang and Kumf *et al.*, 1999 refer mostly to the marine areas over the continental shelves. For these reasons, only capture statistics of species spending most of their life cycles in the shelf areas have been considered in the analysis, excluding all species items classified as oceanic.

As the short period of data availability did not allow a thorough analysis of trends by LMEs, the study mainly focuses on the fishery characteristics of LMEs with

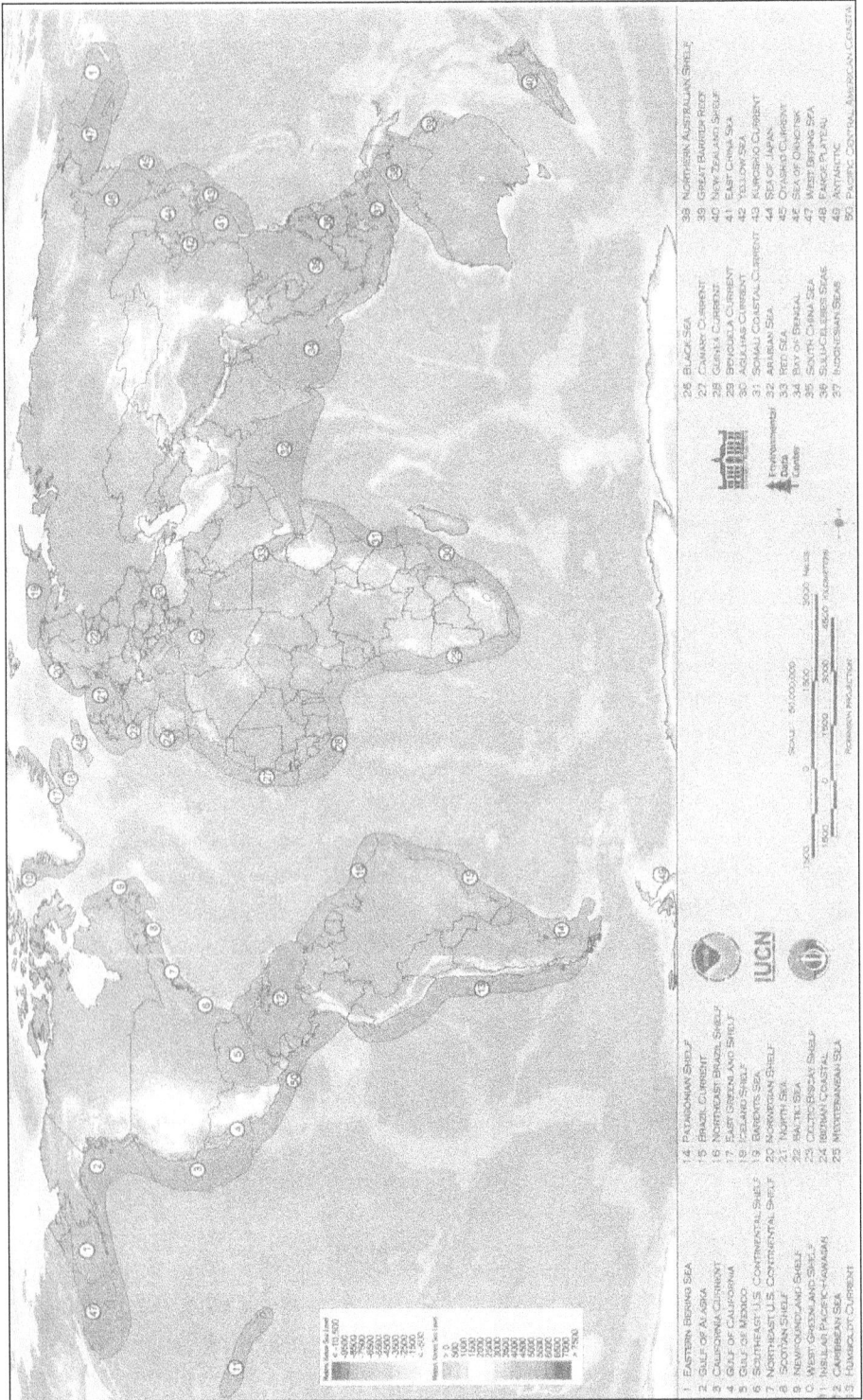

**Figure 54: Map of the 50 LMEs (Modified from Anonymous, 1998).**

reference to the major species groups caught in each LME and tries to identify similar patterns among the various LMEs. The ten years series of capture data available for each LME have been grouped on the basis of the " International Standard Statistical Classification for Aquatic Animals and Plants " (ISSCAAP) which has been recently revised and a LME cluster analysis of the similarity of the average total catches of each group for the studied period. This has produced 11 clusters of LMEs which have similar characteristics in their capture profiles.

## Methods

### Re-arrangement of FAO Capture Statistics by LME and Grouping of Species Items

A data sub-set from the FAO capture database was created including the 1990-99 catches for all non-oceanic species items. Only capture production of fishes, crustaceans and mollusks were considered, excluding catches of marine mammals, miscellaneous aquatic animals and products, and aquatic plants. Catches of freshwater and diadromous fishes reported as caught in marine waters (*e.g.* in the Baltic Sea) have also been included. A dataset comprising of 867 species items was obtained. The total catches of these species items represent about 90 per cent of the global marine catches as the oceanic species constitute the remaining 10 per cent . This figure is close to a previous estimate of LMEs producing approximately 95 per cent of the world total marine capture production (Sherman, 1994).

The data obtained from different sources and harmonized to the FAO data were used to build 1990-1999 time series for 43 Large Marine Ecosystems. For the seven LMEs (*i.e.*, 41, 42, 43, 44, 45, 46, and 47) of the Northwest Pacific area, this was not possible either by using the data from the FAO database or by obtaining additional detailed data either at the regional or national level, and therefore they have not been considered.

### Cluster Analysis

Catches by species groupings were summed up along the ten years period and their percentages in each LME calculated. A cluster analysis, aiming at identifying clusters of LMEs that present similarities in terms of catch composition by species groupings was performed using the analytical method "partitioning around medoids" or *pam* as in the statistical software S-Plus, 2000. The cluster analysis was based on eleven of the groups as the ISSCAAP group 39 (Marine fishes not identified) was excluded from the calculations of the percentage used in the cluster analysis. Catches reported in this group may indeed include very different species in different LMEs.

### Cluster Characteristics

Each cluster is briefly described evidencing the common characteristics among the LMEs that have led to their classification into the same cluster. Large Marine Ecosystems assigned to the cluster are listed together with the relevant ocean, hemisphere and a general categorization of the climate.

## Cluster – 1

Eastern Bering Sea (LME 1) belonging to Pacific Ocean of Northern hemisphere is characterized with sub-arctic climate. The first cluster is comprised with only one LME. The capture trends of the cluster (1990-1999) is characterized by;

1. Freshwater and diadromous fishes
2. Flounders, halibuts, soles
3. Cods, hakes, haddocks
4. Miscellaneous coastal fishes
5. Miscellaneous demersal fishes LME – 1 Marine fishes not identified – 0.1 per cent
6. Herrings, sardines, anchovies
7. Tunas, bonitos, bill fishes
8. Miscellaneous pelagic fishes
9. Sharks, rays, chimaeras
10. Crustaceans
11. Molluscs

Catches of Gadiformes (ISSCAAP group 32) are predominant in this LME; other groups of some importance are flatfishes, salmons and crustaceans.

This is an LME characterized by an extreme environment at high latitude, in which temperature, currents and seasonal oscillations influence the productivity. According to SeaWiFS global primary productivity estimates, this LME has been classified as a moderately high productive ecosystem.

The ten year trend shows decreasing catches of all major species groups in recent years with the only exceptions being diadromous fishes and crustaceans.

## Cluster – 2

The second cluster, Gulf of Alaska, situated in the Pacific Ocean of Northern hemisphere with sub-arctic climate, adjacent to the LME in cluster 1, is also "monotypic" The Gulf of Alaska is highly productive ecosystem (SeaWiFS data). It also presents a significant upwelling phemenon linked to the presence of the counter-clockwise gyre of the Alaska Current (NOAA, 2002).

The capture trends of the LME during 1990-1999 includes;

1. Freshwater and diadromous fishes
2. Flounders, halibuts, soles
3. Cods, hakes, haddocks
4. Miscellaneous coastal fishes
   LME – 2 Marine fishes not identified -13 per cent
5. Miscellaneous demersal fishes
6. Herrings, sardines, anchovies

**Capture Trends (1990-1999) of each LME by Cluster.**

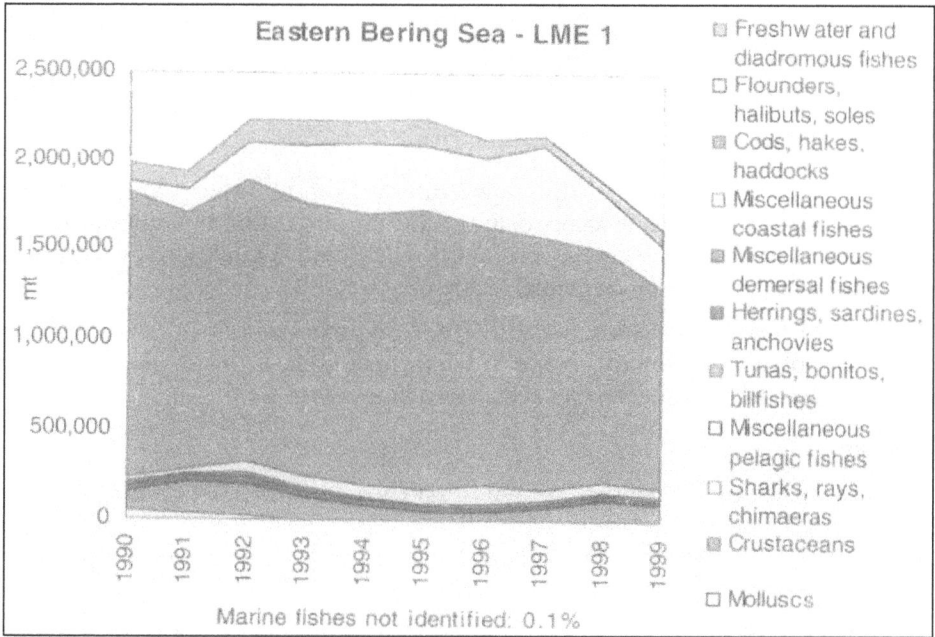

Figure 55: Cluster 1: Capture Trends of LME 1.

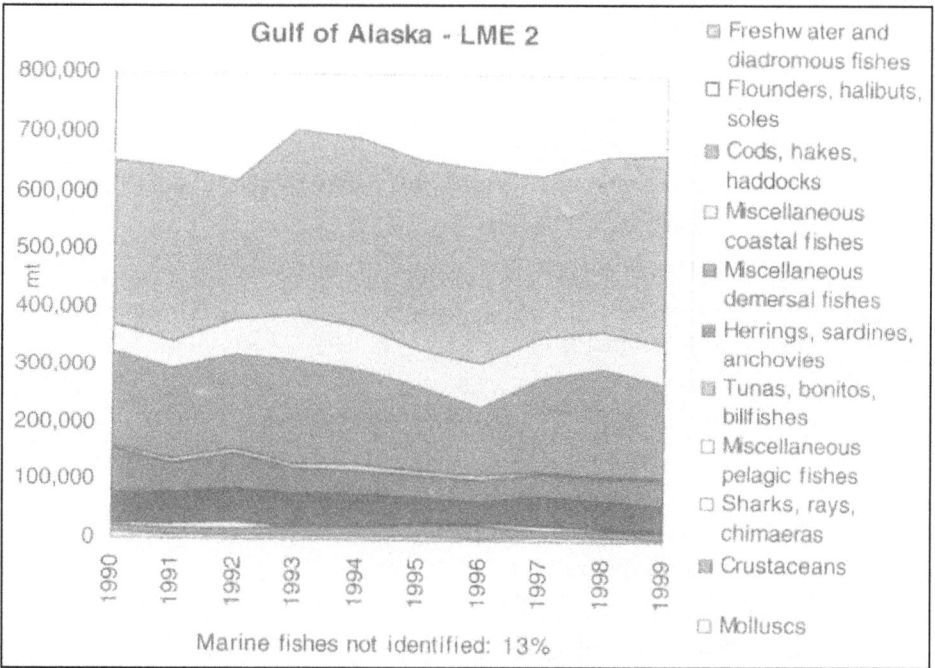

Figure 56: Cluster 2: Capture Trends of LME 2.

7. Tunas, bonitos, billfishes
8. Miscellaneous pelagic fishes
9. Sharks, rays, chimaeras
10. Crustaceans
11. Molluscs

The catch composition of this LME differs from all other LMEs in being characterized by a strong prevalence of the freshwater and diadromous group, linked to the rich salmon fisheries. Gadiformes are also predominant followed by flatfishes, herrings and miscellaneous demersal fishes.

Recent researches (Brodeur *et al.*, 1999) have hypothesized changes in the future production of salmons as a consequence of long term shifts in the plankton biomass in the last decades. However, recent catch trends are rater stable.

## Cluster – 3

This cluster group consists of California Current (LME 3), of Pacific Ocean; Northeast U.S. continental Shelf (LME 7); Scotian Shelf (LME 8) and Newfoundland Shelf (LME 9), all of Atlantic Ocean of Northern hemisphere having temperate climate in first three (LMEs 3, 7, and 8) and sub-arctic climate in LME 9.

The capture trend of these four LMEs for ten years (1990-1999) are;

### LME – 3

1. Freshwater and diadromous fishes
2. Flounders, halibuts, soles
3. Cods, hakes, haddocks
4. Miscellaneous coastal fishes
5. Miscellaneous demersal fishes: Marine fishes not identified – 8 per cent
6. Harrings, sardines, anchovies
7. Trouts, bonitos, billfishes
8. Miscellaneous pelagic fishes
9. Sharks, rays, chimaeras
10. Crustaceans
11. Molluscs

### LME – 7

1. Freshwater and diadromous fishes
2. Flounders, halibuts, soles
3. Cods, hakes, haddocks
4. Miscellaneous coastal fishes: Marine fishes not identified – 0.4 per cent
5. Miscellaneous demersal fishes

**Figure 57: Cluster 3: Capture Trends of LMEs 3–7–8–9.**

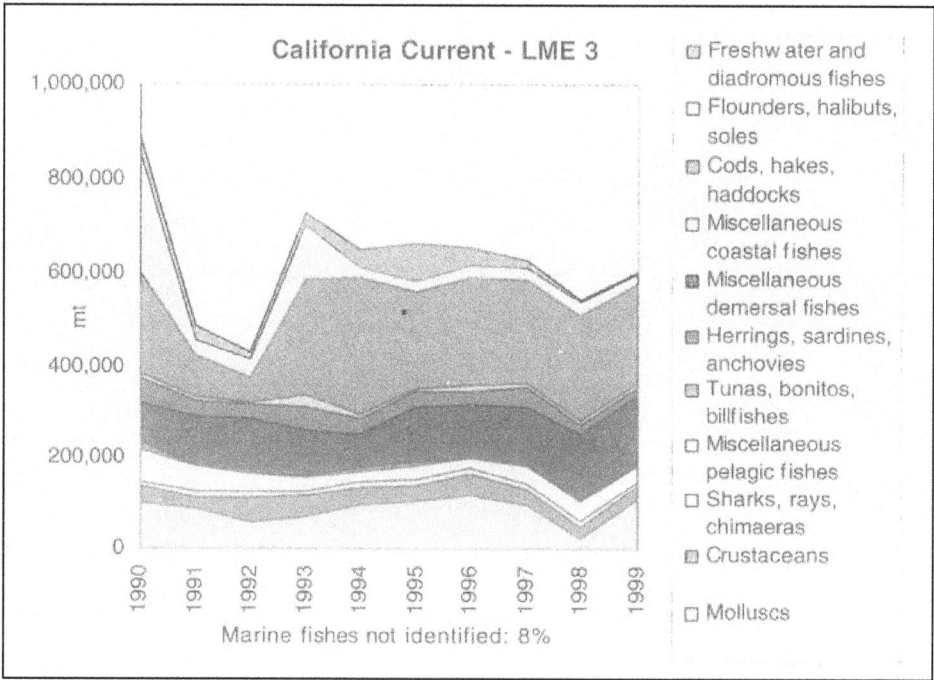

California Current - LME 3

Legend:
- Freshwater and diadromous fishes
- Flounders, halibuts, soles
- Cods, hakes, haddocks
- Miscellaneous coastal fishes
- Miscellaneous demersal fishes
- Herrings, sardines, anchovies
- Tunas, bonitos, billfishes
- Miscellaneous pelagic fishes
- Sharks, rays, chimaeras
- Crustaceans
- Molluscs

Marine fishes not identified: 8%

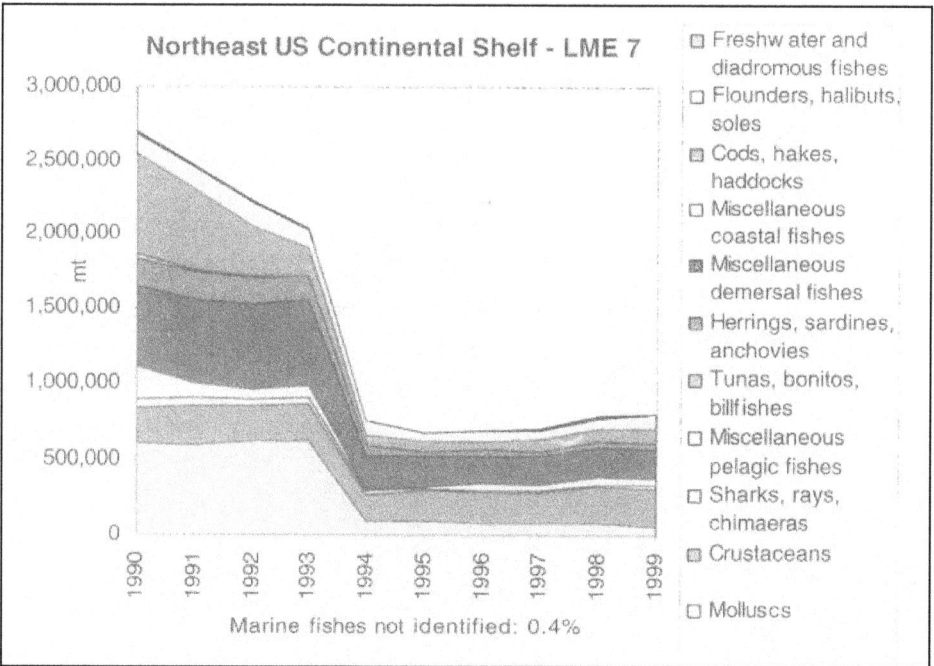

Northeast US Continental Shelf - LME 7

Legend:
- Freshwater and diadromous fishes
- Flounders, halibuts, soles
- Cods, hakes, haddocks
- Miscellaneous coastal fishes
- Miscellaneous demersal fishes
- Herrings, sardines, anchovies
- Tunas, bonitos, billfishes
- Miscellaneous pelagic fishes
- Sharks, rays, chimaeras
- Crustaceans
- Molluscs

Marine fishes not identified: 0.4%

*Contd...*

**Figure 57–** *Contd...*

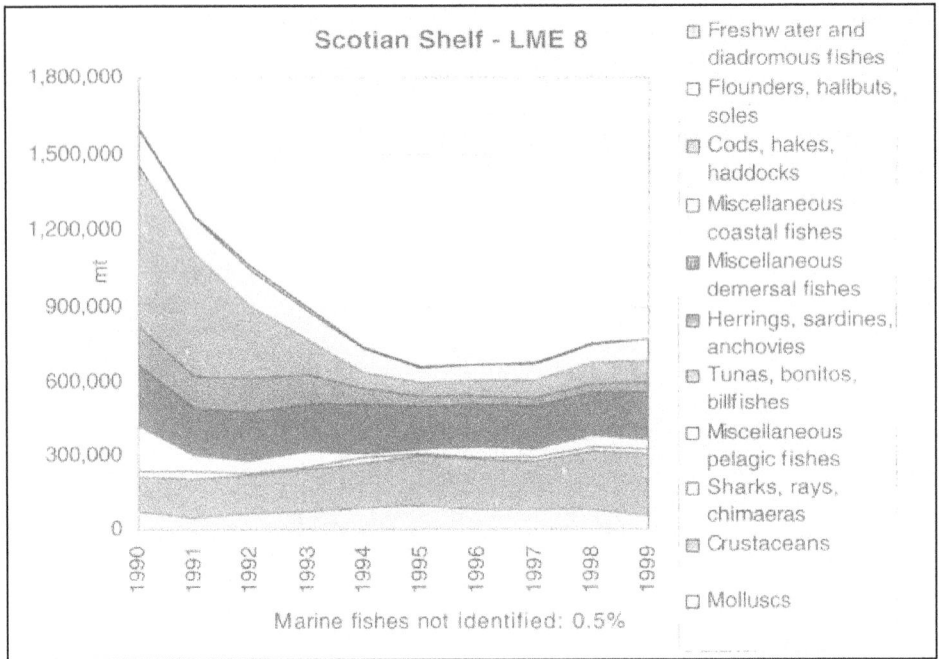

Scotian Shelf - LME 8

Legend:
- Freshwater and diadromous fishes
- Flounders, halibuts, soles
- Cods, hakes, haddocks
- Miscellaneous coastal fishes
- Miscellaneous demersal fishes
- Herrings, sardines, anchovies
- Tunas, bonitos, billfishes
- Miscellaneous pelagic fishes
- Sharks, rays, chimaeras
- Crustaceans
- Molluscs

Marine fishes not identified: 0.5%

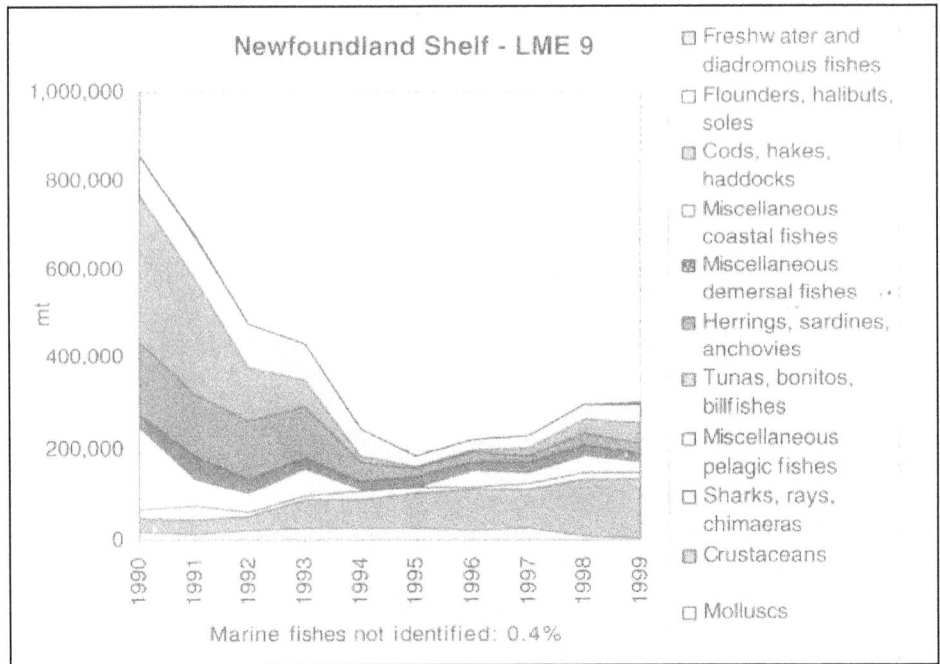

Newfoundland Shelf - LME 9

Legend:
- Freshwater and diadromous fishes
- Flounders, halibuts, soles
- Cods, hakes, haddocks
- Miscellaneous coastal fishes
- Miscellaneous demersal fishes
- Herrings, sardines, anchovies
- Tunas, bonitos, billfishes
- Miscellaneous pelagic fishes
- Sharks, rays, chimaeras
- Crustaceans
- Molluscs

Marine fishes not identified: 0.4%

6. Herrings, sardines, anchovies
7. Tunas, bonitos, billfishes
8. Miscellaneous pelagic fishes
9. Sharks, rays, chimaeras
10. Crustaceans
11. Molluscs

## LME – 8

1. Freshwater and diadromous fishes
2. Flounders, halibuts, soles
3. Cods, hakes, haddocks
4. Miscellaneous coastal fishes
5. Miscellaneous demersal fishes: Marine fishes not identified – 0.5 per cent
6. Herrings, sardines, anchovies
7. Tunas, bonitos, billfishes
8. Miscellaneous pelagic fishes
9. Sharks, rays, chimaeras
10. Crustaceans
11. Molluscs

## LME – 9

1. Freshwater and diadromous fishes
2. Flounders, halibuts, soles
3. Cods, hakes, haddocks
4. Miscellaneous coastal fishes
5. Miscellaneous demersal fishes: Marine fishes not identified – 0.4 per cent
6. Harrings, sardines, anchovies
7. Tunas, bonitos, billfishes
8. Miscellaneous pelagic fishes
9. Sharks, rays, chimaeras
10. Crustaceans
11. Molluscs

Cluster 3 groups four of the historically most productive LMEs of the northern hemisphere, three in the Northwest Atlantic and one in Northeast Pacific. They are all classified as moderately high productive ecosystems, with the exception of the Northeast U.S. Continental Shelf, which is considered as highly productive and is structurally more complex than the other three, with marked temperature and climate changes, river runoff, estuarine exchanges, tides and complex circulation regimes.

For what concerns the California Current ecosystem, this is a transition ecosystem between subtropical and subarctic water masses with an upwelling coastal phenomenon (Bakun, 1993) that determines strong interannual oscillations of the productivity of the ecosystem and, consequently, of the catch levels of different species groups.

The catch composition of this cluster is quite diverse as six species groupings contribute, on average among the four LMEs, at least 10 per cent of the total shelf catches. These groups are, Gadiformes, clupeoids, crustaceans, mollusks, flat fishes and miscellaneous demersal fishes. However, the trend charts show the marked decreases of Gadiformes catches in the Atlantic LMEs in the early 1990s up to the cod collapse in 1993-94, while in the same years the Gadiformes catches (mainly of (*Merluccius products*) in the California Current increased and have remained high since then. An increase of crustacean catches in the three Atlantic LMEs can be noted in recent years although it is not clear if this is due to ecological or to economical reasons (Caddy and Garibaldi, 2000).

## Cluster – 4

The cluster is composed of Gulf of California (LME 4) of Pacific Ocean in Northern hemisphere, Gulf of Mexico (LME 5) of Atlantic Ocean in Northern hemisphere, Humboldt Current of (LME 13) of Pacific Ocean in Southern hemisphere, Baltic Sea (LME 22) of Atlantic Ocean in Northern hemisphere, Black Sea (LME 26) in Northern hemisphere, Canary Current (LME 27) of Atlantic Ocean in northern hemisphere, Guinea Current (LME 28) of Atlantic Ocean and Pacific Central American Coastal (LME 50) of Pacific Ocean in Northern hemisphere. The LMEs 4, 22, 26 and 27 have temperate climate, while tropical climate prevail in LMEs 5, 28 and 50. The mixed climate has been observed in LME 13.

The capture trend of these LMEs for the period of 1990 to 1999 was;

### LME – 4

1. Freshwater and diadromous fishes
2. Flounders, halibuts, soles
3. Cods, hakes, haddocks
4. Miscellaneous coastal fishes
5. Miscellaneous demersal fishes: Marine fishes not identified – 22 per cent
6. Herrings, sardines, anchovies
7. Tunas, bonitos, billfishes
8. Miscellaneous pelagic fishes,
9. Sharks, rays, chimaeras
10. Crustaceans
11. Molluscs

### LME – 5

1. Freshwater and diadromous fishes

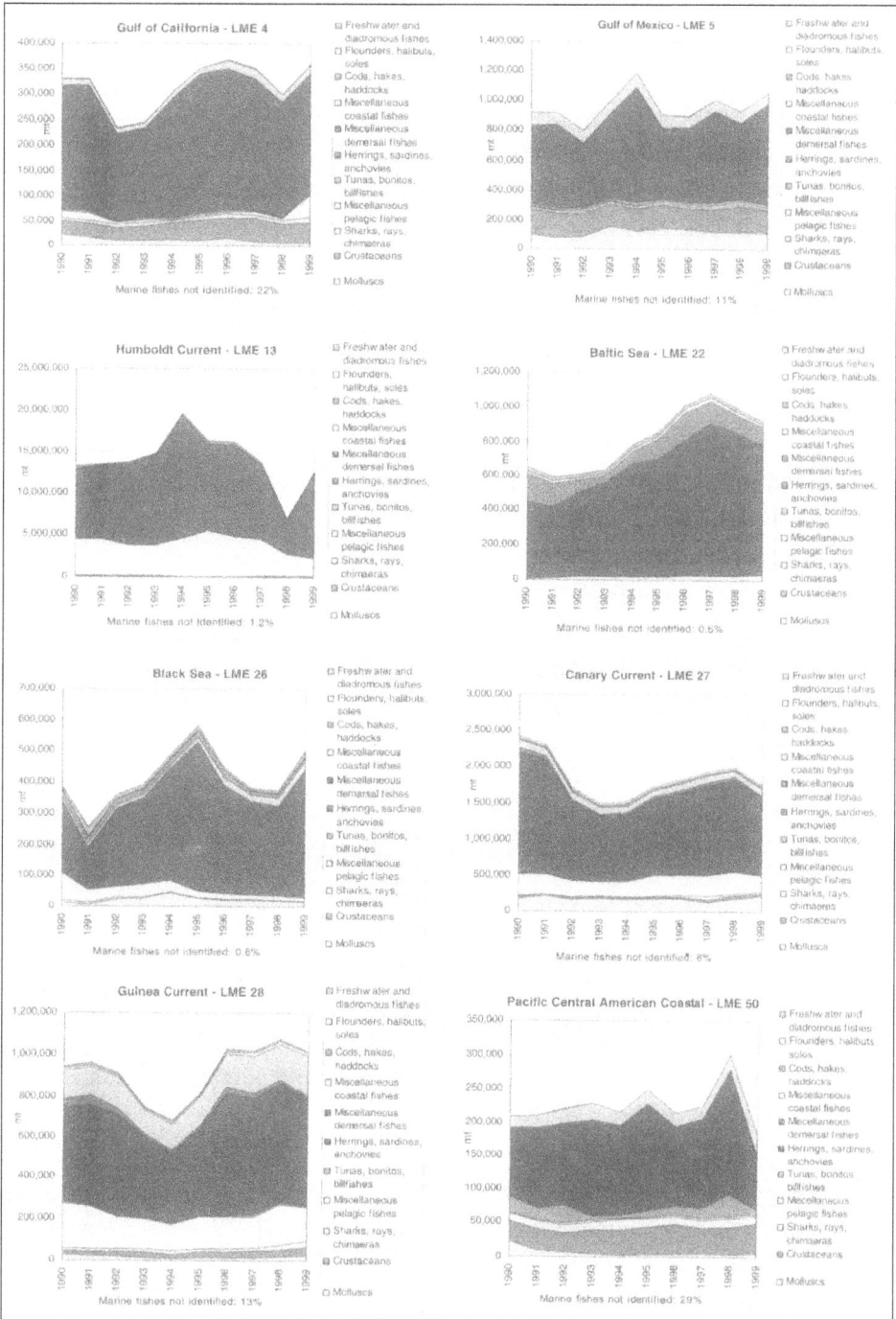

**Figure 58: Cluster 4: Capture Trends of LMEs 4–5–13–22–26–27–28–50.**

2. Flounders, halibuts, soles
3. Cods, hakes, haddocks
4. Miscellaneous coastal fishes
5. Miscellaneous demersal fishes: Marine fishes not identified – 11 per cent
6. Herrings, sardines, anchovies
7. Tunas, bonitos, billfishes
8. Miscellaneous pelagic fishes
9. Sharks, rays, chimaeras
10. Crustaceans
11. Molluscs

## LME – 13

1. Freshwater and diadromous fishes
2. Flounders, halibuts, soles
3. Cods, hakes, haddocks
4. Miscellaneous coastal fishes
5. Miscellaneous demersal fishes
6. Herrings, sardines, anchovies: Marine fishes not identified – 1.2 per cent
7. Tunas, bonitos, billfishes
8. Miscellaneous pelagic fishes
9. Sharks, rays, chimaeras
10. Crustaceans
11. Molluscs

## LME – 22

1. Freshwater and diadromous fishes
2. Flounders, halibuts, soles
3. Cods, hakes, haddocks
4. Miscellaneous coastal fishes
5. Miscellaneous demersal fishes Marine fishes not identified – 0.6 per cent
6. Herrings, sardines, anchovies
7. Tunas, bonitos, billfishes
8. Miscellaneous pelagic fishes
9. Sharks, rays, chimaeras
10. Crustaceans
11. Molluscs

## LME – 26

1. Freshwater and diadromous fishes
2. Flounders, halibuts, soles
3. Cods, hakes, haddocks
4. Miscellaneous coastal fishes
5. Miscellaneous demersal fishes
6. Herrings, sardines, anchovies
7. Tunas, bonitos, billfishes
8. Miscellaneous pelagic fishes
9. Sharks, rays, chimaeras
10. Crustaceans
11. Molluscs
    Marine fishes not identified-0.6 per cent

## LME – 27

1. Freshwater and diadromous fishes
2. Flounders, halibuts, soles
3. Cods, hakes, haddocks
4. Miscellaneous coastal fishes
5. Miscellaneous demersal fishes
6. Herrings, sardines, anchovies
7. Tunas, bonitos, billfishes
8. Miscellaneous pelagic fishes
9. Sharks, rays, chimaeras
10. Crustaceans
11. Molluscs
    Marine fishes not identified – 8 per cent

## LME – 28

1. Freshwater and diadromous fishes
2. Flounders, halibuts, soles
3. Cods, hakes, haddocks
4. Miscellaneous coastal fishes
5. Miscellaneous demersal fishes
6. Herrings, sardines, anchovies
7. Tunas, bonitos, billfishes
8. Miscellaneous pelagic fishes
9. Sharks, rays, chimaeras

10. Crustaceans
11. Molluscs
    Marine fishes not identified – 13 per cent

## LME – 50

1. Freshwater and diadromous fishes
2. Flounders, halibuts, soles
3. Cods, hakes, haddocks
4. Miscellaneous coastal fishes
5. Miscellaneous demersal fishes
6. Herrings, sardines, anchovies
7. Tunas, bonitos, billfishes
8. Miscellaneous pelagic fishes
9. Sharks, rays, chimaeras
10. Crustaceans
11. Molluscs
    Marine fishes not identified – 29 per cent

After the cluster 6, this is the second cluster for number of LMEs in the present analysis. It is composed by eight LMEs, which although in different manners, are all enriched by high level of nutrients. This cluster can be subdivided into two main sub-groups; enclosed and semi-enclosed seas (Gulf of California, Baltic Sea and Black Sea), which are strongly influenced by human induced eutrophication, river runoff and/or by a lack of rapid exchange with the adjacent oceans (NOAA, 2002; Kullenberg, 1986; Caddy, 1993) and upwelling ecosystems (two in the Pacific Ocean; Humboldt Current and Pacific Central American Coastal, and two in the Atlantic Ocean, Canary Current and Guinea Current) that show important upwelling and other seasonal nutrient enrichments (Bernal *et al.*, 1983; Bakun *et al.*, 1999; Bas, 1993, Binet, 1983). The Gulf of Mexico, although it is partially isolated from the Atlantic Ocean and water enters into it from the Yucatan Channel and exits from the Straits of Florida creating the Loop Current which is associated to nutrients flow and upwelling phenomena (Lohrenz *et al.*, 1999), can not be considered as a semi-enclosed sea. Furthermore, this large scale and complex LME is affected by such levels of enriching river runoff (especially from the Mississippi) that large hypoxic areas have been detected in the Gulf in recent years (Rabalais *et al.*, 1996).

All of these ecosystems are characterized by predominant catches of small pelagic clupeoids that represent over half of the total identified shelf catches in all LMEs. Catch trends, although referring to a limited number of years, show that ups and downs do not occur only in LMEs driven by upwelling regimes, but that also enclosed and semi-enclosed LMEs have a high variability in catches.

## Cluster – 5

The cluster covers; Southeast U.S. Continental Shelf (LME 6) of Atlantic Ocean in Northern hemisphere; with temperate climate; West Greenland Shelf (LME 10) of Atlantic Ocean in Northern hemisphere with subarctic climate; Agulhas Current (LME 30) of Indian Ocean in Southern hemisphere with mixed climate; Northern Australian Shelf (LME 38) of Pacific Ocean of Southern hemisphere with tropical climate; Great Barrier Reef (LME 39) of Pacific Ocean in Southern hemisphere with tropical climate.

The capture trends of these LMEs for ten years period (1990-99) are;

### LME – 6

1. Freshwater and diadromous fishes
2. Flounders, halibuts, soles
3. Cods, hakes, haddocks
4. Miscellaneous coastal fishes
5. Miscellaneous demersal fishes
6. Herrings, sardines, anchovies
7. Tunas, bonitos, billfishes
8. Miscellaneous pelagic fishes
9. Sharks, rays, chimaeras
10. Crustaceans
11. Molluscs
    Marine fishes not identified – 5 per cent

### LME - 10

1. Freshwater and diadromous fishes
2. Flounders, halibuts, soles
3. Cods, hakes, haddocks
4. Miscellaneous coastal fishes
5. Miscellaneous demersal fishes
6. Herrings, sardines, anchovies
7. Tunas, bonitos, billfishes
8. Miscellaneous pelagic fishes
9. Sharks, rays, chimaeras
10. Crustaceans
11. Molluscs
    Marine fishes not identified – 0.4 per cent

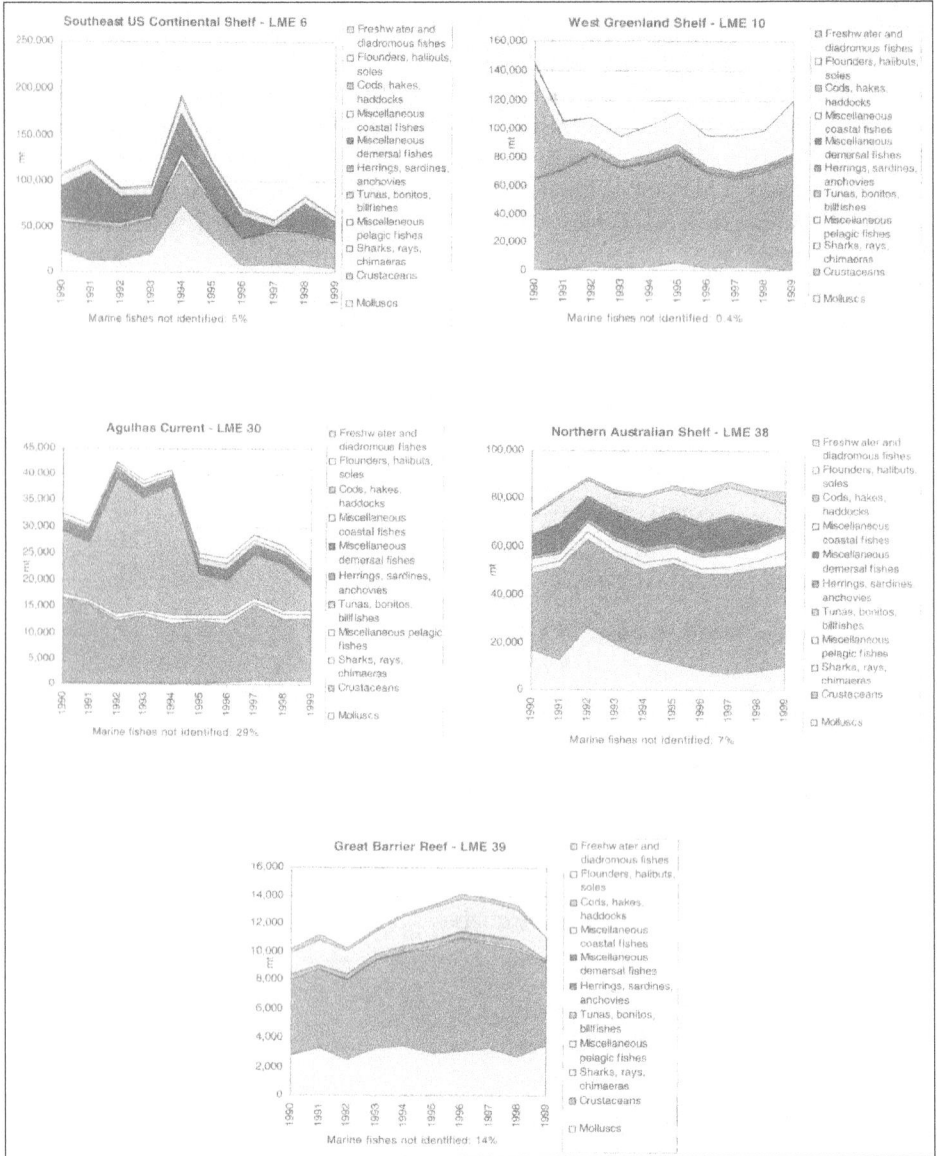

**Figure 59: Cluster 5: Capture Trends of LMEs 6–10–30–38–39.**

## LME – 30

1. Freshwater and diadromous fishes
2. Flounders, halibuts, soles
3. Cods, hakes, haddocks
4. Miscellaneous coastal fishes
5. Miscellaneous demersal fishes

6. Herrings, sardines, anchovies
7. Tunas, bonitos, billfishes
8. Miscellaneous pelagic fishes
9. Sharks, rays, chimaeras
10. Crustraceans
11. Molluscs
   Marine fishes not identified – 29 per cent

## LME – 38

1. Freshwater and diadromous fishes
2. Flounders, halibuts, soles
3. Cods, hakes, haddocks
4. Miscellaneous coastal fishes
5. Miscellaneous demersal fishes
6. Herrings, sardines, anchovies
7. Tunas, bonitos, billfishes
8. Miscellaneous pelagic fishes
9. Sharks, rays, chimaeras
10. Crustaceans
11. Molluscs
   Marine fishes not identified – 7 per cent

## LME – 39

1. Freshwater and diadromous fishes
2. Flounders, halibuts, soles
3. Cods, hakes, haddocks
4. Miscellaneous coastal fishes
5. Miscellaneous demersal fishes
6. Herrings, sardines, anchovies
7. Tunas, bonitos, billfishes
8. Miscellaneous pelagic fishes
9. Sharks, rays, chimaeras
10. Crustaceans
11. Molluscs

The ecosystems in this cluster are distinguished by a high percentage of crustacean catches. The second species group in terms of catches is clupeoids in the Southeast U.S. Continental Shelf, flatfishes in the West Greenland Shelf, non-oceanic tunas in the Agulhas Current and mollusks in the Northern Australian Shelf and

Great Barrier Reef. Catch trends in recent years are very diverse and it is difficult to find common elements.

These ecosystems are characterized by a rather wide range of productivity levels, from low (West Greenland Shelf) and moderate (Southeast U.S. Continental Shelf and Agulhas Current) to moderately high and high productivity Great Barrier Reef and Northern Australian Shelf respectively) according to the SeaWiFS estimates. Geographically, with the exception of the West Greenland Shelf and, partially, of the Northern Australian Shelf, these LMEs all lay along the eastern margins of the continents. Nutrient enrichment and mixing are due to different factors; offshore upwelling regime, although not as intense as in the higher latitude regions, in the Southeast U.S. continental Shelf (Yoder, 1991; NOAA, 2002); tidal effects in the Great Barrier Reef (Brodie, 1999; NOAA, 2002); changes in sea and air temperature in the West Greenland Shelf (Hovgard and Buch, 1990); current-associated in the Agulhas Current (Beckley, 1998); and tidal mixing, monsoons and tropical cyclones in the Northern Australian shelf (Furnas, 2002).

## Cluster – 6

The cluster includes Insular Pacific-Hawaiian (LME 11) of Pacific Ocean in Northern hemisphere having tropical climate, Northeast Brazil Shelf (LME 16) of Atlantic Ocean with tropical climate, North Sea (LME 21) of Atlantic Ocean in Northern hemisphere having temperate climate, Somali Coastal Current (LME 31) of Indian Ocean in Northern hemisphere with tropical climate, Arabian Sea of Indian Ocean of Northern hemisphere having tropical climate, Red Sea (LME 33) of Indian Ocean in Northern hemisphere having tropical climate, Bay of Bengal (LME 34) of Indian Ocean in Northern hemisphere having tropical climate, South China Sea (LME 35) of Pacific Ocean in Northern hemisphere having tropical climate, Sulu-Celebes Sea (LME 36) of Pacific Ocean in Northern hemisphere having tropical climate.

The capture trends of all these LMEs of the cluster are grouped for ten years period (1990-1999) includes;

1. Freshwater and diadromous fishes,
2. Flounders, halibuts, soles,
3. Cods, hakes, haddocks,
4. Miscellaneous coastal fishes,
5. Miscellaneous demersal fishes,
6. Herrings, sardines, anchovies,
7. Tunas, bonitos, billfishes,
8. Miscellaneous pelagic fishes,
9. Sharks, rays, chimaeras,
10. Crustaceans,
11. Molluscs
    1. LME – 11 – Marine fishes not identified – 38 per cent
    2. LME - 16 – Marine fishes not identified – 53 per cent

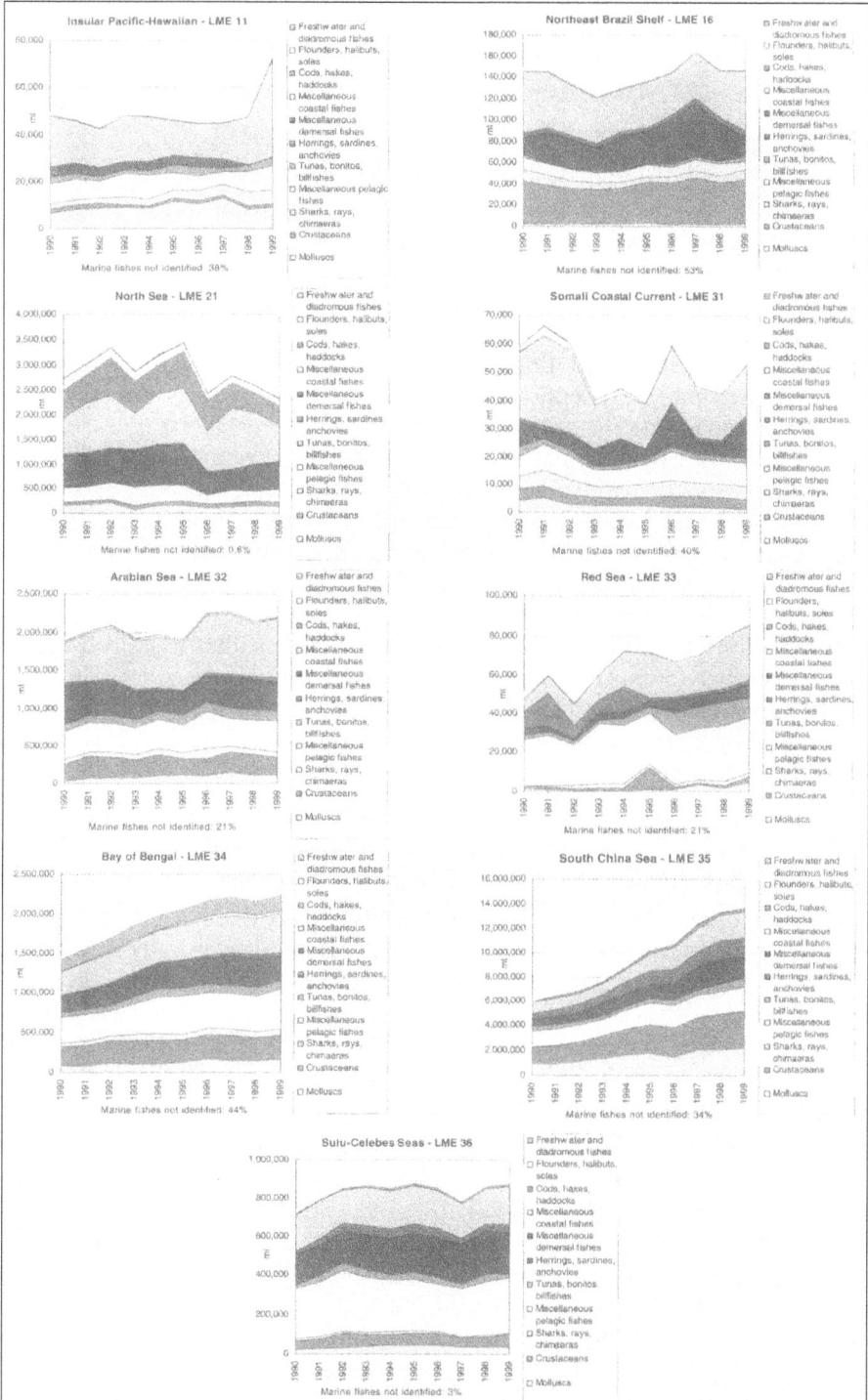

**Figure 60: Cluster 6: Capture Trends of LMEs 11–16–21–32–33–34–35–36.**

3.  LME - 21 – Marine fishes not identified – 0.6 per cent
4.  LME - 31 – Marine fishes not identified – 40 per cent
5.  LME - 32 – Marine fishes not identified – 21 per cent
6.  LME - 33 – Marine fishes not identified – 21 per cent
7.  LME - 34 – Marine fishes not identified – 44 per cent
8.  LME - 35 – Marine fishes not identified – 34 per cent
9.  LME - 36 – Marine fishes not identified – 3 per cent

This is the cluster with highest number of LMEs. These nine ecosystems are probably less characterized than others and for this reason they have been grouped together by the clustering routine. Geographically, this cluster groups all tropical ecosystems, with the sole exception of the North Sea, and it includes four out of five of the Indian Ocean LMEs. The general greater marine biodiversity of tropical regions is so reflected in the catch composition. The main distinguishing feature is the high catch percentages for miscellaneous coastal fishes and miscellaneous pelagic fishes. Secondly catches of herrings, sardines and anchovies and of crustaceans in the nine ecosystems exceed 10 per cent on average. Most of these ecosystems are characterized by fishing activities mainly concentrated, for different reasons, on the coastal areas and this explain the high percentages of miscellaneous coastal fish catches. Catch trends in the 1990-99 period are quite diverse and it is difficult to identify a common pattern. However, for most of these ecosystems, with the only exception of the North Sea and Sulu-Celebes Sea, statistics are reported with poor species breakdown, as can be deducted by the higher percentage of catches included in the " Marine fishes not identified" category.

Primary production ranges from low (Insular Pacific-Hawaiian and Sulu-Celebes Sea) to high (North Sea, Northeast Brazilian Shelf and Arabian Sea) with the remaining LMEs classified as moderately or moderately high (South China Sea) productive.

It should be noted that according to the LMEs web site (NOAA, 2002), the Insular Pacific-Hawaiian LME does not include only the Hawaii, as usually shown in the maps representing the LMEs, but it extends also to shelf areas of several other Pacific islands. Catch statistics have been considered accordingly. This region is dominated by the equatorial currents system (NOAA, 2002). Fishery production in the Insular Pacific-Hawaiian and Sulu-Celebes Sea LMEs is mostly concentrated in the coastal waters as the islands are usually surrounded by very narroe shelf areas.

The Northeast Brazil Shelf is characterized by high levels of nutrients in the inner part of the shelf (Medeiros *et al.*, 1999). The North Sea includes one of the most diverse coastal regions of the world, with a great variety of habitats (NOAA, 2002). Three of the Indian Ocean ecosystems (Somali Coastal Current, Arabian Sea and Bay of Bengal) are influenced by monsoons. In the Somali Coastal Current and in the Arabian Sea, the southwest monsoon from May to October cause seasonal upwelling phenomena that are on the other hand lacking in the Bay of Bengal (information derived, respectively, from Bakun *et al.*, 1998; NOAA, 2002; Dwivedi, 1993). In the Arabian Sea, about 65 per cent of fish landings derive from artisanal fisheries and this would explain the prevalence of coastal species catches, but it may also be influenced by the presence of low-oxygen water, which restricts productivity at depths of 200 m and more (Dwivedi and Choubey, 1998; NOAA, 2002). The elongated and narrow shape, semi-enclosed character and circulation patterns of the Red Sea protect the coast from storms and provide habitats for a large number of marine coastal species (Baars, *et al.*, 1998). Different sub-systems within the ecosystems have been identified in the South China Sea (Pauly and Christensen, 1993).

## Cluster – 7

The cluster consists of Caribbean Sea (LME 12) of Atlantic Ocean in Northern hemisphere having tropical climate, Brazil Current (LME 15) of Atlantic Ocean in Southern hemisphere with mixed climate, Mediterranean Sea (LME 25) in Northern hemisphere having temperate climate and Indonesian Seas (LME 37) of Pacific Ocean with tropical climate.

Capture trends of these LMEs for ten years (1990-1999) are;

### LME 12

1. Freshwater and diadromous fishes
2. Flounders, halibuts, soles
3. Cods, hakes, haddocks
4. Miscellaneous coastal fishes
5. Miscellaneous demersal fishes
6. Herrings, sardines, anchovies
7. Tunas, bonitos, billfishes
8. Miscellaneous pelagic fishes
9. Sharks, rays, chimaeras
10. Crustaceans
11. Molluscs
12. Marine fishes not identified – 19 per cent

### LME 15

1. Freshwater and diadromous fishes
2. Flounders, halibuts, soles
3. Cods, hakes, haddocks
4. Miscellaneous coastal fishes
5. Miscellaneous demersal fishes
6. Herrings, sardines anchovies
7. Tunas, bonitos, billfishes
8. Miscellaneous pelagic fishes
9. Sharks, rays, chimaeras
10. Crustaceans

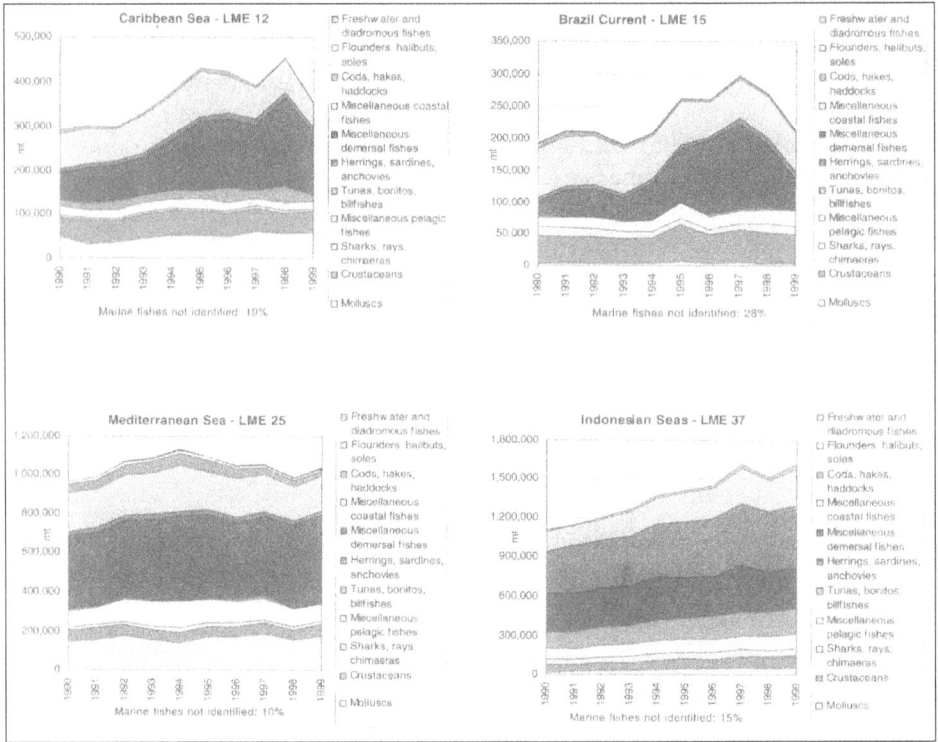

**Figure 61: Cluster 7: Capture Trends of LMEs 12–15–25–37.**

11. Molluscs
12. Marine fishes not identified – 28 per cent

## LME – 25

1. Freshwater and diadromous fishes
2. Flounders, halibuts, soles
3. Cods, hakes, haddockd
4. Miscellaneous coastal fishes
5. Miscellaneous demersal fishes
6. Herrings, sardines, anchovies
7. Tunas, bonitos, billfishes
8. Miscellaneous pelagic fishes
9. Sharks, rays, chimaeras
10. Crustaceans,
11. Molluscs
12. Marine fishes not identified – 10 per cent

## LME – 37

1. Freshwater and diadromous fishes
2. Flounders, halibuts, soles
3. Cods, hakes, haddocks
4. Miscellaneous coastal fishes
5. Miscellaneous demersal fishes
6. Herrings, sardines, anchovies
7. Tunas, bonitos, billfishes
8. Miscellaneous pelagic fishes
9. Sharks, rays, chimaeras
10. Crustaceans
11. Molluscs
12. Marine fishes not identified – 15 per cent

In this cluster, clupeoids; herrings, sardines and anchovies is the most important species group in shelf catches but, unlike cluster 4, other groups (*i.e.*mostly coastal fishes, but also crustaceans, mollusks and miscellaneous demersal fishes for the Indonesian Seas) also contribute significant capture production. Catch trends have been rather stable in recent years with moderate increases in total shelf catches if comparing the last yeas (1999) with respect to the first year (1990) of the considered period, with the exception of the Indonesian Seas where catches have been quite steadily increasing.

As for the catch composition, the Mediterranean Sea seems one of the most diverse and stable LME in terms of species groupings, their shares in total catches and trends. Its unusual biodiversity for a temperate sea is confirmed by the fact that the Mediterranean and Black Sea together cover only the 0.8 per cent of the total surface of the oceans, but represent about 5.5 per cent of the total world marine fauna (Fredj *et al.*, 1992).

According to the productivity classification by SeaWiFS, the four LMEs in the cluster are moderately-high (Indonesian Seas), moderately (Brazil Current) or low naturally productive ecosystems (Caribbean Sea and Mediterranean Sea) but the productivity of the last two LMEs is increased by nutrient input from rivers, estuaries and human induced activities. These LMEs have in common a composite structure of environmental conditions, with local areas of upwelling, wind-driven currents, high water temperatures at least in some periods of the year, nutrient inputs from rivers or human activities (studies on the single LMEs; Richards and Bohnsack, 1990, for the Caribbean Sea; Bakun, 1993, for the Brazilian Current; Caddy, 1993 for the Mediterranean Sea; Zijlstra and Baars, 1990, for the Indonesia Seas)

## Cluster – 8

The single LME – 14, Patagonial Shelf of Atlantic Ocean in Southern hemisphere with mixed climate is characterized by high catches of mollusks, mostly cephalopods

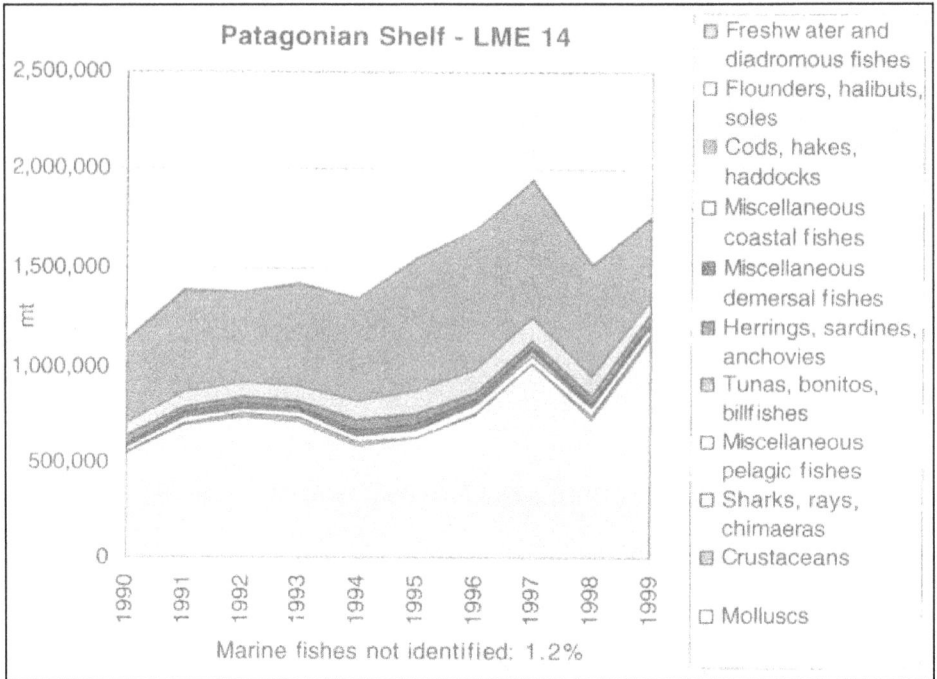

**Figure 62: Cluster 8: Capture Trends of LMEs 14.**

and Gadiformes. Cephalopod fisheries developed in the early 1980s by Distant Water Fleets but, since the early 1990s, also local fleets (*i.e.* Argentina and Uruguay) are actively targeting these species. Following a drop in 1998, cephalopod catches in this area are still increasing. Instead, catches of Gadiformes, mostly by local fleets, increased continuously since the 1970s but from mid-1990s are declining.

The catch trends of 1990-1999 of the cluster includes;

1. Freshwater and diadromous fishes
2. Flouders, halibuts, soles
3. Cods, hakes, haddocks
4. Miscellaneous coastal fishes
5. Miscellaneous demersal fishes
6. Herrings, sardines, anchovies
7. Tunas, bonitos, billfishes
8. Miscellaneous pelagic fishes
9. Sharks, rays, chimaeras
10. Crustaceans
11. Molluscs
12. Marine fishes not identified – 1.2 per cent

These fisheries take place in one of the most extensive continental shelf of the world. According to the SeaWiFS estimates of global primary productivity, the Patagonian shelf is an area of high productivity and it is influenced by intense western boundary currents and wind-driven and tide-driven upwelling (Bakun, 1993; NOAA, 2002).

## Cluster – 9

East Greenland Shelf (LME 17) of Atlantic Ocean in Northern hemisphere with sub-arctic climate; Icelanf Shelf (LME 18) of Atlantic Ocean in Northern hemisphere with sub-arctic climate; Barents Sea (LME 19) of Atlantic Ocean in Northern hemisphere with sub-arctic climate; Celtic-Biscay Shelf (LME 23) of Atlantic Ocean in Northern hemisphere with temperate climate; New Zealand Shelf (LME 40) of Pacific Ocean in Southern hemisphere with temperate climate; Faroe Plateau (LME 48) of Atlantic Ocean in Northern hemisphere with sub-arctic climate have been included in the cluster.

Ten years capture trends of the six LMEs of the cluster are;

### LME – 17

1. Freshwater and diadromous fishes
2. Flounders, halibuts, soles
3. Cods, hakes, haddocks
4. Miscellaneous coastal fishes
5. Miscellaneous demersal fishes
6. Herrings, sardines, anchovies
7. Tunas, bonitos, billfishes
8. Miscellaneous pelagic fishes
9. Sharks, rays, chimaeras
10. Crustaceans
11. Molluscs
12. Marine fishes not identified – 0.05 per cent

### LME – 18

1. Freshwater and diadromous fishes
2. Flounders, halibuts, soles
3. Cods, hakes, haddocks
4. Miscellaneous coastal fishes
5. Miscellaneous demersal fishes
6. Herrings, sardines, anchovies
7. Tunas, bonitos, billfishes
8. Miscellaneous pelagic fishes

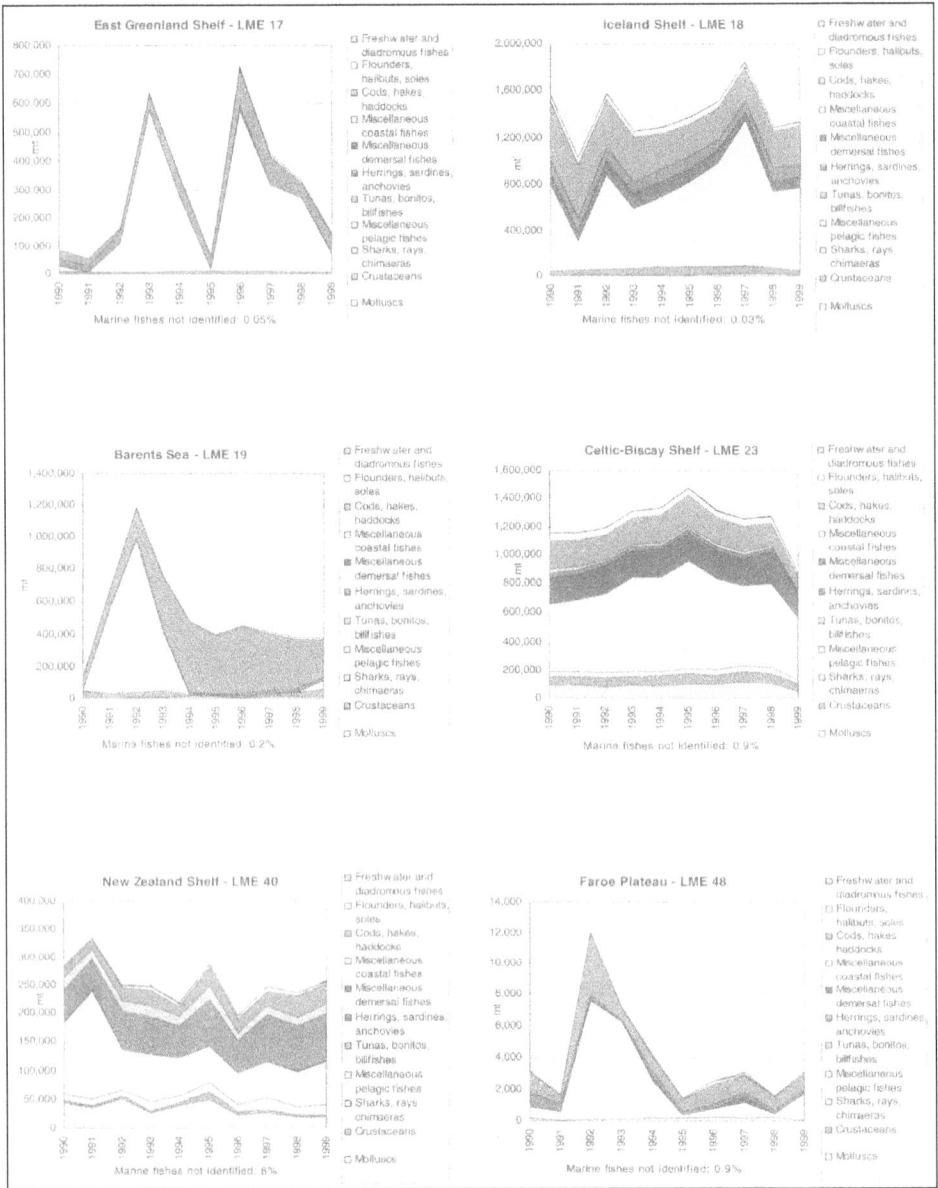

**Figure 63: Cluster 9: Capture Trends of LMEs 17–18–19–23–40–48.**

9.  Sharks, rays chimaeras
10. Crustaceans
11. Molluscs
12. Marine fishes not identified – 0.03 per cent

## LME – 19

1. Freshwater and diadromous fishes
2. Flounders, halibuts, soles
3. Cods, hakes, haddocks
4. Miscellaneous coastal fishes
5. Miscellaneous demersal fishes
6. Herrings, sardines, anchovies
7. Tunas, bonitos, billfishes
8. Miscellaneous pelagic fishes
9. Sharks, rays, chimaeras
10. Crustaceans
11. Molluscs
12. Marine fishes not identified – 0.2 per cent

## LME – 23

1. Freshwater and diadromous fishes
2. Flounders. Halibuts, soles
3. Cods, hakes, haddocks
4. Miscellaneous coastal fishes
5. Miscellaneous demersal fishes
6. Herrings, sardines, anchovies
7. Tunas, bonitos, billfishes
8. Miscellaneous pelagic fishes
9. Sharks, rays, chimaeras
10. Crustaceans
11. Molluscs
12. Marine fishes not identified – 0.9 per cent

## LME – 40

1. Freshwater and diadromous fishes
2. Flounders, halibuts, soles
3. Cods, hakes haddocks
4. Miscellaneous coastal fishes
5. Miscellaneous demersal fishes
6. Herrings, sardines, anchovies
7. Tunas, bonitos, billfishes
8. Miscellaneous pelagic fishes
9. Sharks, rays, chimaeras

    10. Crustaceans

    11. Molluscs

    12. Marine fishes not identified – 8 per cent

## LME – 48

    1. Freshwater and diadromous fishes

    2. Flounders, halibuts, soles

    3. Cods, hakes, haddocks

    4. Miscellaneous coastal fishes

    5. Miscellaneous demersal fishes

    6. Herrings, sardines, anchovies

    7. Tunas, bonitos, billfishes

    8. Miscellaneous pelagic fishes

    9. Sharks, rays, chimaeras

    10. Crustaceans

    11. Molluscs

    12. Marine fishes not identified – 0.9 per cent

In this cluster, the six ecosystems have a temperate or sub-arctic climate and five of them belong to the same ocean region, the Northeast Atlantic. With the exclusion of the New Zealand Shelf and the Celtic-Biscay Shelf, which are influenced also by warm currents, respectively the South Equatorial and the Gulf Currents, the other ecosystems are categorized as high latitude and extreme environments, in which temperature, currents, tides and seasonal oscillations affect productivity. The same division in two sub-groups applies also to data on primary productivity SeaWiFS, 2002 : the New Zealand Shelf and the Celtic-Biscay Shelf are considered highly productive ecosystems, the Iceland Shelf, the Barents Sea and the Faroe Plateau are moderately highly productive ecosystem, and the East Greenland Shelf is a low productive ecosystem.

The marine environment of the New Zealand Shelf is very diverse and includes estuaries, mudflats, mangroves, sea grass and kelp beds, reefs, seamounts communities and deep sea trenches (NOAA, 2002). The Celtic-Biscay Shelf is characterized by strong interdependence of human impact and biological and climate cycles (Koutsikopoulos and Le Cann, 1996). The East Greenland and Iceland LMEs are both characterized by a seasonal ice cover and by marked fluctuations in salinity, temperature and phytoplankton. Factors that can contribute to variations of annual catches of cod and small pelagics (Skjoldal *et al.*, 1993). In the Barents Sea, the ice coverage extends over one third to two thirds of the LME and it varies considerably during the year and inter-annually (NOAA, 2002). The shallow parts of the shelf in the Faroe Plateau are well mixed by extreme tidal currents and no stratification occurs during the summer (NOAA, 2002)

With regard to catch composition, these ecosystems have in common high percentages of miscellaneous pelagic fishes which, for the Northeast Atlantic areas, are mostly due to peak catches of capelin in 1992-93. In the LMEs 17, 19 and 48 these peaks have a "boom and bust" profile and, in the latest years of the observed period, catches of capelin are markedly decreased. Another fish group that shows relevant catches in all ecosystems of this cluster is cods, hakes, haddocks, with the sole exception of the East Greenland LME that has been affected by the cod collapse of the early 1990s. In the other three northern most Atlantic LMEs, total catches of the whole gadiform group have been rather stable during the 10 years examined. (Jakupsstovu and Reinert, 1994; Jacobsen, 1997; Nakken, 1998). In the two temperate ecosystems (*i.e.* New Zealand and the Celtic-Biscay shelves), the second species group in terms of catches is respectively, miscellaneous demersal fishes and clupeoids.

## Cluster – 10

The cluster is composed with Norwegian Shelf (LME 20) of Atlantic Ocean in Northern hemisphere with sub-arctic climate; Iberian Coastal (LME 24) of Atlantic Ocean in Northern hemisphere with temperate climate; Benguela Current (LME 29) of Atlantic Ocean in Southern hemisphere with temperate climate.

The capture trends during 1990-1999 period from the LMEs of the cluster are;

### LME – 20

1. Freshwater and diadromous fishes
2. Flounders, halibuts, soles
3. Cods, hakes, haddocks
4. Miscellaneous coastal fishes
5. Miscellaneous demersal fishes
6. Herrings, sardines, anchovies
7. Tunas, bonitos, billfishes
8. Miscellaneous pelagic fishes
9. Sharks, rays, chimaeras
10. Crustaceans
11. Molluscs
12. Marine fishes not identified – 0.07 per cent

### LME – 24

1. Freshwater and diadromous fishes
2. Flounders, halibuts, soles
3. Cods, hakes, haddocks
4. Miscellaneous coastal fishes
5. Miscellaneous demersal fishes
6. Herrings, sardines, anchovies

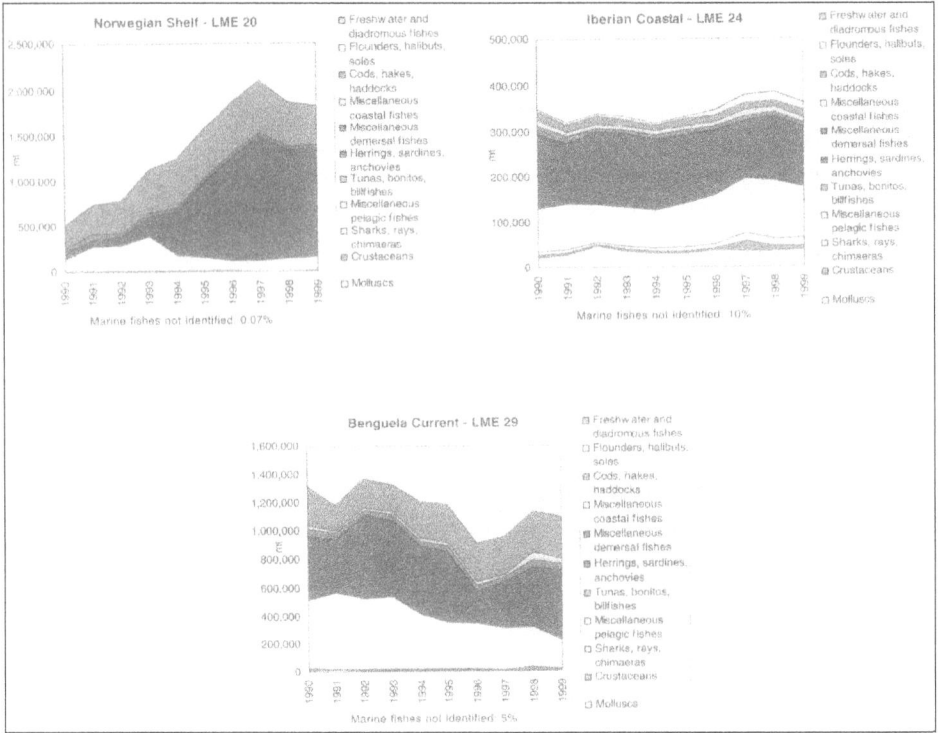

**Figure 64: Cluster 10: Capture Trends of LMEs 20–24–29.**

7. Tunas, bonitos, billfishes
8. Miscellaneous pelagic fishes
9. Sharks, rays, chimaeras
10. Crustaceans
11. Molluscs
12. Marine fishes not identified – 10 per cent

### LME – 29

1. Freshwater and diadromous fishes
2. Flounders, halibuts, soles
3. Cods, hakes, haddocks
4. Miscellaneous coastal fishes
5. Miscellaneous demersal fishes
6. Herrings, sardines, anchovies
7. Tunas, bonitos, billfishes
8. Miscellaneous pelagic fishes
9. Sharks, rays, chimaeras

10. Crustaceans
11. Molluscs
12. Marine fishes not identified – 5 per cent

The three ecosystems in this cluster are all western boundary ecosystems. The Norwegian Shelf and the Benguela Current are characterized by a high productivity according to the SeaWiFS classification, whereas the Iberian Coastal LME is considered as moderately productive. The catch composition pattern is dominated by three groups: herrings, sardines and anchovies; miscellaneous pelagic fishes and cods, hakes and haddocks. Catches of Gadiformes are however very significant, and important for their value, only in the Norwegian Shelf and Benguela Current areas.

The Nowwegian Shelf LME has a complex fishery history with concomitant influences of ecological anomalies, high fishery mortality and early implementation of management measures. Its high productivity is probably to be linked to the nutrient rich, cold arctic waters that characterize this LME (Furnes and Sundby, 1980). Since the early 1990s there has been a significant increase in *Clupea harengus* catches which stock recovered after two decades of very low abundance.

The Iberian Coastal LME's productivity is climate and upwelling driven. It is characterized by favorable factors for the production of clupeoids and other small pelagic fishes (Wyatt and Perez-Gandaras, 1989). Trends in catches by species groupings have been quite steady in recent years.

In the Benguela Current LME is one of the most strongly wind-driven coastal upwelling systems known as it presents favorable conditions for a rich production of small pelagics (Bakun, 1993). Harvests are characterized by stock fluctuations according to the variations in the primary and secondary level productivity.

## Cluster – 11

The single ecosystem cluster includes the Antarctic LME of Antarctic Ocean of Southern hemisphere with Antarctic climate is unique both for its geographic and climatic characteristics. It is classified as a low productivity ecosystem, according to the SeaWiFS data, a consequence of the extensive seasonal ice cover and extreme weather conditions. The ecological and biological characteristics of Antarctic marine species are also unique from a food-chain point of view in that it is peculiarly short and based almost entirely on krill, a key species crucial to the sustainability and production of all other fisheries (Chopra and Hansen, 1997).

Capture trend of the LME for the past ten years (1990-1999) are;

## LME – 49

1. Freshwater and diadromous fishes
2. Flounders, halibuts, soles
3. Cods, hakes, haddocks
4. Miscellaneous coastal fishes
5. Miscellaneous demersal fishes

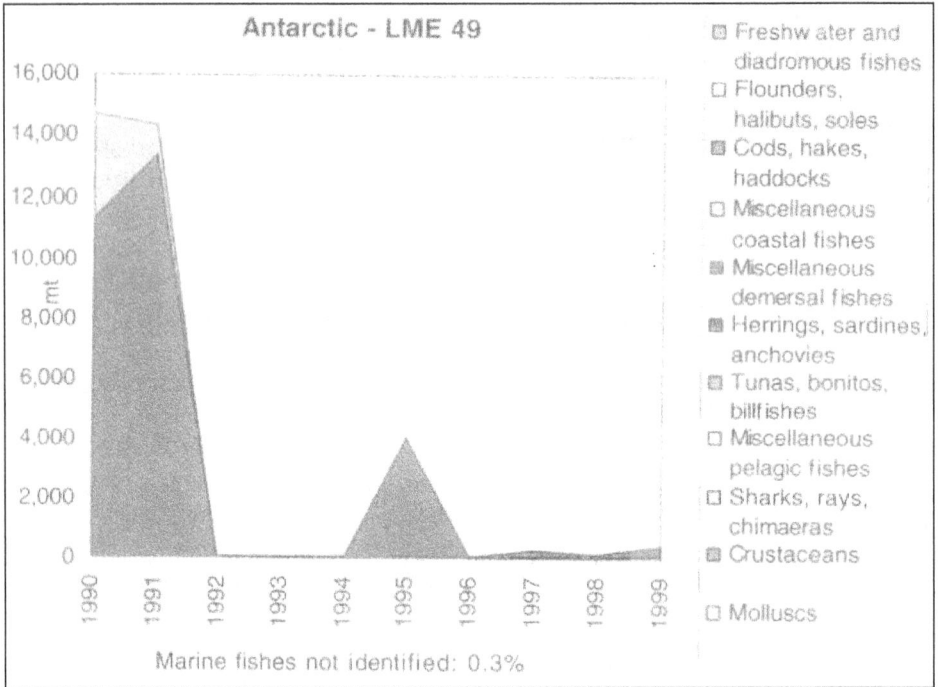

**Figure 65: Cluster 11: Capture Trends of LME 49.**

6. Herrings, sardines, anchovies
7. Tunas, bonitos, billfishes
8. Miscellaneous pelagic fishes
9. Sharks, rays, chimaeras
10. Crustaceans
11. Molluscs
12. Marine fishes not identified – 0.3 per cent

The Antarctic species most significant for fisheries have been considered as oceanic, either epipelagic or deep water. As for catches of shelf species, this LME exhibits a prevalence of miscellaneous demersal catches and a much smaller percentage of coastal fishes, although fitting the Antarctic fishes into the categories of the three miscellaneous groups (*i.e.* coastal, demersal and pelagic) proved to be rather difficult. Catches of shelf species have been remarkably reduced in the early 1990s.

## Conclusion

The general analysis of cluster composition, common characteristics and catch trends of LMEs in the same cluster presented some unexpected analogies between ecosystems of different marine regions and confirmed similarities between areas in which well known ecological phenomena takes place (*e.g.* upwelling regimes).

As expected, ecosystems with extreme characteristics (*i.e.* northernmost Pacific and Antarctic LMEs) have peculiar catch patterns and not presenting similarities with other LMEs, have been included in single clusters. Another cluster that includes only a single LME (Patagonian Shelf), is characterized by predominant catches of cephalopods and Gadiformes.

Three clusters (*i.e.* 4, 7, and 10) are dominated by catches of clupeoids, but some differences between the three groups of LMEs can be noted. The large marine ecosystems in cluster 4 are highly productive, enriched by nutrients as they are either semi-enclosed seas or have upwelling regimes, with clupeoids representing about 50-70 per cent of the catches in their shelf areas (excluding catches reported as "Marine fishes not identified"). Also LMEs in cluster 10 are highly productive and, in addition to clupeoids, they are characterized by catches of Gadiformes and non-clupeoid small pelagics. In contrast, LMEs in cluster 7 have moderate or low productivity and their's catch composition is more diverse with several other groups (i.e coastal fishes, crustaceans, mollusks and miscellaneous demersal fishes) represented by significant catches.

An unexpected finding was a cluster of five ecosystems where the majority (between 30 and 65 per cent) of identified catches on the continental shelf are made of crustacean species. This seems to be the only common feature amongst the LMEs of cluster 5, which are quite diverse in their productivity, climate and second ranking species group in terms of catches. The remaining clusters are characterized by catches distributed quite evenly amongst the major groups of species (*i.e.* clusters 3 and 6) or with a slight predominance of miscellaneous pelagic fishes (cluster 9).

However, given the global coverage and the limitations in data availability, this study only aimed at providing basic information on catch composition by LME for future studies on single LMEs and some possible starting points for more in-depth ecologically oriented researches on fishery trends.

# Chapter 11

# Conservation and Management of Lagoon Fishery Resources

## Definitions

Coastal lagoons are bodies of salt water (from brackish to hypersaline) partially separated from an adjacent sea by barriers of sand or other sediment, with openings through which sea water can flow.

### Italian Lagoon

Italian management of lagoon environment started long ago and shows models that offer a reference point for other geographical areas. Besides traditional activities, in last 80 years, Italian lagoon environments have been affected by the developments of new aquaculture technologies.

It is now clear that socio-cultural and socio-economic aspects predominate in these lagoon systems, besides the biotechnological aspects. Thus in planning lagoon management, one must now consider such elements as; a modified concept of the utilization of coastal areas, considered as an important environmental asset, as well; changed environmental conditions (pollution); new socio-economic necessities of the personnel engaged in resource management.

As far as the biotechnological aspects to increase the yield of lagoon environments are concerned, intensive aquaculture was to be the solution to the microeconomic problems of the undertaking and have positive consequences also in macroeconomics. But experience has shown that such a model is affected by the same problems as traditional lagoon management, i.e. quality of the environment, and requires big quantities of fry. This shows that technological innovations must match traditional methods and that they prove to be valid only when traditional ones are still vital for economics.

The Italian model is a good reference for the development of policies, that must not be traumatic either for the human communities involved in the exploitation and in the management of lagoon resources or for the environment.

The most ancient forms of aquaculture origins date back to the first rudimental fish ponding and fattening systems used along the Adriatic and Tyrrhenian coasts. This technique was developed by the upper Adriatic populations to exploit the seasonal migrations of some fish species from the sea into the lagoon and delta areas which are more suitable for their growth. They return to the sea because of altered environmental conditions (temperature) or for reproduction. To exploit these periodic movements, large brackish water areas were enclosed to prevent the fish descent toward the sea and permanent capture systems. Fish barriers were developed consisting of barriers in the channels communicating with the sea to catch the adults. Later, from the simple ponding of fry freely immigrated into the lagoon, came a man-made seeding of fry fished elsewhere and introduced into the basins to be reared for a few years.

In other coastal lagoons, particular forms of fish management can mostly be found instead of fish culture. Here, in fact, a free ascent of eels, grey mullet and other species can be found. Fishing occurs inside the basins ("wandering" fishing) and, when present, at the fish barriers but without precise seasonal cycles.

## Coastal Lagoons

In the most primitive of cases, a coastal lagoon is without embankments, it receives fresh water from the hinterland without hydraulic control systems and it has one or more mouths to the sea without any defence structure against silting or changing position. The mouth has no fish barrier and there is a lack of control for the water flow. These lagoons are often used as sump pumps to remove water from the surrounding marshes which are reclaimed for agriculture. Some of these lagoons, and in particular those without embankments and without water circulation, are subject to great amounts of silt from outside and therefore to rapid filling processes. In these conditions, there is no way of controlling or managing the fish resources other than through simple fishing activities.

The first step toward active management of fish resources is represented by the presence of fish barriers in the canals communicating with the sea. These have different functional characteristics. They are not in fact, the exclusive fishing gear typical of the lagoon and this is due to the difficult hydraulic management caused by lack of suitable tide levels, of fresh waters and of control possibilities of their flow. Their function is that of preventing escape toward the sea and of allowing partial capture of the fish, as well as to maintain the potential yield represented by the fish fry of marine origin in the lagoon.

A well-structured lagoon should be organized as regards; 1) bottom morphology; 2) external canalizations (sea and fresh waters); 3) sluice gates; 4) fish barrier; and 5) water-changing support systems (pumps).

The maintenance of suitable depths against silting by dredging is fundamental. At the same time it is important to have internal ditches in the lagoon, both radially and circularly, so that water circulation is promoted. External canals parallel to the banks are necessary to prevent silting from adjacent marsh areas. Embankments also give solidity to the shoreline and isolation for the whole lagoon. Embanked feeding canals (carrying fresh or sea waters) are equipped with sluice gates for the control of water flow.

The importance of a means to exchange water should be stressed considering the serious pollution affecting fresh water inlets in most of the coastal lagoons. This situation can cause serious dystrophic crises in the summer. It is often necessary therefore to be able to rely on water sources (through pumping) in those places where the pollution risk is greatest.

## Biological Features

Brackish ecosystems, in their intermediate position between inland and sea waters and as receivers of nutrients of continental origin are among the most productive water environments (Sacchi, 1973; Carrada, 1973; Quignard, 1984; Kapetsky, 1984).

But at many coastal lagoons there is an increasing trophic status because of inputs of organic pollutants. In well-managed lagoons this situation can lead to a growing trend in fish yield, but often causes a dystrophic status with periodic mass mortalities.

Dynamics of energy transfers are far from simple, notwithstanding the reduced species richness and the dominance of a few species. For example, of great importance is the role of detritic and benthic elements as compared to the planktonic one as a basis of the main food chains in the lagoons.

Due to the shallow depth of most lagoons, the wind is often able to mix the whole water mass. This allows a good oxygenation of the deeper layers helping the aerobic decomposition processes of organic substances caused by silt bacteria.

In deeper lagoons with water stratification, oxygen can not reach the lower layers and the bottom; anaerobic decomposition processes then prevail and their final products (sulphur compounds, methane etc.) are toxic and cannot be recycled.

Processes of anaerobic degradation can also be observed in shallow lagoons during the summer season. High temperatures and consequent salinity increase due to heavy evaporation, together with scarce mixing of the waters, bring about a marked decrease in the dissolved oxygen. The simultaneous presence of a thick macrophyte settlement both on the water surface and on the bottom, besides catching the waters so preventing vertical circulation, increases the oxygen deficit during the night. Critical environment conditions are therefore a natural occurrence for many lagoons.

If anoxic conditions in insufficient water circulation cause the development of anaerobic degradation processes, the summer crisis then becomes a dystrophic one, which can bring about serious mass mortality, also affecting the fish species. Similar dystrophic conditions may occur for much shorter periods and during the whole year when phytoplanktonic blooming takes place. In these circumstances, the densities (cells per liter) reached in the top water layers may impair the penetration of light in shallow basins, preventing photosynthesis and triggering anaerobic degradation processes from the bottom toward the surface with consequent mass mortality.

## Planktonic Populations

The extreme variability of phytoplankton should be emphasized for both quality and quantity in a lagoon environment. In fact, it is possible to observe conditions of scarce presence of real planktonic forms with a predominance of benthic or epiphytic forms living passively in suspension (Marchesoni, 1954), which should be considered asticopelagic forms (Regione Toscana, 1978). On the other hand, actual blooming of coastal species is also possible.

It is important to emphasize that algal blooming occurrences should not be interpreted only in terms of nutrients load but also in terms of biotic control processes such as for communities of phytophagus, among which are zooplankton and the filtering benthic organisms.

As far as chlorophyll-*a* concentration is concerned, the most frequent condition in the Italian lagoons has values comprised between 5 and 50 mg/cubic meter. But cases of concentrations higher than 200 mg/cubic meter are also known.

Concerning zooplankton, in coastal lagoons with limited communications with the sea, there is a permanent native population mainly composed of meroplankton, rotifers and copepods of brackish waters, while the neritic component is extremely slight. In lagoons with a large extent of water flow from the sea, it is possible to identify a zonation with hydrologic characteristics over which a structure gradient of zooplankton can be found. Thus it is possible to observe lagoons, or parts of them, with predominance of coastal marine components with copepods, such as, *Acartia clause, A. latisetosa, Oithona nana* and lagoons in which inland species such as *Calanipeda acquaedulcis* and the rotifer *Brachionus plicatilis* have a significant role.

The zooplanktonic role in the productive dynamics of the lagoons seems qualitatively important even if limited in terms of "standing crop". In fact, it is quite significant in the feeding of *Atherina boyeri* and fry (length less than 3 cm) of *Sparus aurate, Dicentrarchus labrax* and various grey mullet.

## Benthic Communities

Three characteristic groupings may be identified regarding phytobenthic population; i) vegetation of aptophyte attached to natural or artificial hard substrata, ii) vegetation of rhizophyte established on soft bottom with sand and mud, iii) vegetation of secondary pleustophyte, not fixed to substrata with acropleustophyte floating on the water surface and with benthopleustophyte lying or rolling on the soft bottom.

The first grouping comprises, among others, some ulvales and species of the *Enteromorpha* genus which in the summer become secondary pleustophyte and should therefore be considered as part of the third grouping (floating algae). This last group include species of the genus *Cladophora* and *Chaetomorpha* which in the extent of their settlements represent a characteristic of a great part of the lagoon environments.

In brackish waters particularly rich in nutrients, *Gracilaria verrucosa* can be found. This red agar-producung alga has a remarkable capacity to catch nutrients and can be cultivated on poles and ropes. This rhizophyte group includes some characea (*Lamprothamnium papulosum*), eel grasses (*Zostera* spp) and *Cymodocea nodosa* in good sea-exchange conditions, while *Ruppia* spp. is more typical of brackish environments and is also often found in the Italian lagoons.

Concerning zoobenthos, three groups of species can be identified;

1. Species with marine affinity, commonly found in coastal semi-enclosed areas, which, even if reproducing at sea, prefer low hydrodynamic environments, such as, lagoons, bays, harbors etc.

2. Species typical of lagoons that reproduce in halolimnobic environments, and which can stand heavy variations in the physical and chemical parameters typically found in those environments. These species inhabit even in the innermost zones of the lagoon and they can be accompanied, according to the extent of inland input, also by freshwater species.

3. Opportunistic species which, owing to their particular strategy (high turnover, brief life cycle, large ecologic valence, low competitive skill) can adapt well to particularly stressed environmental situations, such as those deriving from an excessive organic load with consequently reduced oxygenation of the substratum which can often be found in coastal environments with limited water exchange.

The first group comprises mainly polychaetes, crustaceans amphipods, tenaids, isopods.

The typical species belonging to second group are *Nereis diversicolor* and *Ficopomatus enigmaticus* among polychaetes, *Sphaeroma hookeri* amongst the crustaceans, *Cerastoderma glaucum, Hydrobia acuta* and *Helobia stagnorum* amongst mollusca. The last group includes mostly polichaetes and larvae of dipterous (Chironomidae).

The spatial distribution of macrobenthos obviously reflects the environmental conditions of the lagoon showing the main selective factors operating in it. These should be looked at for both the degree of marine influence (extent of exchanges with the sea) and the trophic levels (extent of exchanges with the continental system).

## Exploited Fish Species

The fish fauna of commercial interest in italian coastal lagoons is mostly made up of euryhaline species. The number of species and the abundance of each species differ according to the environment and depend on both natural fry ascent from the sea and on seeding by man.

The marketing of different fish species is peculiar. Fish such as sea bass and sea bream have high commercial value and strong market demand during the whole year. The eel market is mostly concentrated in the winter period and particularly for the traditional Christmas consumers.

Different conditions are present for the grey mullets; first *Chelon labrosus*, then *Mugil chelon* and *Liza aurata* are the most appreciated species. *L. ramada* and *L. saliens* are low priced species. Differences in commercial value are common in various Italian markets, particularly due to origin and preparation of product.

## Life Cycle of Fish Species in the Lagoon

Fry of eel (*Anguilla anguilla*) entering inland waters are called glass eels and are completely transparent. In the next stage eels pigment progressively and grow and are called elvers. They then have a dark-green or grey back and a light or yellowish abdomen and are called yellow eels. At the start of sexual ripenings the eel changes its appearance; its back becomes black, its abdomen silvery (silver eel) and its eyes larger. From a sedentary yellow stage, the eel change its behavior migrating to the sea for reproduction.

Females reach larger sizes (over 1 m and 3 kg) than the males (not over45-50 cm and 150-200 g). Three to five years are necessary for the males with final sizes of between 100 and 150 g and 4 to 7 years for females (between 200 and 500 g) to reach the silver stage in Northern Italy. In the south the same sizes are reached one year earlier.

The eel is omnivorous but preferably carnivorous and shows twilight and/or nocturnal activity.

The only known reproductive area of this species is the Sargassum Sea. Glass eels migrate from the sea from October to February.

Yellow eels are fished inside coastal lagoons with fyke nets and silver eels at fish barriers during migration (autumn-winter).

Intensive aquaculture of eels is developed in Italy besides extensive activity in coastal lagoons.

Sea Bass (*Dicentrarchus labrax*) fry entering inland waters have fast growth. Sea bass can live a long time in coastal lagoons reaching sometimes 7-8 kg in weight because they are not very attracted by the autumn call of sea water at the first barriers and prefer to take refuge in holes and ditches inside the lagoon.

The sea bass is the major predatory fish in coastal lagoons; it eat sand smelts, elvers, crayfish, crabs, small gobies, and also mollusks and polychaets. In 2-3 years it reaches the commercial size of 250-400 g. It reproduces only at sea in winter. The fry carries out its trophic migration to lagoons in spring. Hard-to-catch fish species. They are caught both in the fish barriers in autumn-winter and with fishing nets.

Extensive and intensive aquaculture are well developed in Italy. Artificial reproduction allows a fairly good production of juveniles for intensive systems.

### Sea Bream (*Sparus aurata*)

Fry enter coastal lagoons and can reach commercial size in one year. Sea bream is very sensitive to cold and often can be killed by low temperature of coastal lagoons in North Italy if it cannot reach the sea.

Its growth is very rapid. In suitable environments, rich in benthic settlement it can reach an average of 150-200 g at the end of the first year, 400 g in the second and 800 g in the third year.

It mainly eats mollusks, also lamellibranches (mussels, clams, oysters), the shells of which it can break with its molars.

It reproduces only at sea at the beginning of winter. Fry carry out trophic migration to inland waters starting in February, about a month earlier than sea bass.

It is one of the easiest species to fish, since it shows up at the first barrier with the first cold. Trammel nets and gill net are employed inside coastal lagoons.

Extensive and semi-intensive aquaculture are well developed in Italy. Artificial reproduction cannot produce large numbers of juveniles. For this reason, intensive aquaculture is rather limited activity, depending on wild fish fry availability.

## Grey Mullet (*Mugil cephalus*)

Fry entering inland waters adapt well to seawater and also to brackish and freshwater, where, however, do not reproduce.

A different growth occurs for the two sexes; males reach between 500 and 700 g in 3-4 years, while females can exceed 1 kg. The species is phytoplankton and detritus feeders. Occasionally it can feed on mollusks and insect larvae. The inorganic component of the diet is around 250 millimicron.

Reproduction of the species is at sea between August and October. The ascent of fry at lagoons takes place in autumn, but it is more abundant in spring.

It is a suspicious fish species. At the end of summer it appears at the fish barriers. During the whole year, it is captured inside the lagoon with trammel gill and surrounding nets.

The species is used for extensive and semi-intensive aquaculture.

Among the Mugilidae there are other species like, *Liza ramada* (Thin-lipped grey mullet); *Liza saliens* (Leaping grey mullet); *Liza aurata* (golden grey mullet); *Chelon labrosus* (Thick lipped grey mullet) and other fish species are found in Italian coastal lagoon, some of them are resident and able to reproduce in the lagoon, while others penetrating into the lagoon following the current flow but not being euryhaline, only feed and grow according to their feeding habits.

## Lagoon Fishing Gear and Techniques

Lagoon fishing gear, characterized by various tradition resulted in fishing techniques that evolved according to local necessities were classified as 28 types of nets, grouped in trawls, nets composed of barrings and basket traps and free nets. A particular system of fish barrier, made of vegetable fibers and composed of many chambers, used for catching the fish that migrate toward the sea without closing the whole canal.

As lagoon fishing techniques evolved, the number of the devices used progressively decreased.

Certain devices, such as, nets, fish weirs, basket traps, harpoons, fishing lines were adapted to local necessities with different names. Fishing was carried out by professionals, but also by occasional fishermen, who acting or against the law, made use of devices that were not so expensive as harpoons.

Trammel nets and gill nets are the main fishing gear used for fin-fish such as grey mullet, sea bream and sea bass, particularly in coastal lagoons without fish barriers. Until a few years ago, the only device used was the trammel net; the gill net has been used only recently. In sufficiently deep lagoons, local fishermen use surrounding nets to catch grey mullet.

Another fishing gear is the seine net, although it is used less and less because of its scarce selectivity, which causes high death rates in juveniles. Now it is used almost exclusive for sand smelts.

Other fishing gear, such as harpoons and long lines are not used any longer in most Italian lagoons.

Cages are commonly used for eels to preserve animals alive for long periods (at Christmas-time), so as to get the best selling prices.

## Traditional Fishing Management

Lagoon management consists in traditional methods of so-called extensive breeding, based on cycles completely supported by natural productivity.

The traditional system essentially consists of mixed breeding, since different species with individuals of all sizes are bred in the extensive basins at the same time. It is clear that growth is proportional to the biological characteristics of each species and to the availability of food in the environment.

The negative aspects of this breeding technique are competition and predation, which can also result in cannibalism. As a consequence, only few fish survive and the catch composition is not proportional to the seeding. Besides, the impossibility of intervening on fish growth and survival, other problems connected with extensive breeding are the length of breeding cycle and the very low yield compared to the land utilized,

An annual cycle includes some basic phases; fry stocking, growth, catch and sale or wintering of the fish. The lagoon cycle begins in spring, when the fry is let into the basins and goes on with those operations that allow its preservation and growth. The final catch phase may take place after only 1-2 years (for sea bream) or up to 6-7 years (for eels). On the contrary, fry stocking in the lagoons is most natural and ordinary artificial stocking is still sporadic.

One of the fundamental problems in lagoon management is the overcoming of the winter phase; only sea bream reach a harvestable size at the end of first breeding year. As far as other species are concerned (grey mullets and sea bass), it must be reckoned that they barely stand low winter temperatures; below 4-5 degree Celsius, the risk of death is very high. In autumn, when all the species breed (except yellow eels) tend to leave the lagoon under the effect of their reproduction and of thermic impulses, whatever their age, and gather in the collecting basins, it is the time to favor the entry of immature fish that can not be sold on the market into special wintering fish ponds. Only eels can remain quiescent in the lagoon by sinking in the mud.

The basis for the success of these methods are those operations that concern the lagoon management, *i.e.*, interventions to control the internal water flow and the hydro-biological balance of the environment.

## Hydrological Management of Coastal Lagoons

Hydrological management is fundamental in every coastal lagoons, even though it is used for different purposes.

Hydrological management is based on 1) the constant opening/closing of the sluice gates to regulate sea water inputs (quantity and quality); 2) the periodic inlet of fresh water; 3) the movements of internal water masses. The regulation of sluice gates depends first on the requirements of breeding, but also on the distance from the sea, the tide extent and the physical and chemical characteristics of internal and external waters, in order to obtain the best conditions of temperature, oxygen and salinity. Where the tide extent is around 1 m, it is sufficient. However many lagoons are provided with water-scooping machines to improve both charge and discharge and internal circulation. Management choices are made according to the experience of the single manager. Nevertheless, there are some general needs and rules in lagoon management that can be summarized below.

1.  Spring – the lagoon water is changed as much as possible; the outflow of brackish water attracts young fish running up naturally. As soon as seeding is done the water is raised to the highest level.

2.  Summer – in this season the water level progressively decreases due to evaporation. It is necessary to refill with freshwater to moderate salinity, carefully taking into account possible dystrophic phenomena resulting from the eutrophication of the lagoon.

3.  Autumn – Water is reduced to the lowest level to foster the gathering of the fish in the channels. Usually at the moon dark in October (rarely in September), the inlet of sea water flows during the peak of high tide stirs the migration instinct of the fish, which gather in the catching gear. In this period the sluice gates are lowered to empty the lagoon during low tide and to foster fishing during high tide.

4.  Winter – Once fishing is completed, the basic problem is to assure the best conditions of temperature and oxygen in the wintering fish ponds, where the immature fish is kept for wintering. For this purpose, the water level must be kept as high as possible. What is particularly important is the availability of freshwater (excellent is the water of artesian wells, whose temperature is generally not lower than 15 degree C) which forms a thin layer of ice on the surface sheltering the fish from sudden changes in temperature.

The coastal lagoons without fish barriers is not always possible to carry out active hydrological management as many of them are not provided with sluice gates in the canals linking them to the sea and fresh waters. Water inflow and outflow are therefore related to tide rates, sea storms, rainfalls etc. Where control systems for water flow exist, they are used for water exchange and for influencing the fish movements.

Water exchange is particularly necessary in spring to control possible dystrophic crises and in those lagoons with strong eutrophic inlets. The necessity of controlling fish movement is instead linked to the running up of the juveniles and to the catch of adults by means of fish barriers. In fact, the essential elements of lagoon fish management are the flowing brackish waters that attract the juveniles running up from the sea into the lagoon and the sea water stimulating the adults in the lagoon.

## Management of Lagoon Environment

The management of lagoon environments has greatly evolved over the years and shows the increasing importance of the public role. As regards their role, lagoons went through various phases in which at first they represented a part of the wide private coastal areas utilized for recreation purposes, such as fishing and hunting to becoming environmental assets owned by public bodies, where private people are engaged one by one or in associations of various kinds, in fishery management.

a) Private lagoons – At present the water bodies belong to these lagoon areas. Fishermen are employees, variously paid and engaged full or part time.

b) Lagoons with exclusive fishing rights – This condition is derived from old permits and often has time limits. The licensee, alone or associated, owns the fish production connected with the management he performs. The fishermen may be employees or associated when the licensee is a company (cooperative society).

c) Public lagoons – There are no specific management obligations or rights. Fishermen are generally free or associated in cooperatives.

The type of lagoon ownership directly determines production strategies and fishery organization. The fishing gear used substantially the same, but they may be employed in different ways, also according to the competitiveness among fishermen.

An interesting case is that of the valli, because of the old tradition they represent. The management differs remarkably according to the environment, but, as a general rule, it follows some typical schemes of agricultural enterprises; since 1982, in fact, aquaculture has been classified as an agricultural- and no longer industrial activity. The model most often followed is that of capitalistic ownership; the entrepreneur, either a real person or a company.

For manual operations, he hires a certain number of workers. The entrepreneur himself is rarely the manager; in some cases his intervention is limited to technical and organizational management, and his appearance is only for control purposes. More frequently, running of the estate is entrusted to a full-time administrator, especially if the concern is also connected with an agricultural activity.

Conditions of ownership, fishing rights and management vary widely for other Italian lagoons.

## Fisheries in Relation to Coastal Zone Management

### The Lagoon in the Coastal System

In a highly populated and developed nation with peninsular topography, the coastline represents a focal point for various interests.

It is in fact the center of economic interests connected, for example, with tourism and the exploitation of biological resources (agriculture, breeding, fishing), but it is also a seat of continental water discharges originating from domestic and industrial uses.

Considering the lack of national coordinated planning, coastal lagoons in their interface position between water and land are particularly subject to aggression from such interests. These normally develop in direct relation to the income level that can be generated; fishing and aquaculture as well as qualitative conservation of very important environments, even from a naturalistic point of view, often receive only marginal attention

The environmental protection now existing for the Italian lagoon areas can be considered as deriving from Act 1497 of 29 June 1939 on landscape bonds, from Act 3267 of 30 December 1973 on hydrogeologic bonds, and from the International Ramsar Convention on wet lands (D.P.R., 448 of 13 March 1975). Many areas are also part of existing parks or oases and of proposals for others.

Any discussions about the overlapping of interests and exploitations in lagoon areas is naturally very complex but dealing with the main aspects that could interact with fishing and aquaculture management., four principal points can be underlined;

1. Various and uncontrolled fishing efforts (sports fishing, trawler fishing, small-scale coast and lagoon fishing) interacting on unitary fish stocks (sea-lagoon);
2. Introduction of polluting waters often with high eutrophyzing loads;
3. Tourism and urban development;
4. Naturalistic needs with preservation of biotopes and protection of species of particular interest.

## Interactions among Fisheries

This aspect is particularly evident in those lagoons where fish recruitment is still mostly tied to the natural ascent from the sea.

Environments such as lagoons being dependent for their production on seeding by man are now in a situation of relative autonomy from natural stocks. For other lagoons, it is fundamental to preserve the renewable fish resources through accurate control of the exploitation state of the various stocks. Only recently, however, has a series of studies for the assessment of such fish resources been started. Up to now the regulations of various types of fishing effort have no effect. This condition is particularly serious along the coastal belt (inside 3 miles) where trawler fishing operates illegally in conflict with small-scale coastal fishing, sports fishing and, indirectly, lagoon fishing.

Thus numerous fishing categories operate on the same stock completely independently and without any control. For example, the following types of fishing are practiced on species such as sea bass and sea bream;

1. Small-scale coastal fishing with gill nets, trammel nets, long lines, small purse seine;
2. Coastal trawling inside three miles;
3. Sports fishing (lines and diving);
4. Fry fishing along the shores, at the mouth and in the canals;
5. Lagoon fishing.

With so many different and intensive types of fishing, over-fishing conditions are inevitable and so is the progressive reduction of fish recruitment in lagoons. Hence the necessity of artificial seeding for those lagoons situated in coastal areas that are most heavily exploited. From this point of view, the Italian lagoons are in the worst conditions.

Fish restocking and defensive actions to eliminate trawler fishing inside three mile zone have been affected through artificial reefs in some Italian areas, and they could create interesting reproduction oasis in sea areas opposite coastal lagoons, to restore the over-exploited stocks to their original levels.

## Integrated Aquaculture

Modern aquaculture of marine fish species in Italy is developing in lagoon areas, where tradition and available land suitable to this type of development are present.

The concept of integrated aquaculture was developed on the criterion of creating intensive units in the lagoon areas.

Intensive farms are mainly concerned with eels, sea bass and sea bream. The principle of the integrated units is that of re-using the flowing waters from intensive to extensive or semi-intensive, both to reduce electricity costs for pumping and to utilize the residual trophic energy.

At present, these technologies are in the course of definition, because the management of the fertilized effluents of intensive units is not easy, especially in relation to the development of impressive biomass of sea weed (*i.e. Ulva, Enteromorpha* etc.) when operating with salinities close to that of sea water.

Within the lagoon system, another limit to the development of integrated activities is the quality of the waters, because it is often necessary to use waters without the qualities required for the correct management of intensive units.

Of greater interest as management models of lagoon environments are semi-intensive rearings established in lagoon areas. These approaches prompt the consideration that, with sufficient availability of hatchery seed, the lagoon itself might be run, in the future, as a very light semi-intensive holding unit.

Rearing experiments with brackish water earthen ponds of various dimensions (from 1000 m to 5-10 ha) have been carried out in recent years. Experiments have been made with fish undersized for the market caught at the fish barriers and reared in ponds. In these basins the diet was based on fresh fish and mixed foods. Sea bream of 140 g reached commercial size averaging around 400 g in about 12 months, with an 86 per cent survival rate.

Other semi-intensive rearing experiments significant for the running of lagoon environments concern the *Penaeus japonicus*. Besides the mention seeding experiment in the lagoons, many trials are being conducted at the production of these shrimps in earthen ponds.

The easiness with which the seed of *P. japonicus* can be obtained is encouraging many operators to rear this species in eutrophized earthen ponds. The average production is around 250 kg/ha/yr. With an average seeding of two post-larvae(p.22-p.30) per square meter obtaining in monoculture, a survival percentage of 70 per cent and in association with other species, around 20 per cent .

In general, the development of semi-intensive rearing seems promising in the field of research of management strategies for coastal lagoons, and once some limiting factors such as seed availability and conflicts in land utilization area are overcome, this could be the future exploitation trend in lagoon environments.

From the analysis of the Italian experience, the following general recommendations may be drawn, above all directed to those responsible for taking decisions at technical, administrative and political level.

1. Coastal lagoons constitute ecosystems with peculiar productive characteristics whose potential resources, generally of high economic value, may be exploited and transformed with modest means. Therefore, lagoons must be protected and managed as a national resource of primary interest, especially where the food deficits call for serious political commitment tending to the rational exploitation of all renewable resources.

2. The lagoon, or a part of it, properly delimited, represents a true "aquaculture farm" preset by nature in which it is possible to seed, increase productivity and supply food as any practice of aquaculture requires.

3. It has been found that the best productive strategies in coastal lagoons are those based upon optimization of the ecological characteristics of the system; for instance, a correct hydraulic management guarantees a correct supply of nourishment, a rich migration of juveniles from the sea (where this resource still exists), a possibility of seasonal catch during the migratory phase. Intensive fish farming utilizing lagoon surfaces and lagoon water not given good results. In this case, the selection of an autonomous site instead of a body of lagoon water is better.

4. From the viewpoint of resource management, all the methods of highly selective capture for commercial sizes have to be magnified; most advanced models of fish barrier has to be selected. The non-commercial sizes of the valuable species may also be routed toward cages or intensive fish farming

points, so creating other opportunities of income for the lagoon, while exploiting a collective resource.

5. The problem of lagoon management must be approached as a complex part of environmental management in which all the components of an environmental character have to be analyzed in physical, biological, economic, social and cultural terms. On ly a correct collection that accounts for the other components and the conflicts among the potential users of the lagoon, fisheries and aquaculture may find a just collocation.

6. Italian experience teaches that where the various components of the lagoon reality are not accounted for, fisheries and aquaculture have been the most penalized sector, just because they are directly dependent upon environmental quality. Fisheries and aquaculture are even instruments of environmental conservation; the fishermen are in fact supervisors and permanent witnesses of the environmental status, because their income depends upon it.

7. Finally the evolution of Italian aquaculture shows that it is possible to implement projects that, starting from traditional lagoon management, can develop production strategies based on even more complex biotechnologies.

# Indian Lagoons

A number of lagoons are present on the east and west coast of India. There are 17 noteworthy lagoons (8 on the east and 9 on the west) along the Indian coasts. The lagoons on the east coast are; Chilka, Pulicat, Pennar, Bendi, Nizampatnam, Muttukadu, Muthupet and Gulf of Mannar. Along the west coast of India, there are nine important coastal lagoons. They are Vembanad, Ashtamudi, Paravur, Ettikulam, Veli, Murukumpuzha, Talapady, Lagoons of Bombay coast and Lagoons of Lakshadweep atolls.

# Pulicat Lake

Pulicat lake is the largest lagoon on the Coromandel coast of India, extending between the South Andhra Pradesh and the North Tamil Nadu States, running north to south parallel to the coast, being separated by a narrow of strip, called the Sriharikota Island.

Its water spread area was about 461 sq. km, but the lake has been shrinking so fast due to siltation, particularly in the northern regions, that its water spread area may be hardly about 300 sq. km today.

The lake can be divided into two regions, the northern region with shallow and turbid (15-20 cm) and the southern region with deeper and less turbid (35-40 cm). The turbidity has a profound influence on faunal composition of the lagoon.

The lagoon, at its southern end, opens through a narrow lake mouth, just about 200 m wide and hardly one meter deep, which during post-monsoon seasons gets partially closed up, by the formation of sand bar, extending from the southern end to a variable extent towards the north. During some years, after persistent drought, year after year, the lake mouth gets closed up completely, bringing about drastic changes in the hydrological as well as biodiversity composition in the lake.Two monsoon rivulets, that flow into the lake only during monsoon, bring in a lot of silt. The Buckingham Canal (East Coast Canal) also flows through the lake for a short distance.

## Physico-chemical Characteristics

Temperatures range between 25-32,8 degree Celsius in the northern region, and between 25.2 and 30.8 degree Celsius in the southern region of the lake, both regions, however, have two peaks in the year, during April-June and August-October. Temperature is higher than in normal years, when the lake mouth closes completely.

Salinity has a single peak during the year, and it fluctuates widely in the northern region (0.5-51.5 ppm) whereas in the southern region, it may fluctuate between 7.3 and 40 ppm. In the years of the lake mouth closure,it may rise to hyper-saline conditions, with salinities between 52-57 ppm.

Higher values of dissolved oxygen are noted in the lake during the monsoons and post-monsoon months, and lower values during simmer and pre-monsoon months. During the closure of the lake mouth, it may go down to 2.1-3.3 ml/l, particularly during the months of May-August, and more so in the northern region.

## Biodiversity

Pulicat lake, as lagoon, is unique in India, because through the Buckingham canal that runs through the lake, it is inter-connected with four major rivers (Godavari, Krishna, Pennar and Palar), 18 small rivulets and numerous brackish waters on the Coromandel coast, so that the lake receives as well as discoerses a wide variety of biodiversity to all these water bodies, and it is a reservoir for the brackish water biodiversity.

As per the records maintained, 168 varieties of fish, 12 varieties of prawns, 34 varieties of crabs, 19 varieties of bivalves, 8 varieties of gastropods, 2 varieties of cephalopods and 2 varieties of turtles were recorded form the lagoon.

Nearly 50 thousand traditional fisher folk, living in 52 villages around the lake and another 50 thousand backward people living a little further away from this lake are dependent directly or indirectly on the resources of the lagoon for their livelihoods. All these one lakh of poor people, with their daily activities of fishing, hand-picking juvenile prawns and shell mining in the lake have a profound influence on the biodiversity of the lagoon

Pulicat lake offers ideal habitat for certain species endemic to the region, like the edible oyster, *Crassostrea madrasensis* and the southern region of the lagoon provides for extensive beds for this oyster, although harvesting and conservation are uncared for by all stakeholders. Similarly, the mud crab or the lagoon crabs, *Scylla serrata* and *Scylla tranquebarica* are endemic to the brackish waters of the South East Asia, and in fact, Pulicat Lake in India yields the largest amount of these crabs in the country. Tiger prawn, *Penaeus monodon*, the fastest-growing giant prawn contributes up to 10 per cent of the total catches consisting of 12 species of prawns in te Pulicat Lake. All these three species are over-exploited from the lagoon for local consumption as well as for export.

Since past thirty years, local fishermen have been complaining that nine species of fish and the tiger prawn have been rapidly dwindling in numbers in Pulicat Lake, and another eight species of fish and the mud crabs are also declining since last ten years.

## Threatened Biodiversity and Restoration

Most of the threats to the ecosystem and biodiversity of Pulicat lake are man-made, but occasionally, severe cyclones, like the one which hit the lagoon directly during November, 1984 and brought about lasting ecological and biodiversity degradations. Super-numerary lake-mouths were formed and lake bottom was severely churned and deep pits and high mounds of sand were formed at unusual places in the lake, siltation was severe, choking navigational channels and killing all benthic biodiversity, prawns were washed away in the floods to several kilometers into the coastal waters, strange deep-sea fish and other species drifted into the lake, and fishing was unproductive for several months after the cyclone.

## Over-fishing

Ever since prawn and crab exports from the Pulicat Lake have started in early 1970s, over-fishing for prawn, day and night resulted rapid depletion of stocks in the Pulicat Lake. Even non-fishermen used destructive drag-nets (Konda valai) at night, and traditional fishermen used fine meshed stake net (Ara valai) during the day, resulting the depletion of prawn stocks of the lake by 24-hour fishing. Mud crabs have gone down in numbers and in size, indicating the incidence of over-fishing.

There are several indigenous methods of fishing, including hand-picking of juvenile prawns from shallow waters in the southern region by tribal women, of which many are destructive to habitats as well as to species.

Oyster beds (*Crassostrea madrasensis*) planted by the Madras Fisheries Department during 1920s flourished very well in the southern region of Pulicat Lake and got established. But the oyster-meat was not of any commercial use, not even the local people including the tribal were relishing it as food.Only oyster shells were used for burning them into lime, with the ultimate result that clandestine trade was established for these shells. Consequently, oyster beds began to disappear in the Pulicat Lake. Some species of fish have become rarer and even disappeared. Earlier they have been flocking to the oyster beds as to fish aggregating devices and with the disappearance of these oyster-beds, such fish also have disappeared.

In other words, oysters have been functioning as keystone species in the southern region of the Pulicat Lake, but with the over-exploitation of such keystone species, the whole benthic biodiversity in the lake was annihilated Therefore, in eco-restoration and biodiversity restoration in the Pulicat Lake, it is necessary to restore first, the vanishing oyster beds, the keystone species, in order to restore the whole benthic biodiversity composition, associated with oyster beds.

## Conservation of Biodiversity of Pulicat Lake

1. Lake mouth – Unless the Pulicat lake mouth into the adjacent sea (Bay of Bengal) is permanently kept open, Pulicat Lake ceases to be a coastal lagoon, and the whole biodiversity composition of this lagoon would not only change but would even dwindle down. Therefore, the lake-mouth should be permanently kept open either through the construction of a groyne or break water at the southern end of the lake mouth or by dredging annually during the monsoon either mechanically or manually.

2. Dredging the Lake – Strip dredging or deepening of the lake, in a phased could be done scientifically, taking care not to destroy the benthic biodiversity in one indiscriminate dredging. Creation of deep pits would help to retain water and biodiversity for a longer duration in the year, and also to provide shelters and breeding sites for some species.

3. Mangroves could be planted, all along thr lake margins, not only to bind the soil but also to prevent top-soil erosion and siltation of the lake. Mangroves have other multiple benefits for a brackish water ecosystem.

4. Restoration of biodiversity

    i) Habitat improvement – Artificial habitats to replace the destroyed natural habitats could be innovated and implemented, Development of weed beds, benthic vegetation that ultimately promote detritus, so necessary for benthic life, and hard artificial substrata like roof tiles, coconut shells and oyster shells for promoting the settlement of encrusting bio-foulers could be tried. N

    ii) Keystone species – Edible oysters in the Pulicat Lake, which are the keystone species should not be destroyed, but should be propagated.

    iii) Captive breeding – Nurseries for the production of prawn, crab and fish-seed could be developed at a cottage level, in fishing villages around the lake, and seed so produced could be stocked in to the lake, at a proper stage.

    iv) Juvenile stocking – Wild seed of prawn, crab and fish could be collected from the lake-mouth, during the season when they ingress into the lake, and stocked into the lake to supplement the seed that naturally ingresses into the lake through the lake-mouth.

5. Regulating fishing – Fishing regulation on Pulicat Lake, through extension of the Paadu management system to all the villages around the lake and strengthening the system may achieve a more sustainable management of the lake resources.

Ban on destructive gear like scoop-net, shore seine, stake net and drag net could be imposed, since some of them disturb the bottom habitat and others destroy the juveniles. Mesh size of other nets could be regulated as not to trap juveniles and sub-adults.

Some destructive indigenous methods of fishing, like oothu, vallikodi and hand picking, practiced by tribals should be discouraged by providing alternate means of livelihoods for those who have been exclusively depended on such traditional but destructive methods of fishing in the lake.

Mechanized trawlers should not be allowed to operate within 12 km from the Pulicat Lake mouth, particularly during the breeding migration of prawns, so that their reproductive potential is not destroyed.

## Conservation and Management of Fisheries in Chilka Lagoon

Chilka Lake, the largest brackish water lagoon in Asia, like other lake or lagoon is not static, reaches the late stage of natural evolution from marine to brackish water to fresh water system. The rate of this transition has been accelerated due to land use practices, which increased erosion and sedimentation and reduced tidal exchange and flushing.

Significant physical changes are occurring in the lake; exhibiting;

1. Shrinkage of water spread area of the lake from 906 sq.km in 1915 to 790 sq km in 1986;
2. Ten-fold increase in weed covered areas between 1973 and 1985, estimated to be expanding by 14.6 sq km per year;
3. Being remarkably shallow and getting shallower (the minimum depth of 0.38-1.5 m and maximum depth of 2.15-3.85 m during high water in 1990-91 as against the maximum depth of 3.9 m).
4. Highest salinity of 8-12 ppt in the southern end of the lake, which gradually decrease toward the north;
5. Hardly perceptible tidal effect in Rambha and at the mouth of Daya and Bhargabi rivers; and
6. Dynamic nature of the shifting mouth of the lagoon over decades.

The potential loss of marine influences and lagoon characteristics due to evolution of fresh water system in Chilka Lake, would likely cause significant decline in the diversity and value of the fisheries of the lake.

## Lagoon Ecology

Relevant features of the ecosystem directly supporting or contributing to fisheries and aquaculture production in Chilka lagoon from lower trophic levels to commercial aquatic resources have been indicated.

High nutrient concentrations are often present in the lagoon as a result of both riverine nutrient inputs and effective nutrient recycling between the sediments and the water column.

The food chain of Chilka Lake is poorly described. While species descriptions exist for the different trophic levels, the functional relationships between macrophytes, herbivores, detritivores and carnivores are unavailable. Published information on decomposition rates of *Potamogeton pectinatus* (Howard-Williams and Davies, 1079) suggests that this macrophyte rapidly breaks down to form usable detritus in aquatic food chains. A number of commercial species, including mullets and prawns consume aquatic plants and detritus directly. There is a likelihood that the spread of aquatic vegetation has stimulated the production of herbivorous species within Chilka Lake, mediated by increases to their food supply.

Time series records for fish landings do not support the notion that the spread of vegetation has had a deleterious effect on the overall fish production within the lagoon. It is likely that the expansion of vegetation has affected fish production through alterations in fish community structure, and this impact is confounded by simultaneous changes to lagoon salinity conditions and harvesting effects associated with operation of the fishery.

Both zooplankton and benthic organisms (secondary producers) provide an important trophic link between the plant and detrital carbon sources produced within Chilka Lake and the fish species consume them.

## Fish, Prawn and Crab Fauna

The Chilka lagoon harbors 225 species of fish, prawn and crab and is an important source of fish, prawn and crab in Odisha. Of these, 158 species of fish and prawn have been identified from the lagoon of which 27 species belong to freshwater and the rest are of marine origin (three more freshwater fishes and five marine speccies were added later).

The lagoon forms the breeding ground for 44 species of fish besides Gobiids and some mullets. Fishes of commercial importance contributed more than54 percent of the average annual landings of the lagoon. More than 50 percent of the lagoon's commercial species need sea water for completion of their life cycle.

Successful lake-ward or sea-ward migration essentially depend upon the salinity gradient, which decreases from about 34 ppt to a very low level and a gradual rising and falling salinity gradient exercises directive influence on the migration of Chilka fish either way.

The most important conditions pertinent to the fisheries of the lagoon are favorable environment and food for their growth and access to move to the sea for spawning and the same for the entries of post larvae and juveniles of all varieties into the lagoon.

## Commercial Activities in the Lagoon

Fishing is the single largest commercial activities of the lagoon. The fisheries of central part of the lagoon that remained full of water all the year round, remained the exclusive right of the government in pre-independence, while the waters of creeks and channels, which becomes dry in summer were owned private estate holders. Fisheries in the areas belonging to their land holdings were leased out to private fish merchants, who used to sub-lease them to the fishermen at a higher rate. The right of land holders over fisheries was later transferred to the government under Orissa Estate Abolition Act.

## Fishing Methods

Depending on the following methods, there are only 14 well defined fishing gears are in use in the Chilka Lagoon; (a) Jano fishing – a community fishing, enclosing fish in shallow water areas by bamboo screens. To-day, due to very shallow water close to land, the major part of the enclosement is made of low mud bundhs. Bamboo screens are used only in some openings of the mud wall. In little deeper water split bamboo screen are used to close the jano in a few minutes with the help of 30 to 40 nahas. Between 13 to 22 percent of lagoon's annual catches are accounted by janos and the production from a normal jano was estimated to be 124 kg/ha per person. Mullets, sea bass, perches are the main catches from janos.

The net fishing contributes nearly 50 to 66 percent of annual fish catch from the lagoon. Many of the nets are more selective in respect of particular fish species. The net fishing intensity varies during the year and is low during October-December coinciding with jano season.

Three types of trap are in operation in the Chilka lagoon of which large prawn trap made of split bamboo are set in shallow waters to catch prawn. Smaller prawn traps are operated by Tiara fishermen of the lagoon. Besides a rectangular box type bamboo traps are used in large numbers to catch crabs

A box type net trap, made of HDPE twine has replaced the bamboo traps and thattas and is popularized in the lagoon for its comparatively low cost and more catching efficiency.

To catch catfish, a long line of 70-100 m attached with hooks at an interval of 3 to 3.5 m is stressed across the water with one end tied to pole and the other with the boat. Rotten prawn and fish are used as baits.

Spear fishing is practiced in the lagoon during dark nights. A burning lamp is so hung from the fore-deck of the boat that remains just above the water level. A man holding four pronged iron spear attached to a bamboo pole measuring 3 m stands at the end of the fore-deck, while another noiselessly punts the boat from rear end. The man in the fore-deck spears the fish as it comes close to the boat, being attracted with naked light. Chiefly mullets are speared in large quantities.

## Fishery

A distinct rising trend of prawn and fish catch of Chilka lagoon have been noticed from 1929 to 1994. Downward trend persisted for two years in 1952 and 1953; nine years in 1958 to 1966; three years years in 1975 to 1977, two years in 1987 to 1988 and for four years in 1991 to 1994.

The fishery of the lagoon after each spell of low annual catch showed upward trend, which some times take as long as nine years to recover. As such, it will not be proper to apprehend depletion of fish prawn population in the lagoon after noticing downward trend for a few years.

The crab landings of the lagoon, however, show a distinct downward trend after initial rise from 1972 onwards till 1982 reaching its peak and there after fall in the catch for last 11 years.

While considering the percentage of fish and prawn groups of the lagoon in three spells, prawn and mullets, the prized species of the lagoon, exhibited a downward trend, while cat fish and miscellaneous fish as a group were dominant in the annual catch in recent years when compared from their percentage composition of initial years.

It has been estimated that the annual fish yield from the lagoon averaged about 90 kg per hectare during 1980s, range being 65 to 122 kg per ha.

## Conservation of Fishery Resources

From time immemorial, the lagoon has supported a subsistence and commercial fishery, providing a means of transportation and most of the population depends on the in-lake and coastal fishery as major and minor occupations.

During last two decades, the lagoon has come under increasing use pressure by an expanding local population. Nutrient loading of the lake is increasing caused by domestic wastes, agriculture and aquaculture practices. Sedimentation rates in the upper and more sheltered areas have increased.

Residents have noticed reduced fish catches, deteriorating water quality and increasing problems associated with increasing fresh water conditions The annual fishery yield of the lagoon is declining to 3329 tonnes (1993-94). Overfishing, deteriorating water quality associated with increasing nutrient loads are probably contributing factors to declining lagoon fishery.

## Impact of Shrimp Farming on Lagoon Ecology

Extensive shrimp farming in the lagoon area presently utilize an estimated 25 per cent of the lake margin strip, which normally dries up during non-monsoon season. Some impingement of culture area on the permanent lake waters also occurs. As a result, the use of these areas by wild fish population of the lagoon is restricted. Such removal of productive areas of the lagoon is believed to have impacts on lagoon fish population and consequently on the capture fisheries.

It is therefore necessary to find out scientific basis about the limits to how much of this habitat can be used for prawn farming without negative impacts on wild fish population of the lagoon.

Prawn farming in Chilka is now causing conflicts with ongoing traditional fisheries and other water uses (*e.g.* water transportation, animal grazing etc). Expanding prawn farming in the lagoon will change the present land uses and the conflicts will intensify.

## To Protect Ecology of the Lagoon

Renewable fisheries resources within Chilka lagoon provide a sustainable protein source and economic commodity of critical habitats and population of the lagoon can be protected and maintained. Political, social, economic and technical factors all pose significant constraints for effective fisheries management in Chilka lagoon.

Chilka lagoon without enhancement of salinity level from the present level, will undergo a steady transformation from the current state to a system that is increasingly less productive without increased circulation, rising nutrient load, increased sedimentation ultimately leading to anoxic bottom condition. This process will affect aquaculture operations as well as natural fish populations of the lagoon.

Without enhanced circulation and salinity, any aquaculture activity would likely be at increasing risk of these dystrophic events. Earthen ponds or pen enclosures isolated from the direct lake circulation will risk the water management measures leading to lower production level. The successful aquaculture activities of Chilka lagoon, will therefore be to manage larger areas, preferably the lagoon as a whole, without creating any isolated areas and obstructions in the lagoon system with lower rates of production.

The Chilka lagoon itself can be stocked with prawn seeds like the Seto Island of Japan, to get more catch of prawn. As the lake is shallow and eutrophic in nature having optimal salinity range not exceeding 20 ppt, it provides better conditions for faster growth of prawns than in sea. The escape of stocked seeds is highly restricted as the lake is connected to the sea with narrow channel.

Increased fresh water influence in the Chilka Lagoon will preclude many of the organisms that are currently found in the brackish water system. This will have impact on both existing aquaculture practices, as well as, many of the brackish water and salt water species represented in lagoon's flora and fauna. For the impact that these changes would have on the local and regional economics, it is advisable to intervene by enhancing the circulation of sea water to the lake system to protect the estuarine character of Chilka ecosystem with all its genetic diversity, optimizing of salinity condition of the lagoon for improving fishery potential which will have significant bearing on the socio-economic condition of large numbers of poor fishermen living in and around the lake.

De-silting of the lagoon and especially of Magarmukh and Palur canal by dredging will ensure the flow in and out of Chilka to Bay of Bengal and help in restoring the salinity gradient of the lagoon

Steps may also be taken to augment fishery potential by higher recruitment of prawn and fish juveniles from adjacent Bay of Bengal to the lake.

The stabilized brackish water environment (5 to 27 ppt), after initial enhancement efforts in Chilka lagoon will offer opportunities strongly in favor of production of marine shrimps (*Penaeus monodon, P. indicus*) and fish (mullets, seabass, perches and other oceanic varieties) with the following advantages

1. They are of high economic values;
2. There are existing marketing infrastructure and contacts;
3. Seed for auto-stocking and supplementary stocking available locally;
4. Technical know-how available locally.

## Fisheries Management in and around Chilka Lake

Awareness among residents in and around Chilka lake and general public are to be promoted about the lake system and their participation in the management process have to be ensured.

A fisheries management program for protecting important fish habitats, fish stocks and regulating fishing activities have to be strictly enforced. For that a community based resource conservation and development with extensive local village participation and responsibility is necessary.

Fisheries management within Chilka lake occurs primarily through the allocation of leases. There are few fishing regulations, and limited capabilities for enforcement. While this system operated reasonably effectively in the past, the increased demands placed upon the resource by an ever-increasing number of participants in the lagoon fishery have caused over-exploitation and inefficient utilization of the resource. In future it will be necessary to develop effective mechanisms which control total fishing effort, and serve to allocate fishery resources in an equitable fashion. Any such mechanisms need to be carefully and sensitively designed, in view of the dependence of many local communities and fisherfolk upon Chilka fishery resources. Potential harvesting over harvesting of several marine species (including prawns) within the lagoon is offset by the recruitment of juveniles from the neighbouring marine areas within the bay of Bengal. It is critical for the sustained operation of the Chilka lake fishery, that such marine areas are maintained as reserves and protected from fisheries exploitation in future. Within Chilka Lake there are currently no conservation zones, where fish stocks are protected from exploitation (with the exception of the Palur Canal and the lagoon mouth). Such conservation zones need to be established in areas, where fish spawning is localized.

In the past fisheries management within the Chilka Lagoon was primarily through allocation of leases of fisheries sources of the lake primarily for capture fisheries (except Jano fisheries, where impoundment of fishes and prawns for 2 to 4 months have been made so as to grow and catch in intervals).

Since 1985, higher prices for prawn has led to the commercialization of prawn farming in Chilka lagoon, which has made non-traditional fishermen, particularly farmers living in and around the lagoon, to enter into prawn culture. This resulted more and more illegal occupation of land and water in and around the lake for prawn farming.

With the advent of prawn culture technology in early eighties and to protect the Chilka lagoon from ecological hazards, conflict and litigation in the present " no change" condition, the culture and capture fisheries together with the areas which will be considered for culture and capture fisheries in Chilka lake with minimum ecological disbalance was defined as follows;

## Capture Fishery

Capture sources in Chilka mean the traditional sources like, Jano, Dian, Uthapani and Bahanis, but shall not include;

(a) the areas earmarked for culture of fish and prawn;

(b) the areas conserved for migration of fish and prawn including their juveniles;

(c) the areas earmarked as nursery and grazing grounds of juveniles of prawn and fish;

(d) the areas declared as birds and wildlife sanctuaries in the lake;

(e) the areas earmarked as migratory path of fish and prawn including their juveniles;

(f) natural navigation channels of the lake, from, where the aquatic produce (fish and prawn) can not be totally harvested/taken out at any point of time.

## Culture Fishery

The culture sources will include, the controllable confined areas between inter-tidal zone of Chilka lake, where the aquatic animals (fish and prawn) can be held up for certain time inorder to fatten them to grow, and the produce from the area can be totally harvested at any point of time, but shall not include;

(a) the areas conserved for migration and nursery and grazing grounds of fish and prawns including their juveniles;

(b) the areas declared as bird and wildlife sanctuaries in the lake, and

(c) areas earmarked as migratory path and navigational channels of the lake.

## Explanation

The inter-tidal zone of Chilka means the area between high and low water mark of the lake in patches (not contiguous) excluding the areas earmarked for nursery and grazing ground of fish and prawn and their juveniles, migratory path of fish and prawn including their juveniles, natural navigation channel of the lake, the area declared as sanctuaries for birds and wildlife, which get fully dried and exposed to solar radiation, at least some part of the year so as to have a natural disinfected and easily bio-degradable top soil before starting the next culture operation.

All capture sources may be leased out to the Central Fishermen Cooperative Marketing Society, Balugaon who in turn shall sub-lease them to the affiliated primary societies. The capture fishery sources may be divided into convenient operational size in the interest of better management. In no case, the operational size shall exceeds 1000 acres. The annual lease value of each capture source (prawn and non-prawn) shall be fixed at by adding 10 percent to the preceding years lease value.

Each such primary society shall be given a culture fishery source of not more than 100 acres at the offset price of 800 rupees per acre per annum with 10 percent increase in successive years.

Rest of the culture sources can be leased out to the societies/organizations formed by the inhabitants of the neighbouring villages who are not members of the primary societies of fishermen.

The period of lease shall be for three years beginning from the 1st day of January every year with 10 percent increase in lease value every year. On the expiry of the period of lease the right of the lesee to operate the source shall automatically cease.

The settlement of fishery sources as indicated above shall be subjected to the following stipulations.

(a) In the culture fishery only extensive prawn culture will be allowed without addition of any organic and/or inorganic fertilizer, supplementary feed, chemicals, pesticides and antibiotics at any time.

(b) The outer channel, Palur canal and navigational channels of the lake together with conserved areas earmarked for nursery and grazing grounds of fish and prawn juveniles shall not be obstructed in any way by fixing any device, such as, earthen embankment, netting of any sorts, fixing pen materials etc.

(c) The radius of one kilometer area in the lake mouth and at the opening of outer channel to the lake, Rushikulya mouth and at the opening of Palur canal into the lake shall be kept free from any obstruction as indicated above.

(d) The areas for prawn culture and conservation for nursery and grazing grounds of the prawn and fish juveniles already identified shall be demarcated in consultation with noted fishery scientists and ecologists and the identification of such areas will be reviewed and monitored at an interval of every three years keeping the above principles in view before leasing the areas afresh.

(e) The lesee shall operate the source directly and shall under no circumstances sub-let/sub-lease/permit the sources to any body and in the event of such sub-letting the source lease shall be forfeited and the lessor shall be competent to enter upon, take over possession of the fishery sources and lease it out to the others. In such circumstances the lesee shall not be entitled to any compensation and lessor in addition to taking over the sources shall realize the full lease value if not realized till then.

(f) The lessor (or any officer duly authorized by him) shall retain the right to enter into the fishery sources for the purpose of inspection, survey, measurement, enforcement of lease condition or any other purpose as deemed necessary. The lesee shall be bound to assist the lessor or any of his subordinate officer duly authorized by him) to take up such survey monitoring etc.

(g) The lesse shall always be liable to make payment of lease amount by the date as may be determined by the lessor failing which he shall always be liable to pay interest at the rate of 12 percent per annum from the date of such default over and above the outstanding lease amount.

(h) No mud wall embankment shall be erected to enclose culturable source, thus identified but with pen netting materials not below 3 mm square mesh pen wall supported by bamboo and wooden poles so as to allow free exchange of water between the culturable area and the main lake.

(i) The extent of fishery source so determined shall be in conformity with that of the map if the source maintained by Collectors of Puri, Khurda, and Ganjam districts and the Tahasildars concerned. For this purpose boundary marks shall be fixed on the spot to identify the sources and distinguish one source from the other which are to be indicated in the map prepared for the purpose.

(j) Not more than 5 (five) leader lines may be laid in a prawn source and distance between two leader lines may not be less than half a kilometer.

(k) Leader line may be laid only on the one side of the source extending from the land mass up to the main channel/Bahar Chilka. But in no case length of the leader line should exceed 250 m. indicating the maximum distance between the land mass up to the midstream of Bahar Chilka and if the distance is less than 250 m. then the length of the leader line may be limited to that extent. In other words, if the distance of the leader line from the land mass up to midstream of Bahar Chilka will be limited to only 250 m. only.

(l) The leader lines shall be removed after the prawn season is over, but the lesee society shall have the right to catch fish by other means till the lease period expires subject to the condition as above.

(m) The period of operation for different types of sources shall be as follows subject to the restrictions imposed above

  (i) Bahani Throughout the year

  (ii) Jano From September to January

  (iii) Uthapani From July to September

  (iv) Dian From July to October

  (v) Prawn From February to July.

  Size of traps and nets etc. used as devices for catching fish shall be as follows;

  1. Bazza: Its height, length and breadth shall not exceed 32, 21 and 8 inches respectively.

  2. Dhaudi: Its height, length and breadth shall not exceed 12, 36, and 12 inches respectively.

(n) Collectors and the concerned Tahasildars shall have the power to seize boats/nets/bazza/dhaudi etc. involving clandestine catching of fish. On every such seizure minimum penalty of 1000 rupees shall be imposed on boats including out-board engine fitted boats having hull length of less then 25 feet and 2500 rupees for boats having hull length of more than 25 feet and 5000 rupees for mechanized boats such as trawlers.

(o) Violation of any one or more of the aforesaid conditions shall be sufficient for termination of lease by the collectors concerned.

(p) The machinery for enforcement of this lease principles shall consist of one platoon of Armed Force with an Executive Magistrate who shall move frequently in the lake and shall be answerable to Collectors of the concerned district.

(q) The license fee of fifty rupees each per annum shall be paid by all boats which are not larger than full length of 25 feet and 100 rupees for boats larger than this size. They shall be allotted a serial number which would prominently be displayed in red color over white both on the stem end and on the stern.

(r) The conditions of the lease deed that shall be executed between the collector and the Cooperative Marketing Federation, Bhubaneswar shall form part of the lease deed to be executed between the Primary Fishermen Cooperative Society and the Cooperative Marketing Federation, Bhubaneswar.

(s) Restrictions as would be imposed by the Fisheries and Animal Resources Development Department, under the Orissa Marine Fishing Act, 1981 shall be followed scrupulously, which relates to conservation of Chilka lake fisheries as under;

The State Government do hereby regulate fishing in the Palur Canal and Chilka in the following manner;

(i) Fishing by any method is prohibited in Palur Canal throughout the year.

(ii) Capture of Khainga, Kabla. Bhekti below one hundred fifty mm size and prawns like Bagda and Chapra varieties below hundred mm size by any means is prohibited throughout the year in Chilka lake.

(iii) Fishing is completely prohibited in the outer channel of Chilka lake during the months of December and January.

(iv) Prawns which are not growing above 2 inches (5 cm) as specified below can be caught in the outer channel of the Chilka lake during the months of February and March.

| Description of prawn (Scientific Name) | Local name (in Oriya) |
| --- | --- |
| Metapenaeus monoceros | MORODA |
| Metapenaeus dobsonii | PANU |
| Metapenaeus affinis | GHASUA |

(v) No fishing by means of net shall be allowed in the outer channel throughout the year. Fishing, however, by other means like Khanda, Thatta and Baza can be undertaken in the outer channel. But no Khanda shall enter into the deeper zone of the outer channel.

The areas of outer channel and Palur Canal are as stated below;

Outer channel – Starting from tip of Retamati (Satpada) up to mouth of Chilka lake.

Distance 25 kilometer within     Latitude 19.39 to 19.44 degree;

                                 Longitude 85.26 to 85.38 degree.

Palur Canal Starting from Rambha Bay up to mouth of River Rushikulya;

Distance – 15 kilometer within Latitude 19.22'45 to 19.29'30 degree Longitude – 85.04'45 to 85.08'30 degree.

The State Government do hereby prohibit fishing of prawn larve (PL-20) and juveniles (30-50 mm size) from (a) Krushna prasad up to 2 km, north of Chilka lake mouth in Puri district (b) 2 km of South of Chilka Lake mouth covering Rushikulya estuary and Palur Canal in Ganjam district.

# Chapter 12

# Development and Management of Reservoir Fisheries

Reservoirs, also known as man-made lakes, are formed by impounding rivers or other flowing waters by way of construction of dams across them. Reservoirs are defined as "Man-made" impoundments created by erecting dams across rivers, streams or any water courses. In Asia, including India, reservoirs play an important role in inland fishery development. The primary purposes of reservoirs are hydel-power generation, agriculture, industries and flood control.

In India, there are 19370 reservoirs, spread over in 15 States, covering an area of 3.15 million ha. This area is expected to increase in the near future due to the execution of various water projects in the country for irrigation and power.

Reservoirs provide vast opportunities of culture-based-capture fisheries. Based on the water spread area, reservoirs are categorized as small (above 10 ha to less than 1000 ha), medium (1000 ha -5000 ha) and large (more than 5000 ha). Tamil Nadu has the highest number of small reservoirs followed by Karnataka and Andhra Pradesh with 8895,4651 and 2898 units respectively. So far as medium category of reservoirs are concerned, Madhya Pradesh is at the top in total area, as well as in water spread area, followed by the States of Karnataka and Andhra Pradesh. The maximum number of large reservoirs is in the State of Karnataka (12 units) but the total area is less when compared to that of Andhra Pradesh which has 7 units. Considering vastness of the resource and its production potential, these reservoirs have become the main inland capture fisheries sources for the future fisheries development in India.

Nearly half of the projected annual demand of 3 million tonnes of additional inland fish can be contributed by the reservoirs by the end of 2012 (Sugunan, 2009).

# Reservoir Fishery Resources of India

Sugunan (1995) has categorized 19370 reservoirs, covering an area of 3,153,366 ha of different sizes (area) having fishery resources as below;

1. Small (less than 100 ha) – 19134 covering an area of 1465557 ha.
2. Medium (between 1000-5000 ha) – 180 covering an area of 527541 ha
3. Large – 56 covering an area of 1140268 ha

### State-Wise List of Important Reservoirs in India

| Sl.No. | State and Reservoirs | River on which Located | Location | Area (ha) |
|--------|----------------------|------------------------|----------|-----------|
| **Andhra Pradesh** | | | | |
| 1. | Osmansagar Dam | Musi | Medan | 4200.99 |
| 2. | Himayatsagar Dam | Issi | Medan | 3807.00 |
| 3. | Nagarjunasagar Dam | Krishna | Nalagonda | 30303.00 |
| 4. | Nizamsagar Dam | Mowgina | Nizamabad | 14636.09 |
| 5. | Mopad Dam | Mammore | Nellore | 1693.00 |
| 6. | Other reservoirs | – | – | 78326.00 |
| **Bihar** | | | | |
| 1. | Panchet Dam | Damodar | Santal Parganas | 7511.00 |
| 2. | Maithon Dam | Barakar | Santal Parganas | 11491.00 |
| 3. | Konar Dam | Konar | Santal Parganas | 2792.00 |
| 4. | Tilaiya Dam | Barakar | Hazaribagh | 6435.00 |
| 5. | Mayurakshi Dam | – | Hazaribagh | 6734.00 |
| 6. | Other reservoirs | – | – | 2245.00 |
| **Gujarat** | | | | |
| 1. | Mahi Stage II | – | – | 16576.00 |
| 2. | Ukai | – | – | 51282.00 |
| 3. | Other reservoirs | – | – | 15081.00 |
| **Jammu and Kashmir** | | | | |
| 1. | Lidder Project | – | – | 116550.00 |
| **Kerala** | | | | |
| 1. | Periyar Barage | Periyar | Kottayam | 606.00 |
| 2. | Neyyar Dam | Neyyar | Trivandrum | 9065.00 |
| 3. | Other reservoirs | – | – | 9755.62 |
| **Madhya Pradesh** | | | | |
| 1. | Tawa multipurpose project | Tawa | Hoshangabad | 29553.77 |
| 2. | Gandhisagar | Chambal | Mandisaur | 64750.00 |
| 3. | Barodia | – | Shajapur | 6879.04 |
| 4. | Other reservoirs | – | – | 50883.93 |

*Contd...*

*Contd...*

| Sl.No. | State and Reservoirs | River on which Located | Location | Area (ha) |
|---|---|---|---|---|
| **Tamil Nadu** | | | | |
| 1. | Bhavanisagar | Bhavani | Coimbatore | 7861.84 |
| 2. | Stanley reservoir | Cauvery | Salem | 15343.75 |
| 3. | Poondi reservoir | Koraliyar | Chingelpet | 3263.40 |
| 4. | Other reservoirs | – | – | 23408.16 |
| **Maharashtra** | | | | |
| 1. | Shivajisagar | Koyna | Satara | 12100.48 |
| 2. | Darwa Dam | Darwa | Nasik | 3367.00 |
| 3. | Other reservoirs | – | – | 135647.23 |
| **Karnataka** | | | | |
| 1. | Tungabhadra | Tungabhadra | Hospet | 37814.00 |
| 2. | Vanivilasagar | Vedavathi | Chitradurga | 7252.00 |
| 3. | Linganamakki | Sharavathi | Shimoga | 38850.00 |
| 4. | Krishanrajasagar | Cauvery | Mysore | 12924.00 |
| 5. | Other reservoirs | – | – | 55932.00 |
| **Odisha** | | | | |
| 1. | Hirakud | Mahanadi | Sambalpur | 74592.00 |
| 2. | Other reservoirs | – | – | 5275.83 |
| **Punjab and Himachal Pradesh** | | | | |
| 1. | Beas Dam | Beas | Kangra | 26418.00 |
| 2. | Govindsagar | Sutlej | Kangra | 16838.00 |
| 3. | Other reservoirs | – | – | 111.37 |
| **Rajasthan** | | | | |
| 1. | Ranapratap sagar | – | – | 20720.00 |
| 2. | Bajajsagar | – | – | 10950.00 |
| 3. | Other reservoirs | – | – | 10250.43 |
| **Uttar Pradesh** | | | | |
| 1. | Sardasagar Dam | Chukasanda | Nainital | 7303.80 |
| 2. | Nanaksagar | Desha | Nainital | 4662.00 |
| 3. | Matatila | – | – | 20720.00 |
| 4. | Rihand | Renda | Mirzapur | 46620.00 |
| 5. | Other reservoirs | – | – | 46419.75 |
| **West Bangal** | | | | |
| 1. | Kangasabati | – | – | 11396.00 |
| 2. | D.V.C. Donar Dam | – | – | 2331.00 |
| 3. | Other reservoirs | – | – | 9840.88 |

## Reservoir Ecosystem

In reservoirs, the quality of the impounded water varies from one place to the other, depending on the type of soil, climatic condition and on the anthropogenic activities. It also varies with shape of reservoir basin, photoperiod and wind action. The quality of water changes owing to these variables.

Though reservoirs are a combination of fluviatile and lacustrine systems, a close examination of their bioptpes reveal that they have certain characteristic features of their own. The riverine and lacustrine characters coexist in reservoirs, depending on the temporal and spatial variations of certain habitat variables. For example, the lotic sector of a reservoir sustains a fluviatile biocoenos, whereas the lentic zone and the bays harbor lentic communities. During the months of heavy inflow and outflow, the whole reservoir seems to be a lotic environment whereas in summer, when the inflow and outflow from a reservoir dwindles, a more or less lentic condition prevails in most parts of it. Another unique feature of reservoirs that makes them distinctly different from their natural counterparts is the water renewal pattern marked swift changes in levels, inflow and outflow.

In India, most of the precipitation takes place during the monsoon months which contribute substantially to the surface flow. During this period, due to heavy inflow of water into the system, all outlets of the dam are usually opened. This results in total flushing. This process dislodges a considerable part of the standing crop of biotic communities at the lower trophic level and disturbs the natural primary community succession. The sudden level fluctuations also affect the benthos by exposing or submerging the substrata. Factors determining the water and soil quality in reservoirs are different from those of natural lakes. In the later, the basin soil plays a predominant role in determining the chemical water quality through soil water interphase. In the reservoirs, on the other hand, the nutrient input from the allochthonous source often determines the water quality, nutrient regime and the basic production potential. This is because of the fact that the catchment length of parent rivers is very often situated far away from the reservoir, under totally different geoclimatic conditions. Deep drawdown, wind-mediated turbulence, locking up of nutrients in the deep basins, etc, are but some of the factors that impart uniqueness to the reservoir ecosystem.

## Development and Management of Fisheries in Indian Reservoirs

A number of large, artificially constructed reservoirs came into existence as a result of the completion of various multipurpose river-vally projects for the development of the country's fishery resources. Fish production in Indian reservoirs varies from reservoir to reservoir depending upon its fisheries development. It was estimated to be 6.2 kg and 39.0 kg per ha in Tungabhadra and Stanley reservoir respectively and 250 kg/ha in Keetham, the average fish production from Indian reservoirs being only 6-7 kg/ha.

**Fish Production in Various Types of Reservoirs in India.**

| Category | Area (ha) | Production (t) | Yield (kg/ha) |
|----------|-----------|----------------|---------------|
| Small | 1485557 | 74129 | 49.90 |
| Medium | 507298 | 6488 | 12.30 |
| Large | 1160511 | 13033 | 11.43 |
| **Total** | **3153366** | **93650** | **20.13** |

Various steps usually adopted in the development of the fisheries of the Indian reservoirs are;

1. Survey of the fish fauna of the river before impoundment of the reservoir;
2. Clearance of submerged obstructions, like tree trunks, buildings etc, preferably at the pre-impoundment stage and weeds to permit easy exploitation;
3. Establishment of a fish farm to produce fish seed for seeding the reservoir;
4. stocking of the reservoir with quick growing, compatible fish seed;
5. Survey of fish seed resources to decide the necessity and intensity from extraneous sources;
6. Rehabilitation of fishermen communities on the periphery of the reservoir;
7. Organization of cooperative societies for proper marketing of fish;
8. Topographical survey of the reservoir substrata;
9. Experimental fishing before throwing open the reservoir for commercial exploitation;
10. Transporting and marketing of the fish catch;
11. Conservation and management of fish stock in the reservoir

## Pre-Impoundment Fisheries Survey of the River Basin

In few of the river valley projects completed in 1940s and 1950s, fish and fishery survey of the river basins were conducted before the construction of dams and the potential effects of impoundment on the fisheries anticipated. While recommendations regarding the provision of fish-ways, seeding, conservation etc. were made and followed with varying degree of success at different reservoirs, no efforts were made in any case to determine how the autochthonus fish fauna reacted to the deep lentic environment. Only a lone instance of Stanley reservoir may be cited wherein Raj (1941) opined that prawns, once abundant on the sandy beds of Cauvery, have disappeared after the impoundment. A complete survey of the fish and fisheries of the reservoir together with an inventory of the fishing villages, fishermen population, fishing craft and gear, so essential for planned development, is however, lacking in most cases.

## Removal of Submerged Obstructions

To facilitate easy fishing and the use of modern and effective methods of exploitation, the reservoir bottom, at least in its light penetration sections, should be free from obstructions. However, while impounding streams or rivers, no attention is generally paid by the project authorities to this important development aspect and the magnitude of the problem would become clear from the fact 629 houss in Tilaiya, 118 in Konar, 1588 in Maithon and 2119 in Panchet Hill reservoir and 90 villages and 366 towns and villages in Govindsagar Lake have been submerged apart from large forest tracts, rocks, boulders, etc. The problem of the clearance of submerged obstruction was squarely tackled in a number of smaller reservoirs constructed recently in Madhya Pradesh, Chillar (Shajapur district) and Benisagar (Panna district) being well known examples wherefrom the trees standing on reservoir beds were cut and the wood auctioned. However, it may be borne in mind that even after the reservoir is filled, it is possible to clear the obstructions at least in the reservoir margins, but at that stage the work can be taken up only in the summer months when the water level goes down and the shore areas are exposed. In Madhya Praesh, Harsi (Gwalior district), Jamonia (Sehore district) and Ghatera (Vidisha district) were completely cleared of forests of datepalm trees. An area of about 61.4 square kilometer was cleared during 1955-56 in Hirakud when the reservoir bed was dry.

Presence of aquatic vegetation not only hampers fishing but also suppresses growth of benthic fauna as it occupies the productive zones. Many of the smaller reservoirs of Madhya Pradesh and Uttar Pradesh have the menance of aquatic vegetation. Suraha Tal (Ballia district) in Uttar Pradesh is almost fully overgrown with aquatic vegetation. Use of mechanical winches may bring good results.

## Raising Fish Seed at Dam Sites

The reservoirs in Uttar Pradesh and Madhya Pradesh, being connected with Ganga river system, have a natural stock of major carps, but in view of a large volume of water impoundment by these dams, the original stock is being supplemented by stocking them regularly with major carp fingerlings. The reservoirs across other river basins, however, do not have a natural stock of major carps, hence major carp fingerlingd were planted in them.

Effective seeding operations are possible only when the fingerlings are reared near the reservoir site as the long distance transportation is an uneconomic venture. In many reservoirs fish farms were constructed. But in most cases, where the fish farms were constructed, little attention was paid either to the suitability as to their site or to the requirements of their water area commensurate with the production expected to be raised. Fish farms attached to poondi and Mettur (Tamil Nadu), Krishnarajasagar (Karnataka) and govindsagar (Haryana) reservoirs clearly bring out the fact that raising the desired number of fingerlings for stocking these may never be achieved. These sites had the greatest disadvantage of possessing porous soil where retention of water was a serious problem. The farms at poondi, Mettur and Krishnarajasagar have since been brick-lined and these are now utilized for rearing major carp fingerlings. Wet paddy fields serve as nurseries for the Amaravathy (tamil Nadu) reservoir.

# Seeding of Reservoirs

A dense stock of commercially important species of fish should be maintained in the reservoir to procure a maximum sustained yield on an economically sound basis. The reservoirs may, therefore, have to be stocked from outside sources.

It is noteworthy that even where a faunistic survey has indicated the presence of reptiles, birds and mammals, no attempts have been made to eradicate them or even to reduce their numbers. Sirsi and Lower Khajuri (Mirzapur district), Nanaksagar (Nainital district) and Sardasagar (Pilibhit district) reservoirs in Uttar Pradesh have large populations of crocodiles which need to be controlled. The Indian darters, *Anhinga melanogaster* not only take direct toll of the fishes of the Damodar Valley Corporation group of reservoirs (Bihar), but are also indirectly harmful in as much as they act as permanent hosts of certain cestode worms which parasitize the commercially important fishes particularly, *Catla catla* . The parasitized fishes have a low market value. Shooting of birds, considerably brought down the incidence of disease.

The population of predatory fishes, namely, *Mystus* spp, *Channa* spp, *Wallago attu, Silonia silondia* and others dominates the catches of many reservoirs. A study of the catch composition of some of the reservoirs of uttar Pradesh has shown that catfishes constituted 23.30 per cent and 36.8 per cent in Matatila (Jhansi district) and Sardasagar (Pilibhit district) during 1963-64; 39.79 per cent in Sardasagar during 1964-65; 27.20 per cent in Chandraprabha, Nuagarh, Bhainsura and Latifshah (Varanasi district) and 60.945 in Sardasagar and Nanaksagar during 1965-66. Similarly, in the Tungabhadra reservoir (Bellary district, Karnataka) catfishes dominate both by numbers and weight. Effective control of these and other predatory fishes is imperative for building up a population of commercially important fishes feeding on lower links of food chains.

It has been observed that certain species of fish are unable to withstand the changed hydrological conditions of the reservoiras, for example, the mahseers present in the rivers Mahanadi, Tungabhadra and Cauvery could not come up as fishery in the Hirakud (Odisha), Tungabhadra and Krishnarajasagar reservoirs (Karnataka) respectively, while *Tor tor* dominates the catches of Govindgarh reservoir (Rewa district, Madhya Pradesh) and forms a high percentage of catches in the Jaisamand Lake (Udaipur district, Rajasthan0. The catches of *Labeo fimbriatus*, present in the parent stream, declined in a few years in Nizamsagar (Nizamabad district, Andhra Pradesh) and that of *Puntius dubius*, also initially present in the Cauvery, declined in the Mettur Dam (Salem district, Tamil Nadu). The failure of *Etroplus suratensis* to establish in Mettur reservoir might have been due to the fact that disturbed waters of mettur could not prove congenial to the adhesive nature of the eggs to suberged objects and parental care exhibited by these fishes. Restricted fecundity and abundance of predatory fishes also would have been causative factors. While stocking with major carps proceeded in Shardasagar, their percentage in the catches declined continuously and is almost negligible now. The introduction of milk fish (*Chanos chanos)* in the mettur reservoir did not meet with success. The success of recent introductions of mahseers in the Damodar Vally Corporation reservoirs and Powai Lake (Greater Bombay, Maharashtra) and of *Macrobrachium malcolmsonii* in the Tungabhadra reservoir has yet to be assessed.

The reservoirs in Kerala have been stocked with major carps, peninsular carps, *Cyprinus carpio, Chanos chanos, Etroplus suratensis* and *Orieochromis mossambica*, the latter species forming sizeable catches in many of the reservoirs, particularly, Walayar.

While, *Puntius curmuca* forms an important fishery in Malampuzha and Mansalam reservoirs (Kerala), *Thynnichtys sandkhol* dominates the catches of Nizamsagar (Andhra Pradesh).

Investigations in Tungabhadra dam have shown that stocking of major carps in the reservoir has not been successful, mainly because it was done near the dam site which is the deepest portion of the reservoir and is almost a biological "desert". Stocking operations should therefore be taken up in areas which are not deficient in fish food and where the introduced species can take refuge against the larger predatory forms.

The size of fish stocked also vary from reservoir to reservoir. In some of the reservoirs of Uttar Prodesh, fingerlings measuring 38 mm to 76 mm in size have been stocked, while emphasis is now shifting to fingerlings above 15 cm in length.Of late, 25-30 cm long yearlings are being stocked in the Tungabhadra reservoir. Breeders of major carps have been stocked in Mettur reservoir and in the reservoir of Indore Division in Madhya Prodesh.

The rate of stocking the reservoir also varies from one region to another. While in Uttar Pradesh and Madhya Pradesh, the smaller reservoir have been stocked at 3719 to 4950 fingerlings per hectare, no definite rate of stocking has been followed elsewhere.

## Location of Fish Breeding Grounds in the Reservoir

In many instances, fish breeds either in the reservoir itself or in the tributaries or streams which drain into the river or reservoir. Fishing experiments in the Hirakud and river Ib have shown that mature fishes migrate into the rivers Mahanadi and Ib for breeding where large congregations of the spawning fishes are caught and destroyed.

Breeding ground of the fishes migrating upstream from Pilwa and Kotwal reservoirs (Morena district, Madhya Pradesh) have been located near Niraoli (Gwalior district, Madhya Pradesh) respectively (Dubey and Tuli, 1961). Recent investigations have shown that catla, rohu and mrigal spawn in the tail ends of the Tilaiya reservoir while mrigal and calbasu in Panchet Hill. A spawning ground of major carps has been located at the confluence of Badua river with the reservoir in Bihar The collection of fingerlings of mrigal and catla from the Mettur reservoir and the age-group-wise record of fishery indicate that these species have established themselves well in the reservoir. Spawning of carps has also been observed within the reservoir as in the Nagda (Shivpur district) and Bilaoli reservoir (Indore district).

## Fishermen Habitation and Cooperative Societies

In most of the villages in the vicinity of the reservoirs or on their periphery, there is hardly any fishermen population. Rajasthani fishermen are domestic survents and a very few of them earn a living by fishing. Fishermen parties from Uttar Pradesh migrate to Rajasthan and carry out fishing operations in reservoirs. The situation of Madhya Pradesh is also more or less the same, though a few fishermen have organized themselves into cooperative societies to undertake fishing exploitation in the eastern region.

Fishermen parties in Uttar Pradesh itself move from place to place. There is hardly any fishermen population at Govindsagar reservoir. Although a few fishermen from Andhra Pradesh have settled on Tungabhadra, in all about 125 fishermen live in 47 villages on the periphery of Tungabhadra dam, of which only 50 per cent are active. As 400 fishermen are required for exploitation of the reservoir, a scheme for their rehabilitation has been formulated.

To develop a commercial fishery in a reservoir, it is imperative that a sufficiently large fishermen population is settled around the reservoir at places which are near good fishing grounds and are easily accessible, so that collection and disposal of catches do not pose a problem. These fishermen may find it difficult to fish with gill nets or use other methods of fishing in deep waters and have, therefore, to be trained. The fishermen of Damodar Valley Corporation reservoirs were trained by the Mettur fishermen while about 300 fishermen have been trained departmentally in gill net fishing at Hirakud.

Once the number of fishermen and the catch from the reservoir increases or where such condition already exists, the middleman generally appears on the scene. This undesirable element has to be rooted out. The organization of fishermen cooperative societies being the only solution, all-out Government help should be given to them. The cooperative societies organized at Mettur and Gandhisagar are doing very good work and can serve examples to others.

## Experimental Fishing

The results of experimental fishing undertaken by Gulbadamov-designed nets during 1960-61 at Mettur, Krishnarajasagar and Tungabhadra dam showed that 50 mm and 63 mm meshed nets were the most efficient at Mettur and Krishnarajasagar respectively, but no definite results were available in case of Tungabhadra Dam. The ratio of catch in five experimental nets at these three reservoirs was 0.242 (Mettur), 0.614 (Krishnarajasagar) and 0.145 (Tungabhadra Dam) respectively. The relative abundance of different species (per cent by weight) was shown below;

| Mettur | Krishnarajasagar | Tungabhadra |
|---|---|---|
| *C. cirrhosa* (36.18) | *P. dubius* (70.80) | *S. silondia* (31.16) |
| *S. silondia* (21.08) | *P. carnaticus* (21.70) | *P. kolus* (16.67) |
| *C. mrigala* (16.25) | *W. attu* (3.27) | *L. fimbriatus* (12.82) |
| *P. pangasius* (9.94) | *T. tor* (2.33) | *M. seenghala* (8.36) |
| *M. aor* (3.87) | *L. kontius* (0.92) | *P. dobsoni* (7.13) |
| *M. seenghala* (3.04) | *L. calbasu* (0.84) | *R. vigorsii* (6.07) |
| Misc.species (9.64) | Misc. species (0.14) | *L. calbasu* (4.98) |
| | | *P. pinnauratus* (2.84) |
| | | *E. vacha* (2.69) |
| | | Misc.species (7.28) |

The catches of *Tor* sp. have come down from 15.0 per cent in 1958 to nil in 1961 in the Tungabhadra reservoir

The absence of catla in the experimental nets suggests that the gear used was highly selective, large-meshed nets being required for catla. Krishnamurthy *el al.* (1964) conducted experimental fishing with surface gill nets of similar design and construction but of different mesh sizes on the Tungabhadra reservoir from November, 1960 to October, 1962. The catch comprised mainly *Puntius kolus* and *Silonia chiidrenii* forming 62.2 per cent . The most efficient net was found to be of 38 mm mesh size. The efficiency of nets decreased with an increase in the mesh size.

The production per ha at Mettur and Tungabhadra dam for 1960-61 works out to be 23.9 kg and 1.37 kg respectively. While this ratio was 17.4 : 1, the catch ratio by experimental nets was 1.65 : 1 showing thereby that fishing at Tungabhadra reservoir is 10 times less than what it should be.

Exprimental fishing has also been undertaken departmentally at the Hirakud reservoir. In Tilaiya reservoir, electric fishing with 6 volt D.C. was tried in 1955, but it proved a complete failure. So was an experiment with purse seine in a reservoir in Rajasthan in 1952.

The results of experimental fishing undertaken by the FAO experts, Messrs Gulbadamov and Znamensky, have resulted in the improvement of the local nets, designing of the new nets, use of echo-sounder for charting the bottom as well as locating the fish congregations, and new methods of fishing such as light and electric fishing.

To improve their catching efficiency, Golbadamov (1961) recommended immediate reconstruction of the indigenous gill nets on the following lines;

1. Application of a hanging coefficient of 0.5 while rigging the nets;
2. Complete framing of the nets by attaching breast-lines and a lead line; and
3. Better distribution of the buoyancy along the float line and similarly equal distribution of sinkers along the lead-line.

Znamensky designed framed nets with a hanging coefficient of 0.5 for both the horizontal and vertical lines and found them to be the most effective of all the other types of nets designed by him as well as the indigenous nets.

## Commercial Exploitation

The reservoirs are exploited in any one of the following ways; (a) departmental fishing, (b) lease by auctioning, (c) issuing licences of fishermen to cooperative societies, and (d) royalty basis.

## Conservation and Management

In the belief of procuring a sustained yield of fish from the reservoir, of avoiding waste of fishery resources, and of conserving the stocks, various rules and regulations under the Indian Fisheries Act are in force in various States. These are however, empirically determined in all cases wherever enforced.Till recently there had been no legislation regarding capture of fish in the Tungabhadra reservoir and Hirakud where the river and later the reservoir fishing was free. There still do not exist any conservation measures at Mayurakshi (West Bengal). The existing conservation practices in the Indian reservoirs can be dealt under the following heads;

### (a) Limit on Mesh-Size of Net

The minimum mesh size for nets permitted is 30 mm, others of still smaller meshes are permitted to be used in the marginal areas as in Tilaiya reservoir (DVC) and some reservoirs of Andhra Pradesh and Tamil Nadu.

### (b) Limit on the Size of Fish to be Caught

The minimum size ranges from 229-305 mm in different States, but these are not very effective. At Jaisamand, there is no restriction with regard to mesh size or the fish.

### (c) Closed Season

In all large reservoirs, fishing is closed from June/July to end of September so that fishes are not hampered during their spawning migrations and allowed to breed, at least once. However, this too has not been checked effectively. At Jaisamand, no closed season is observed, though fishing is closed from 1st July to 15th September, in the entire State of Rajasthan. Large scale destruction of fish takes place when they migrate upstream of Tilaiya, Hirakud, Pilwa and Kotwal reservoirs for breeding. It is reported that at Tilaiya over 11 tonnes per day of fishes were caught by the local population in the upper reaches of the reservoir and in the Barakar river.

### (d) Sanctuaries

Certain sections of rivers and reservoirs are closed for fishing for a certain period or all the year round where the fish congregate for breeding or fry and fingerlings are found in large numbers. About 3.2 km of river stretches below the dams (Mettur, Tungabhadra, Gandhisagar etc.) have been declared as sanctuaries.

### (e) Other Methods

In Madhya Pradesh many of the reservoirs are given on lease every alternate years as it is supposed to give the fish a chance to breed and make up the natural stock of the reservoir.

The problem of pollution has always to be kept in mind. While domestic sewage on a moderate scale may be helpful in increasing the fertility of the reservoir, the industrial effluents may be harmful. The waste from Sindri Fertilizer Factory kill spawn in large quantities in the Panchet Hill Dam. Though coal washeries do not seem to have a direct influence on the fishes of the Panchet Hill Dam at present, the deposition of fine coal particles on the reservoir bed may make the bottom inert and render it unproductive in not too distant a future. The effects of effluents from the Orient Paper Mills, Brijrajnagar, discharged into the river Ib which is partly enclosed in the Hirakud reservoir are harmful. However, parasitic infections and diseases of any consequence have not been reported from reservoirs other than that of the D.V.C. group. A case of large scale of fish mortality in Poondi reservoir due to choking of the gills and gullets with mud and filaments of *Oscillatoria* and diatom frustules and reduction of the oxygen content to the lethal limits has been reported by Chacko and Ganapati (1949).

## Determining the Production Potential of Reservoirs

Physical and chemical parameters of water and soil are important ones for determining the production potential of reservoirs. Yield enhancement and management approaches should be finalized by a series of enhancement tools required to be properly assessed and examined with specific objective mainly concerning the better production and scientific management. Based on the current knowledge, it can be concluded that it is possible to get maximum potential production especially for small reservoirs. Thus scientific management of the reservoirs is indispensable to get a sustainable production. Besides, it will help in creating employment opportunities and also meeting the national food scarcity problem to some extent.

Some examples of Indian reservoirs where research and scientific management were bridged up wth launching of the All India Coordinated Research Project under the control of CIFRI, where the project attempted to have in-depth study of all determinants of the reservoir productivity. These studies were eco-oriented under which some reservoirs from different States were investigated. Application of norms of this investigation resulted in remarkable increase in fish yields of all categories. Subsequently, some more reservoirs of other States were also included in the investigation giving recommendations to manage them scientifically. The tables below show the change in production after implementation of scientific management practices in these reservoirs.

**Increase in Fish Yields of Medium and Large Reservoirs by Scientific Management**

| Reservoirs | State | Yield (kg/ha/yr) | |
|---|---|---|---|
| | | Before Management | After Management |
| Yeldari | Maharashtra | 3 | 37 |
| Girna | Maharashtra | 15 | 45 |
| Ravishankarsagar | Chhattisgarh | 0.22 | 1.5 |
| Gandhisagar | Madhya Pradesh | 1 | 44 |
| Tawa | Madhya Pradesh | 1.4 | 28 |
| Ukai | Gujarat | 30 | 110 |
| Govindsagar | Himachal Pradesh | 20 | 100 |
| Pong | Himachal Pradesh | 8 | 64 |
| Bhawanisagar | Tamil Nadu | 30 | 94 |
| Sathanur | Tamil Nadu | 26 | 108 |

**Increase of Fish Yields of Small Reservoirs by Scientific Management**

| Reservoirs | State | Yield (kg/ha/yr) | |
|---|---|---|---|
| | | Before Management | After Management |
| Chulliar | Kerala | 35 | 275 |
| Meenkara | Kerala | 10 | 105 |
| Markonahally | Karnataka | 5 | 70 |
| Gulariya | Uttar Pradesh | 3 | 170 |
| Bachhra | Uttar Pradesh | NA | 150 |
| Baghla | Uttar Pradesh | NA | 110 |
| Thirumoorthy | Tamil Nadu | 70 | 200 |
| Aliyar | Tamil Nadu | 27 | 215 |

## Assessment of Production Potential (Standard Methods)

☆ Morphometric and hydrographic measurements such as water residing time, inflow, outflow and water level fluctuations.

☆ Physico-chemical parameters of water, such as, temperature, transparency, pH, dissolved oxygen, total alkalinity, total dissolved solids, specific conductivity, nitrate and phosphate, estimation of soil organic carbon, available nitrogen and phosphorous in soil.

☆ Quantititative biological aspects, such as, plankton, benthos, periphyton, macrophytes and fish.

☆ Fish population parameters of commercially important fishes and weed fishes

☆ Species-wise and gear-wise fish landings and fishing effort in terms of crafts, gears, and man hours to calculate fish yields and fishing effort.

☆ Potential yield can be estimated from primary production, morpho-edaphic index, morpho-drainage index and maximum sustainable yield (MSY).

☆ Stocking rate is calculated on an average growth rate of individual fish

## Constraints of Reservoir Fisheries

Prime importance for dam construction is given only to hydel-power generation and for agriculture purpose and because of this, the development of fisheries is almost neglected. The reservoir, after formation, passes through three distinct phases- initial high fertility, trophic depression and final fertility characterized by intense development of fish food organisms for first 2-3 years, followed by soaring scarcity of nutrients and then marked by stabilization of reservoirs showing production somewhere near half the magnitude of initial phase respectively. Fish has to struggle for its existence with changed environment. Hence it is essential to give considerable importance for fisheries development by taking necessary action plan for upgrading potential fish yield of the reservoirs.

# Chapter 13

# Conservation of Fish Biodiversity in Riverine Ecosystem

Large rivers are grouped on the basis of their drainage-basin area into major (more than 20000 sq. km), medium (2000-20000 sq. km) and minor (less than 200 sq. km). Accordingly 15 major, 45 medium and 120 minor systems, besides numerous ephemeral streams in the western arid region drain the Indian mainland. The rivers of Indian mainland can be grouped, according to their origin, into Himalayan and Peninsular rivers. The rivers Indus, Ganga and Brahmaputra are major rivers originating from the Hamalayas.

## Threats to Indian Rivers

It is believed that the major sources of pollution in Indian rivers are point sources, namely, domestic sewage, industrial effluents etc., as most of the information available concerning pollution in Indian rivers are those of point sources of pollution. Very little is known about the non-point sources of pollution. Moreover, many of the Indian rivers have large catchment areas from where the pollutants from non-point source sources flow into the rivers. The pollutants like organochlorines, organotins, and heavy metals in the rivers are mainly from the non-point sources of pollution. Some quantitative and qualitative information about such chemicals in some of the Indian rivers are available but almost nothing is known about their exact sources. In most of the cases the concerned industries are usually held responsible if such hazardous chemicals are found in the river system but it may not be always true. The sources of organochlorines, especially DDT, in the arctic environment and in the lakes in high altitudes of Alps were found to be the tropics and subtropics of USA and Africa respectively. Recntly DDT content in the Ganges fish at Haridwar was found to be higher than those places like Kanpur and Patna. These observations are matters of great concern and there is a serious need to understand the chemistry and behavior of such chemicals in our environment, especially in rivers.

In many cases the fishermen use toxic chemicals like organochlorines and organophosphates for fishing especially in the lentic water bodies in the flood plains and riparian zones of the river like the Ganges. Such activities also result in pollution in the rivers as such water bodies get connected with the main channel of the rivers during the monsoon.

The regulation of river flow has severely affected the flow regime of the rivers. Almost all the Indian rivers have been dammed at their heads and many places in their course for irrigation and various other purposes. It causes reduction in flow in the rivers, which in turn eroded the self-purifying capacity of the rivers.

The floodplains and riparian zones are under heavy pressure of farming throughout the year, except during the monsoon when they are inundated. The natural vegetation cover in the floodplains is being removed to get more and more agricultural land. This results into heavy siltation in the rivers. Moreover the farmers use chemical fertilizers and pesticides indiscriminately causing pollution both in floodplains and rivers.

# Decline of Biodiversity

## In the Ganga River

The commercially important fishes, namely, Indian major carps and Hilsa (after construction of Farakka Barrage in 1975) collapsed. The pollution-tolerant species, like tubificids, heavily colonized, to the extent of 1000000 per sq. m, near the city outfalls; pollution-intolerant (sensitive) species like plecopteran and ephemeropteran larvae vanished; primary productivity of the river was adversely affected resulting in decline of not only fish population but the other vertebrates as well. Indiscriminate use of organochlorine pesticides in agriculture and health sectors posed new threats and resulted in high accumulation of these hazardous chemicals in the tissues of fish as well as other vertebrates. Rampant killing of the turtles, especially the soft-shell turtles (*Asoideretes gangeticus, Lissemys punctata* etc.) by the poachers reduced the scavenging capacity of the river as the turtles feed mainly on the dead bodies and carcasses. Directed and incidental killings and the habitat degradation due to various anthropogenic activities pushed the gangetic dolphin (*Platanista gangetica*) on the verge of extinction. Recently the dolphin has been categorized as Endangered by the IUCN- the World Conservation Union.

## Decline of Biodiversity in the River Yamuna

Not only has the flow regime of the River Yamuna been altered but indiscriminate extraction of river water and discharge of untreated city sewage and industrial effluents have changed the status of the river to a cesspool, especially at Delhi. The river has lost its total integrity in and around Delhi. The river used to have plenty of Gangetic dolphins, during the 19th century even in the month of May when water was low

(Anderson, 1879). The last report of the presence of the dolphins in the Yamuna at Delhi was in the year 1967 when a dead dolphin from the river was brought to the Delhi Zoo (K.S.Sankhala, the then Director of Delhi Zoo). Similarly the river lost most of its biota in the last couple of decades. Now scarce population of the dolphins in Yamuna is found mainly betweenPanchnada, the confluence of the Chambal, and Allahabad.

## Fish Fauna in the Ganga

Among the vertebrate fauna, though the number of fish species is high (378 species), the population of most of the economically important fishes, including the Indian major carps (*Labeo rohita, Catla catla* and *Cirrhinus mrigala*), has dwindled in recent years. But the biomass of the catfishes has been found to increasing. Altogether 75 species of fish were identified to have high commercial value. During a fish stock assessment exercise in the Ganga in a stretch of about 30 km in and around Patna between July 1994 and June 1995, 106 species of fish fauna were collected and identified from the river. *Bagarius yarrellii, Silonia silondia* and *Anguila* sp were found to be the most vulnerable and rare. The degradation and loss of habitat in the river Ganga have led to decline of the major carp population, while less economic fishes (minor carps and small catfishes) are increasing in relative abundance. The migratory fishes like Hilsa are also confined to downstream of the Farakka Barrage. After construction of the Barrage, the fishery of Hilsa has collapsed; however in recent years their catch was recorded up to Allahabad. Boulder mining and, dams/barrages resulting in water flow regulation in upper reaches of Ganga have also adversely affected the Mahasheer population. Still the fishes form the largest group of living natural resources in the Ganga and serve as the largest source of fish spawn in India.

## Threats to Riverine biodiversity

For aquatic biodiversity, the root causes of loss can be divided into five broad categories; (i) pollution, (ii) habitat alteration, (iii) competition for water, (iv) introduction of exotic species, and (v) commercial exploitation The first three factors, often acting in concert, are the principal causes of the loss of aquatic biodiversity in aquatic systems.

## Pollution

The pollutants from both point and non-point sources have deleterious effects on aquatic benthic invertebrates. Organic enrichment also has a detrimental effect on insect abundance. Toxicity of metallic ions diminishes benthic abundance as well as catfish population. The impact of industry wastes on aquatic life including fish is most severe in streams and tributaries with low rates of summer flow, especially in the minor tributaries of the Ganges. Inputs of agro-chemicals through run-off not only make the river system a repository of toxic chemicals but also render it eutrophic, especially the small rivers having less discharge.

## Habitat Alteration

### Withdrawal of Water from Rivers

Men become successful competitors for water with fish and other organisms when they withdraw water from rivers, lakes, springs or underground aquifers. Water is withdrawn most often from aquatic environments for irrigation, and urban and industrial consumption. The annual runoff in the Ganges basin is about 469 billion cubic meter. Of this 85 billion cubic meter of water is diverted by canal projects and by hydro-electric and storage reservoirs for irrigation, power and flood control. Canal projects account for a little over 60 per cent of the impounded water. The diversion of water has caused large-scale changes in the channel bed and hydrography of the river in terms of flow, flow-rate, flood-rhythm and regime. Hydraulic structures have changed river morphometry, increased bank erosion and created barriers for migratory species.

# Dam Projects Threatens Ancient Fish

The hefty muddy brown lung fish, *Neoceratodus forsteri*, is thought to have survived virtually unchanged for at least 100 million years, making it one of the oldest known vertebrate species around earning the moniker of "living fossil". It is also one of the closest living relatives of the ancestral fish that crawled on to the land and eventually give rise to all land vertebrates including humans. Being able to study the species is important for understanding how transition took place.

The lung fish is now largely confined to two river systems in Queensland- among the only place that provide the shallow running and weedy water in which the fish likes to spawn. A dam in one of these, the Burnett river to supply drought stricken region is likely to be a huge problem in the future. By flooding or drying them out, the dam will eventually destroy nearly half of the lung fish spawning areas.

The decision to dam the second river, must pass a Federal environmental impact assessment before the project can proceed, because the Australian lung fish is listed as threatened species. But the second dam could be enough to drive the species to extinction. Lung fish experts step up a campaign to block the dam. So far 100 scientists have responded the call to save lung fish. It would be calamitous and irreplaceable loss if this animal went extinct.

There are five other species of lung fish living in South America and Africa. But the Australian lung fish which can live for a century and grow 1.5 meter long is thought to be most closely resemble the last common ancestor of land vertebrates.

Biologists say that living fish can be used for genetic and embryology studies that probe how vertebrates moved from water to land- analysis that would be impossible with preserved specimens.Patterns of gene activity of lung fish is being studied to try to work out how fins became limbs. These things are amazingly important organisms in the history of the earth.

The Queensland government has guaranteed that the dam will include a fish elevator to carry lung fish across the dam. But this is not enough, because the lung fish's old spawning grounds will still be destroyed. Lung fish lay a very few eggs and return to the same spawning sites year after year.

In the question of lung fish breeding center, guaranteeing the species survival in captivity would be tough. Researchers, so far, managed to breed lung fish using two ponds, each the size of an Olympic swimming pool.

## Construction of Dams, Embankments and Barrages

The construction of flood-control dykes and levees in flood-prone low-lying areas has deprived the major carps of their extensive breeding habitats, previously available in a network of interlaced channels connected with the tributaries. In 1965-66, the oxbow lakesof the Burhi Gandak sub-basin in Champaran District of Bihar alone covered an area of 36000 ha and provided a fishery of 2900 tonnes per year. The major carp fishery has declined in many oxbow lakes, as they change to marsh. The ecology of these oxbow lakes is further affected by sluice gates on inlet and outlet channels, which are operated more to serve agriculture than fisheries. Canal projects and flood control measures are two major factors that are especially responsible for the destruction of breeding habitat for major carps.

Large water diversion projects have not only affected freshwater fish and fisheries, but have caused reductions in estuarine and marine fish populations. Reduction of freshwater inflows reduces the amount of nutrients flowing into downstream areas and increases salinities. The effects of dams and barrages on fish faunas in tropical areas are poorly known but likely to be great. The Farakka Barrage commissioned in 1975 at the head of Bhagirathi and Padma distributaries of the Ganges, some 510 km from the river mouth, has nearly eliminated the hilsa fishery upstream of Farakka on the main stem of the Ganges, a fishery which was based on runs of both Padma and Hoogly stocks. The Farakka Barrage has a fish ladder, which is ineffective as a pass from the Padma. The barrage also created a barrier to the movements of the Ganges River dolphins and other aquatic wildlife between the lower reaches of the Ganges system, including the biologically rich Sundarbans and the middle and upper Ganges.

Barrages in upper reaches of the river obstruct migration of mahseers, *Tor* spp that move from lowland to upland reaches for breeding. Decline of *Tor tor* along with other fishes has been reported following construction of a barrage at Tribeni on the Gandak River at the Indo-Nepal border. The Ganges River dolphin became extinct from the main stem of the Ganges upstream of the Middle Ganges Barrage Bijnor, after construction of the same in 1984. Hydro-electric dams on the upper reaches of the Ganges and its tributaries may also prove detrimental to mahseer, catfish, *Bagarius bagarius*, and the carps, *Labeo dero* and *L. dyocheilus*. Dams and barrages not only reduce downstream flows but also reduce the amount of nutrients flowing into downstream areas. This nutrient reduction eventually may affect the productivity of aquatic communities within the river, estuary, or adjacent ocean.

Riverine fish fauna are subjected to a series of habitat changes such as water current, turbidity, fishing pressure, loss of breeding grounds and changes in fish food organisms due to lake formation. Species that are sensitive to habitat variables perish, and the hardy ones take advantage of the vacant niches. Formation of reservoirs has affected a number of riverine fish stocks in India.

**Fishes Affected by Dam Construction in India**

| Sl.No. | River Basin | Affected Species |
|--------|-------------|------------------|
| 1. | Indus | Mahseers, Snow trouts, *Labeo dero, L. dyocheilus*, freshwater prawns |
| 2. | Mahanadi | *Tenualosa ilisha, Puntius sarana, Tor tor, T. mosal, Labeo finbriatus, L. calbasu, Rhinomugil corsula*, freshwater prawns |
| 3. | Cauveri | *Puntius dubius, P. carnaticus, Cirrhinus cirrhosa, C. reba, Labeo kontius, L. fimbriatus*, freshwater prawns |
| 4. | Krishna | *Tenualosa ilisha, Puntius sarana, P. kolus, P. porcellus, P. potail, L. Pangusia, L. fimbriatus, L. calbasu*, freshwater prawns |

The cyclic rise and fall of Asian rivers and lakes are of singular importance because inundated floodplains are the main or exclusive spawning and nursery grounds for many fish species. This cycle also signals and stimulates the breeding and movements of many freshwater species, and any changes in timing and flow rates due to impoundment will have adverse effects on them.

# Construction of Bridges and Approach Roads

Development activities related to transportation also destroy the habitat of many aquatic fauna. Construction of bridges on the river, including the approach roads, destroys the floodplains, which is a breeding ground of many fish species.

# Mining activities in the rivers

Extensive mining, especially sand and china clay, from the riverbed also severely affects the bottom fauna. The River Son and the River Ganga bear the burnt of extensive sand mining in Bihar at several points. China clay is being mined from the Ganga near Rajmahal.

# Channelization of Rivers

Habitat alteration due to channelization of rivers is the single biggest cause of loss of diversity of aquatic life. Channelization typically involves the realignment, clearing, widening, and lining of the stream channel, usually for flood control. Among other effects, channelization may reduce stream length, create uniform habitat conditions (reduce habitat heterogeneity), modify the hydrological cycle, drain adjacent wetlands, eliminate stream cover and riparian vegetation, degrade water quality, and alter trophic relationship.Channelization is often conducted in piecemeal fashion. This result in fragmentation of formerly continuous stream corridors and confines many less-tolerant species to short section of undisturbed stream. Isolated populations within these habitat "islands" become more vulnerable to extinction by natural and human-caused events such as floods or pollution. Channelization also has dramatic effects on the fish faunas of larger rivers. The shallow-water habitats as well as adjacent riparian habitats that flooded annually and are vital to the reproduction and rearing of many riverine fishes, are destroyed due to channelization. Channelized sections of river have fewer fish and lower species diversity.

## Competition for Water

Existing competition for water for various purposes and the ever growing need for water become serious threat leading to the loss of lotic ecosystems and freshwater biodiversity.

## Introduction of Species

Introduction of species occasionally replace native species in natural habitats through competition or predation, but most replacement occurs in altered environments that provide the introduced species an ecological advantage.

One-way that introduced species eliminate native species is through introduction of diseases. Thai magur, and Chinese grass carp are some of the introduced species in the Ganga River system. Details of impact on the native fish fauna are not well understood. In1998, a North American snail *Physa mexicana* was first recorded in the Ganges and Yamuna Rivers for the first time in Indian subcontinent. By 2001 the species was found to flourish profusely. Similarly, a well-known South African aquatic plant, *Eichhornia crassipes*, has badly affected the lentic water bodies in the Gangetic plains.

## Extinction of Native European cyprinid

The deliberate introduction of new species can have unexpected negative consequences. A recently introduced fish, the invasive Asian cyprinid, *Pseudorasbora parva* is causing increased mortality and totally inhibiting spawning of an already endangered native fish, the European cyprinid *Leucaspiys delineatus* . This threat is caused by an infectious pathogen, a rosette-like intracellular eukaryotic parasite that is a deadly non-specific agent. It is probably carried by healthy Asian fish, and could decrease fish biodiversity in Europe as well as having implications for commercial aquaculture.

The sunbleak, *L. delineatus*, is the only representative of its genus and the only nest guarding fish among European cyprinids. Once wide spread in Europe in the past 50 years it was explicably declined and is now on the European list of threatened freshwater fish. By contrast, since its introduction in 1960 into Romanian ponds near the river Danube, the Asian topmouth gudgeon *P. parva* has spread rapidly throughout the Europe and has locally coincided with *L. delineatus* extinction.

## Pike: The Invasive Species

The northern pike (*Esox lucius*), a fish that already is causing trouble in rest of the United States, is decimating salmon population in some rivers, in south-central Alaska. A growing number of creeks and lakes, once teeming with salmon, is now losing the fish. Concern about the threat to salmon populations has focused on overfishing and the effect of farmed salmon on natural ones. But attention in Alaska is now turning to booming numbers of pike which eat young salmon before they reach the sea to breed. A 1999 survey revealed that 80 per cent of tested pike had salmon in their stomach.

The northern pike occurs naturally in parts of Alaska, but was only introduced to the salmon rich south-central area in the 1950s by an angler.

In the late 1980s, flooding spread the pike into the streams of the Susitna and Matanuska river basins. Now it has spread through both basins, in at least a dozen lakes and four rivers, all of which are rich in salmon and trout. Alaskan scientists did not initially undersatand the seriousness of the invasion. When a non-native species shows up, one has to jump on it.

## Over-Exploitation of Species

Over fishing occurs in many rivers of India, but it has not been the subject of detailed studies. For a useful analysis of over fishing, data on the productivity and identity of the stocks are essential. There is an urgent need to gather these basic data. Fish poisoning is a traditional way of fishing for some groups of people, who use plant products or pesticides as poison. This practice results in destruction of almost the entire local biodiversity, including the fishes of the area.

Overfishing, usually combined with other threats, is responsible for the drastic reduction of entire communities, especially in densely populated areas and of some species of particular economic interest. Example would include species of *Tor* spp in many of the rivers.

Exploitation of other aquatic fauna is also prominent in most of the rivers. Killing of freshwater turtles as a food source is a cause of great concern. This has resulted to decrease the population of the Gangetic soft-shell turtle (*Aspideretes gangeticus*). The turtle is endemic to the Ganga river system. Killing of Gangetic dolphin (*Platanista gangetica*) in the Ganga and Brahmaputra river system is posing a serious threat to the population of this animal. Some invertebrates like crabs are also overexploited for consumption by different communities and are highly priced in the market.

## Conservation of Lotic Ecosystems of India

To conserve the lotic ecosystems needs a three-pronged consideration;

1. Maintaining the integrity of river systems;
2. Purposeful research on the riverine ecosystem and its biodiversity;
3. Gaining people's support through their active participation

A minimum flow must be ensured to maintain the ecological integrity of the rivers. Construction of upstream reservoirs has its own consequences on the river systems; however, if release of water from such reservoirs, especially during the lean period, is possible, it will help in maintaining a minimum flow in the river during the period. Proper watershed management will help in this direction.

The natural attributes of a river must be maintained for conserving the biodiversity. In evaluating options for water development, four basic principles of riverine ecology must be kept in mind;

(a) There is no "surplus" water; any large-scale withdrawl will have ecological consequences.
(b) The floodplain is an integral part of the river;

(c) An alluvial river must be allowed to migrate;

(d) Rivers need to maintain their natural temporal and spatial variability

As maximum river water is diverted through irrigation canals, there is a serious need to evolve strategies to minimize the wasteful use of water in agriculture. For this the farmers need to be trained and educated to use minimum water for the maximum yield. Efficient wastewater treatment systems and recycling are required to reduce the pressure on the river water. The crops requiring less water need to be promoted in the area of water deficiency.

Dredging of river channels may not be a good suggestion as it may destroy benthic habitat and ultimately have adverse effects on the fishes.

Dams and barrages must have provisions of functional fish ladders and by-passes.

Most of the dams and barrages in India are fatal for the migratory aquatic species; these often cause complete disappearance of the species in the upstream reaches of the rivers. Though there are provisions of fish ladders in the barrages, they have failed to serve the purpose. With due consideration of local conditions and engineering principles, construction of by-pass channels can be a good suggestion to allow the species to migrate.

To protect river floodplains and areas surrounding all inland water bodies from uncontrolled anthropogenic activities, River Regulation Zones similar to Coastal Regulation Zones can be notified under the Environment Protection Act (1986). The National River Action Plan should widen its perspectives and proper elements of floodplain management should be incorporated with the pollution control and abatement programs of the Indian Rivers.

## Conservation of Fish Biodiversity

Fisheries, being the most important resource of the lotic systems and source of livelihood for millions of riparian communities, need special attention. *In situ* conservation of fish biodiversity in the wild is useful where genetic diversity exists. *In situ* conservation may be attained through declaring protected areas in appropriate places where wild fish diversity is available. Protection in such areas and enactment and enforcement of regulations to prevent destructive methods of fishing and avoiding water pollution can conserve the fish biodiversity. Furthermore, special emphasis should be given to preservation of germ plasm of endangered and vulnerable fish species through *ex-situ* conservation measures.

# References

Ardizzone, G.D, S. Cataudella and R. Rosai. Management of coastal lagoon fisheries and aquaculture in Italy, FAO Fisheries Technical Paper 293, Food and Agricultural Organization, Rome, 1988.

Boerema, L.K. The characteristics of an exploited stock; FAO Fisheries Circular No. 701, Food and Agricultural Organization, Rome, 1978.

BOBP. Report of the consultation on stock assessment for smallscale fisheries In the Bay of Bengal; BOBP/REP/10.1 (GCP/RAS/040/SWE), FAO of the United Nations and Swedish International Development Authority, 1980.

Biswas, K.P. Ecological and fisheries development in wet lands; A study of Chilka Lagoon; Daya Publishing House, Delhi, 1988.

Beaugrand, Gregory, *et al.* Plankton effect on cod recruitment in the North Sea, Nature, vol. 426 2003.

Block, Barbara, A. *et al.* Electronic tagging and population structure of Atlantic bluefin tuna Nature, vol. 434, 2005.

Cyranoski, David. Satellite set to keep track of whales, Nature, vol. 415, 2002.

Doddamani, P.L. K. Pand *et al.* Indian reservoirs- an untapped inland fisheries resource, Fishing Chimes, vol 30, no. 12, 2011.

Dalton Rex. More whale strandings are linked to sonar, Nature, vol 439, 2006.

Dalton Rex. Pike pests ravage Alaska's salmon, Nature, vol 418, 2992.

Daniel Pauly. Much rowing for fish, Nature, vol 432, 2004.

Dalton Rex. Census of marine migration launched to gauge fish stocks, Nature, vol 418/22, 2002.

Dalton Rex. Fishing for trouble, Nature, vol. 431, 2004.

Devine, J.A. *et al.* Deep sea fishes qualify as endangered, Nature, vol. 439, 2006.

Dalton Rex. Plans to track tuna canned amid claims of cash shortfall, Nature, vol.432, 2004.

Dalton Rex. Fishy future, Nature, vol. 437, 2005.

FAO, Fisheries; Capture fisheries production statistics for the year 2011 (on line), website – WWW fao. Org/fishery/capture/en.

Finney Bruce, P. Fisheries productivity in the northeastern Pacific Ocean over the past 2200 years, Nature, vol. 416, 2002.

Gowin Virginia. Panel calls for sea change to fisheries policy, Nature, vol. 423, 2003.

Gales, N.J. *et al.* Japan's whaling plan under scrutiny, Nature, vol. 435, 2005.

Gozian, R.E. *et al.* Disease threat to European fish, Nature, vol. 435, 2002.

Garibaldi, Luca, *et al.* Trends in oceanic captures and clustering of large marine eco-Systems, FAO Fisheries Technical Paper 435, FAO, Rome, 2003

Garibaldi Luca. Trends in oceanic captures; an analysis of 50 years data by FAO fishing areas, FAO Fisheries Technical Paper 435, FAO, Rome, 2003.

Gulland, J.A. Review of the state of world fishery resources, FAO Fisheries Circular No. 710, FAO of the United Nations, Rome, 1978.

Hays, Graeme C. Stemming the tide of turtle extinction, Nature, vol. 433, 2005.

Hoag, Hannah. Atlantic cod meet icy death; Nature, vol. 222/24, 2003.

Hsich Chi-hao *et al.* Fishing elevates variability in the abundance of exploited species, Nature, vol. 443, 2006.

Hutchings, J.A. The cod that got away, Nature, vol. 428, 2004.

Jones, R. Stock and recruitment, FAO Fisheries Circular No. 701 FAO of the United Nations, Rome, 1978.

Jhingran, V.G. *et al.* A review of the measures adopted for the development of the fisheries of reservoirs in India; Proc. Of the Seminar on Ecology and fisheries of freshwater reservoirs, ICAR, New Delhi, 1978.

Limongelli, Luca. Clustering large marine ecosystems by capture data; Fisheries Technical Paper 435, FAO of the United Nations, Rome, 2003.

Ludwig Arne *et al.* When the American sea sturgeon swam east?, Nature, vol. 419 2002.

Marine Resource Service. Review of the state of world fishery resources, FAO Fisheries Circular No. 710, Revision 6, FAO, Rome, 1989.

Marine Resource Service. Review of the state of world fishery resources, FAO fisheries Circular No. 710, Revision 7, FAO, Rome, 1990.

Nagasaki, F. *et al.* Management of multi-species resources and multi-gear fisheries, FAO Fisheries Technical Paper 305, FAO, Rome, 1989.

Nature. Caviar is off the menu as beluga fish is threatened, Nature, vol. 428, 2004.

Nature. Fishing's secretive controller, Nature, vol. 432, 2004.

Nature. Conservationists blast plans for offshore army base, Nature, vol. 431, 2004.

Nature. Not saving the whale; Nature, vol. 446, 2007.

Nature. Fishermen battered by scale of fish quota, Nature, vol. 421, 2003

Nature. Military manoeuvres leave whales high and dry, Nature, vol. 419, 2002.

Nina Tabitha, S. and B. Gunaian. Exploitation of oil sardine, *Sardinella longiceps* of below the harvestable size along the southeast coast of India, Fishing Chimes, vol. 32, No. 11, 2013.

Pearson, Helen. Dam project threatens living fossil, Nature, vol. 442, 2006.

Palumbi, Stephen R. Why mother matters ?, Nature, vol. 430, 2004.

Pauly Daniel, *et al.* Towards sustainability in world fisheries, Nature, vol. 418, 2002.

Prasad, S.N, *et al.* Lentic ecosystems of India, Zoological Survey of India, 2003.

Panayotou, Theodore. Management concepts for small-scale fisheries, economic and social aspects, FAO Fisheries Technical Paper No. 228, FAO of the United Nations, Rome, 1982.

Pauly Daniel. Some simple methods for the assessment of tropical fish stocks, FAO Fisheries Technical Paper No. 234, FAO of the United Nations, Rome, 1983.

Robinson, M.A. Prospects for world fisheries to 2000, FAO Fisheries Circular No. 722, Revision 1, FAO of the United Nations, Rome, 1982.

Rao, G. Syda. Way forward for enhancing Indian marine fish production, Fishing Chimes, vol. 33, No. 1 and 2, 2013.

Schrope, Mark. The real sea change, Nature, vol. 443, 2006.

Schiermeier, Quirin. Climate findings let fishermen off the hook; Nature, vol.428, 2004.

Schrope, Mark. Whale deaths caused by U.S. Navy's sonar, Nature, vol. 415, 2002.

Schiermeier, Quirin. How many more fishes in the sea ? Nature, vol. 419, 2002.

Schiermeier, Quirin. Low stocks prompt calls for North Atlantic fishing ban, Nature, vol. 419, 2002.

Sumaila Rashid, U. Daniel Pauly. All fishing nations must unite to cut subsidies, Nature, vol. 280, 2002.

Schiermeier, Quirin. Harbor threat for Coelacanths, Nature, vol. 458, 2009.

Shina, R.K. and S.K. Shina. Lotic ecosystems in India, Natural ecosystems of India, Zoological Survey of India, 2003.

Troadec, J-P. Fishing and assessment of stocks, FAO Fisheries Circular No. 701, FAO of the United Nations, Rome, 1978.

Trainer, Vera L. Unveiling an ocean phantom, Nature, vol. 418/29, 2002.

Venkataraman, K. Marine ecosystems of India, Zoological Survey of India, 2003.

Wolfgang, K.V. *et al. Pfiesteria shumwayce* kills fish by micro-predation not exotoxin secretion, Nature, vol. 416/29, 2002.

Watson Reg and Daniel Pauly. Systematic distortions in world fisheries catch trends, Nature, vol. 414, 2001.

Yogeesh, C. Rapidly depleting marine fisheries resources adversely impacting common fish consumers, Fishing Chimes, vol. 33, No. 3, 2013.

# Index

www.ingramcontent.com/pod-product-compliance
Lightning Source LLC
Chambersburg PA
CBHW020217290326
41948CB00001B/78